# GEOGRAPHY

## THE WORLD
## AND ITS PEOPLES

A SURVEY OF THE PHYSICAL, CLIMATIC AND
VEGETATIONAL CHARACTERISTICS OF THE EARTH
AS THE ENVIRONMENT OF MANKIND, TOGETHER
WITH A DESCRIPTION OF THE MAIN REGIONS OF
THE WORLD AND OF THE PEOPLES WHO INHABIT
THEM, AND A BRIEF ACCOUNT OF THE PROBABLE
DEVELOPMENT OF MAN'S STRUGGLE WITH HIS
PHYSICAL ENVIRONMENT FROM EARLIEST TIMES

CONTRIBUTORS:

*Professor H. J. Fleure*, D.Sc., M.A., F.R.S.

*Professor A. Austin Miller*, D.Sc.      O. J. R. Howarth, O.B.E., M.A., Ph.D.

*Professor E. Estyn Evans*, M.A., D.Sc., F.S.A.  P. D. Mehta.

*Professor W. Fitzgerald.*          Thomas Pickles, B.Sc.

*Professor F. Kenneth Hare.*       *Professor R. N. Rudmose Brown*, D.Sc.

*E. W. Shanahan*, M.A., D.Sc. (*Econ.*)

ODHAMS PRESS LTD · LONG ACRE · LONDON

# TO THE READER

To DEAL with such a vast subject as the geography of the world in a single volume of some three hundred pages may be thought to be an undertaking likely to baffle the most expert of writers and the most avid reader. Scores of books, some of them much larger than this one, have been written about each of the countries of the world, about the rocks and rivers, the seas and mountains that make up this planet we call the Earth, about weather and climate and vegetation, and about Man himself and his centuries of struggling with his natural surroundings. So it is not to be expected that a single volume can provide all the varied information about the world that lies stored in such a vast reservoir of knowledge.

What the eminent geographers who have written this panoramic view of the world have done is to distil the essence of that knowledge for the general reader and the intending student of geography. Just as you would wish to make a rapid exploration of your new surroundings, if you settled in an unfamiliar district of your own country, so here you will make a series of brief excursions to look at the world in the company of expert guides, who have learnt from long experience what you want to know and what you need to remember about the earth itself and about its countries and peoples. And when you return from your imaginary travels, Professor Fleure, the distinguished geographer and anthropologist, will be waiting to tell you in the last section of the book something of the geographical aspect of the long story of mankind's progress from the primitive hunter and food-gatherer sheltering in his cave to the citizen of such highly complex civilizations as we find today in Europe or North America.

The essential passport for your imaginary excursions will be a good atlas. The maps in this book have been specially drawn by a skilled cartographer to give, chiefly, a realistic impression of the physical appearance of the regions represented. To achieve this aim much detail has had to be omitted. Keep your atlas open at your elbow as you read; and if you can obtain one with vegetation and production maps as well as the usual physical and political ones, your reading will provide you with still more interest and instruction.

You will find as you read that your curiosity will be stimulated concerning this or that aspect of geography or about this or that country and its people. If you will make notes of these special interests as you go, you will find in the *Guide to Further Study* at the end of the book, and especially in the valuable lists of books for further reading, all the information required to set you off on ever new and ever more absorbing voyages of discovery.

# GEOGRAPHY

## THE WORLD
## AND ITS PEOPLES

### MAN IN THE JUNGLE

*New Guinea tribesmen and their families gather on the outskirts of a village to welcome official visitors from Australia. The fuzzy hair of the natives is characteristic of these Papuan peoples, who are the dominant stock in New Guinea.*

# CONTENTS

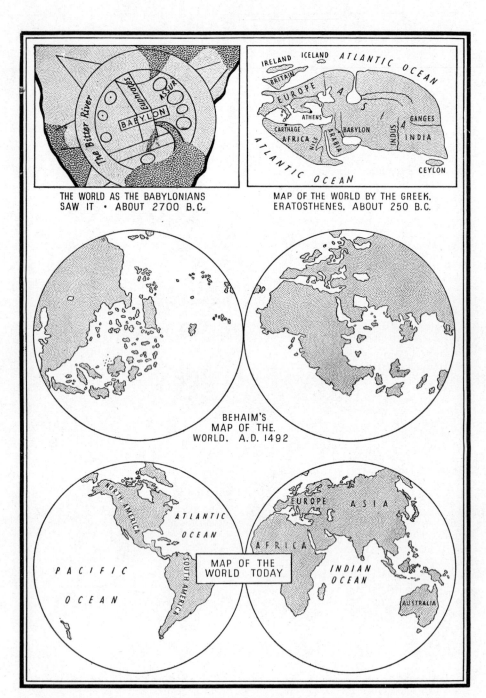

THE WORLD AS THE BABYLONIANS
SAW IT · ABOUT 2700 B.C.

MAP OF THE WORLD BY THE GREEK,
ERATOSTHENES, ABOUT 250 B.C.

BEHAIM'S
MAP OF THE
WORLD, A.D. 1492

MAP OF THE
WORLD TODAY

THE WORLD AS IT HAS APPEARED TO MAN AT DIFFERENT STAGES IN HIS HISTORY

# INTRODUCTION

Most of our forefathers lived out their lives in a village or a little town, hearing of the world through tales of the few who travelled it, perhaps as pedlars or palmers, as raiders or crusaders. The Renaissance brought the beginnings of the more active search for truth; travellers' tales multiplied and aroused so much scepticism that, when Marco Polo told truth that was stranger than fiction, he was not believed. There was still a large element of barbarism in our make-up, and the early map-makers would try to fill up the unknown spaces, of Africa for instance, with elephants and other fanciful representations.

So travellers' tales multiplied, and maps were improved little by little as knowledge of the world increased. Roads as well as sea-routes were inserted, a good indication that communications were spreading and that men were looking out towards more distant horizons. They still depended mainly on local products, but knew there were competitors for the luxuries they wanted and for the control of the seas across which these were brought. The coming of the railway and steamship, the factory and the post office made men jostle one another far more sharply than heretofore. Old-fashioned groups here and there, still living on their own products, were hustled into the new world of big business.

### Geography and Science

Men in their group-life mould their environment and are moulded by it, so that each group and its environment, present and past, must be studied, group and environment together. The discussions in this book are focused on the life of mankind, and so on efforts towards a synthesis of several lines of thought.

It is obvious that the physical features of a country can hardly be understood without some appreciation of the story of its rocks, their uplift or downthrow into their present positions, the work of wind and rain, frost and ice, rivers and waves, in shaping the surface. Geology is thus drawn upon, and with it must be utilized a great deal of physics.

We need physics also to help us to interpret climate and weather, so vitally important to man in his own personal comfort and well-being, also through its master-work on soils and in its control of vegetation and the possibilities of crops and of animal life. Soil science and biology are entering ever more fully into discussions of human welfare. The physiology of vitamins and of the effects of ultra-violet radiation, sometimes in excess and sometimes insufficient for the optimum results, is being analysed, and it is likely that these considerations will enter, far more in the future, into plans for welfare.

Maury, in the mid-nineteenth century, by his study of movements of ocean waters did so much to improve the layout of steamship routes that oceanography has become of vast practical importance.

### Men in Their Homelands

In dealing with the parts of the world, this book seeks to visualize great regions in which there is a considerable growth of common experience widespread among the people. Thus, instead of taking the anciently recognized continents, which have a mainly cartographical justification, i.e. they look rather distinct on the map, the world has been broadly divided according to facts of human experience.

A number of authoritative writers have contributed chapters, in each case based on personal knowledge of at any rate some part of the area dealt with. The book is concerned to arouse interest, and, when possible, to give a picture of men at work in a homeland that they have made, while it in turn made them.

The Mediterranean region, including parts of south-western Asia, has within it the localities in which people first learned to take care of plants, and very probably, too, the first localities in which they added

1

herding to cultivation. Much of the basic pattern of their lives had been laid down on the warm soil five thousand and more years ago, and theirs is a story of mercantile adventure added to craftsmanship in land use as well as in equipment. It brought into existence the oldest cities; it evolved a driving-force that carried ideas to India and China, to Europe and even across the forbidding desert into intertropical Africa, but not to Australia, though some made the longer journey around north-eastern Asia into America. Cultivation, craftsmanship, cities, churches, commerce: these are the great achievements of Mediterranean life.

### Western Civilization

Europe north of the Mediterranean, a poor fringing region until the iron-shod plough came to its aid and the ideas of law and order from imperial Rome filtered in, has found scope for craftsmanship and commerce and ultimately for machine-power to supplement and replace the work of men's hands. And with its coal and steam power it has had a marvellous outpouring over North America, Australia, New Zealand and many another region. We note the contrast between English-speaking North America, with its population of immigrants, and Spanish - Portuguese-speaking America, colonized earlier by small numbers who intermarried with the peoples they found there. The efforts of the maritime Europeans have welded some of them, both in Europe and in the New Lands, into strongly self-conscious national groups, the temporary success of which has encouraged too ready imitation in places where this scheme is not so appropriate.

The Union of Soviet Socialist Republics, with its base in the great northern land-mass of Eurasia, is increasingly seen to differ deeply from Europe-of-the-sea. It owes much to ideas brought from maritime Europe, but we must think of its immense plains, of its broad waterways for summer use, its severe winters, the unique fertility of its "Black Earth," and the marvellous variety of peoples and languages without sharp, obvious contrasts of skin colour. Whereas Europe-of-the-sea has had a pro-digious expansion of its people and their thoughts over lands across the ocean, the U.S.S.R. illustrates just as prodigious an expansion colonizing the "Black Earth," the mineral-bearing regions of the Urals, irrigable lands and coalfields in Inner Asia, and even trying to adapt parts of the Arctic. And all this has been organized under central autocracies of one kind and another, with expansion step by step beyond old borders as the keynote.

### The East

Then there is the great East with its population of half mankind, its four or, perhaps in parts, nearly five thousand years of cultivation under conditions of warm summer rain. It added rice to the millet which had spread to it from south-west Asia. Frugality has developed into dire poverty of hundreds of millions both in India, where jungles offer refuges to still lingering backward folk, and in China, where the great mass of cultivators is almost on one and the same level of life. And in both of these regions, and in Japan, too, a few have achieved hereditary wealth, power and leisure, often misused, but yet more or less concerned with the evolution of Chinese art, one of the greatest achievements of mankind, and with Indian thought, which has contributed more than some realize to European knowledge and belief. In the south-east the Monsoon Lands tell us of the immense growth of population by colonists from mainland Asia, with recent supplements from Europe, in the islands that spread from Asia out towards the Pacific, on the fringes of which linger the lowly folk of Melanesia.

### Africa

In Africa south of the Sahara we find lands that have been full of difficulties of climate and crops, of insect-borne diseases and difficult rivers emerging on to harbourless coasts. If the discovery of America brought new crops to Africa, it immensely extended the age-old slave trade and so undermined much of the social effort that African peoples had maintained in face of a hostile climate and vegetation, insects and parasites. And now, even if slavery has been nearly extinguished, the intrusion of world commerce has presented too often to African peoples the alternative of submission to exploitation or of taking a sudden leap across what it has taken Europeans some thousands of years to pass over. It is only with deeper knowledge that we can hope to mitigate threatened evils, many due less to ill will or selfishness than to the inevitableness of crises following the introduction of scraps of European ideas. But let us make no mistake. The African peoples do not retreat into a background on the way to extinction; they multiply and learn one thing after another from the Europeans, who must give them scope and hope if disaster is to be avoided.

### Racial Differences

Finally, we ask ourselves how men, ultimately of common ancestry, have come to be different from one another in body. That is one great subject of research which has been badly mistreated by seekers after power anxious to find some justification for aggression. We cannot scientifically divide mankind into groups that have been separate since their first divergence. We have rather a series of drifts of men in every direction, often, but not always, retaining immemorial features of their bony structure, but becoming darker-skinned in some environments and paler-skinned in others. We have, therefore, not a white race and a black race, but a series of drifts in two opposite directions, the earlier drifts in both cases having several bony features in common, and late drifts, too, in some measure. Yet in Europe they have paled, in Africa south of the Sahara they have darkened.

How have men, ultimately of common ancestry, come to be different in mind and outlook? Some, generally pushed into unkind deserts and forests by better equipped folk, have clung to the early mode of getting food by hunting and collecting. Others, producing food first by cultivation and in due course by keeping farm animals, have had different accumulations of experience handed down the generations with much forgetfulness on the way. They may, in north-west Europe, have ultimately found oats as a weed in the fields of the wheat their forefathers had brought from south-western Asia. In Africa and parts of Europe they may profit by the maize brought in from America after the voyages of discovery. The efforts made in so many parts of the world to get more people living on a given piece of land are marvellously different results of the power of the reproductive instinct. The areas of river-mud in regions of warm summer rain and the areas of intensive factory industry have the greatest achievements in this direction, and how different they are! And people are beginning to wonder whether this crowding of men is the aim that is worth while, whether it is an inevitable concession to the reproductive instinct, or whether it can be altered by persuasive means.

Increase of population in western Europe slowed down after standards of living rose. Although progress in infant welfare and in medical and sanitary science all tended towards a reduced death-rate, and concealed to some extent the slowing down process; yet this reduced death-rate itself, especially amongst girls, led gradually, by way of more working women, later marriage and consequently smaller families, to an acceleration of the slowing down process. How far a rise in standards of living in Eastern countries would tend to halt the increase of their populations is an open question.

### "We Know in Part"

So in this book the efforts of men towards the good life in many environments are reviewed, it is hoped, with sympathy and a deep conviction that the mixing of thoughts and experiences is the most fruitful, even the most essential, factor of improvement, however difficult it may be to develop and maintain peace when that intercourse brings clashes that give too ready opportunities to the love of power so deeply rooted in our race.

One, as it were, uses a great variety of colours to try to make a picture—never, indeed, a complete photographic reproduction, but rather a selective effort that recognizes to the fullest extent the truth of the ancient saying that "We know in part."

Fig. 1. *Vesuvius during the spectacular eruption of 1944, showing the cone of molten lava. Since the historic eruption of A.D. 79, when the cities of Pompeii and Herculaneum were overwhelmed by ashes and lava, Vesuvius has enjoyed long periods of tranquillity.*

CHAPTER I

# THE PLANET EARTH

THE earth on which we live is a ball of rock and metal nearly 8,000 miles in diameter. It is one of the smaller members of a family of nine such bodies which revolve round the sun. The sun itself is a small star, and its nine principal attendants are called planets. Some of these have their own attendant families of moons. The earth, for example, possesses one such satellite, Mars has two, and Jupiter eleven. The sizes of the planets, as well as the order of their distances, in relation to the sun and to each other, are shown diagrammatically in Figure 2.

### Day and Night

The distance of the earth from the sun varies from 91,300,000 miles in January to 94,500,000 miles in July. During its journey round the sun, which it accomplishes once every year, the earth rotates on its axis very nearly 365¼ times. Each such rotation is called a day, and brings all places on the earth's surface alternately into sunshine (day) and shadow (night).

The two ends of the earth's axis are known as the Poles, and an imaginary line drawn on the earth's surface midway between the Poles is known as the Equator. The Equator thus divides the earth into two parts—the Northern and Southern Hemispheres.

For convenience in defining the positions of places, circles called "parallels of latitude" are drawn round the globe parallel with the Equator, at intervals of one degree of arc (about sixty-nine miles). These circles get smaller and smaller as they approach the Poles, and vanish in a point at the Poles themselves. The Equator is at latitude 0 degrees, and the Poles are at 90 degrees north or south of the Equator.

Once the latitude of a place has been fixed, its exact location can be given by measuring, in degrees, its distance east or west of a line running from the North Pole to the South Pole through Greenwich. By convention, this line (known as the Prime Meridian) is numbered longitude 0 degrees. Similar meridians of longitude are drawn at intervals of 1 degree east and west of Greenwich, longitude 180 degrees marking where they meet on the other side of the globe. Thus, New Orleans is said to be at latitude 30 degrees N. and longitude 90 degrees W., or, more briefly, 30° N., 90° W.

If the earth's axis were perpendicular to the plane of its orbit round the sun, every place on its surface would have twelve hours day and twelve hours night throughout the year. The axis is, however, inclined to this plane at an angle of 66½ degrees, its position at four different times of the year being shown in Fig. 3. This inclination of the earth's axis has far-reaching effects on the climate and geography of the globe, and is, in fact, the prime cause of the seasons—spring, summer, autumn and winter.

### The Seasons

When the North Pole is inclined towards the sun the South Pole is directed away from it, and at such times places situated very near the North Pole will perform their twenty-four-hour rotation in continuous sunshine. This is what is meant when we speak of the "land of the midnight sun." At the same time, places very near the South Pole will undergo periods of twenty-four hours in complete darkness. These extreme conditions are found north of latitude 66½ degrees N. (the Arctic

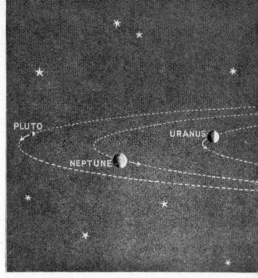

FIG. 2. *The principal members of the Solar System, showing their sizes compared with that of the sun, and the order of their distances from the sun. If their distances were given on the same scale as their sizes the diagram would have to be about 400 yards wide. The planets rotate counter-clockwise on their axes, and also follow their orbits in a counter-clockwise direction. The farther the planet from the sun the longer it takes to complete its orbit, the range extending from Mercury, whose year is about 88 of our days, to Pluto, whose year is probably about 200 of our years.*

Circle), and south of latitude 66½ degrees S. (the Antarctic Circle). Between these two latitudes there is a gradual transition from perpetual day to perpetual night, all places north of the Equator having a longer day than night, and all places south of the Equator having a longer night than day. Only at the Equator itself are day and night always of approximately equal duration.

At such times, the Northern Hemisphere not only gets more than its normal share of sunshine during the twenty-four hours, but the sun's rays also fall more directly on to the ground, giving a greater intensity of light and warmth. The Northern Hemisphere is then enjoying its summer season, in spite of the fact that the earth is—in July—at its greatest distance from the sun. In the Southern Hemisphere it is winter.

Six months later, when the earth has travelled half-way round its orbit, the conditions are reversed. The Northern Hemisphere is now inclined away from the sun, and is undergoing its winter, while the Southern Hemisphere has its summer. At the intermediate stages, in March and September (the "Equinoxes"), the earth's axis, though still inclined, is directed neither towards nor away from the sun,

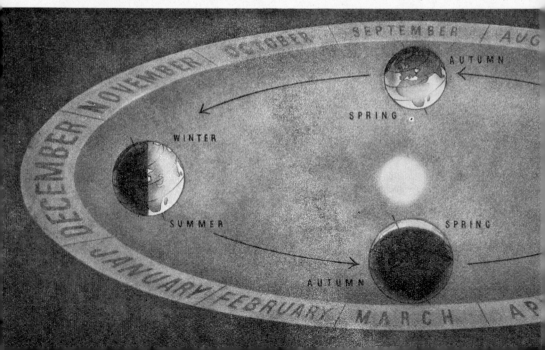

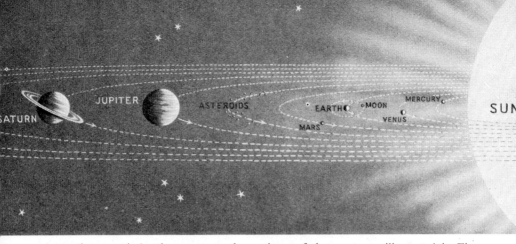

and at these periods there are twelve hours day and twelve hours night all over the world.

There is visible evidence of these astronomical changes in the height of the sun above the horizon at noon. In summer the noonday sun is much higher in the sky than it is in winter. In March and September the midday sun is overhead at the Equator, but in June it is overhead at latitude $23\frac{1}{2}$ degrees N. (the Tropic of Cancer), and in December at latitude $23\frac{1}{2}$ degrees S. (the Tropic of Capricorn). The apparent paths of the sun through the sky at different places, and at different times of the year, are illustrated in Figs. 4, 5 and 6.

Throughout history men have speculated on the mode of origin of the earth and other planets. Many modern theories suggest that the matter of which they are composed was torn out of the sun by the disruptive action of a passing star, and that the ejected matter coalesced to form the individual planets.

Such conjectures as to the origin of the earth appear to receive confirmation from investigations into the constitution of the earth itself. Physicists have "weighed" the earth, and say its average density is

FIG. 3. *The position of the earth at the four seasons. The earth's axis remains tilted in the same direction throughout the year, its North Pole pointing approximately to the Pole Star. Note that the edge of the shadow runs through the Poles at spring and autumn, but not at summer and winter. Though the earth rotates on its axis about $365\frac{1}{4}$ times while it makes one revolution about the sun, a Calendar Year is reckoned to consist of 365 days only. The odd quarters of a day amount to a whole day every four years, when an extra day is added to the month of February, such years of 366 days being called "Leap Years." This adjustment rather overdoes the necessary correction, therefore the last year of each century is not treated as a leap year unless it is exactly divisible by 400. Thus, at the end of last century, 1900 was not treated as leap year, but the year 2000 will be.*

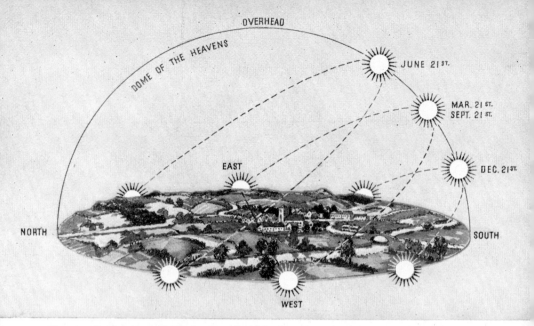

FIG. 4.    *In Temperate latitudes—i.e. latitudes lying outside the Arctic and Antarctic Circles, but not between the Tropics—the sun rises due east and sets due west on two occasions only each year, in spring and autumn respectively.   In the northern summer the sun rises to the north of east and sets to the north of west, giving long days and short nights. In winter, it rises to the south of east and sets to the south of west, which means that days are short and nights are long.   In the Southern Hemisphere the opposite takes place.*

FIG. 5.    *On the Equator there is very little variation in either the length of the day or the altitude of the noonday sun throughout the year, and in consequence there is no division of the year into seasons.   The noonday sun is exactly overhead in March and September. Sunrise and sunset always occur at about 6 a.m. and 6 p.m. respectively, and take place rapidly, the twilight being of very short duration.*

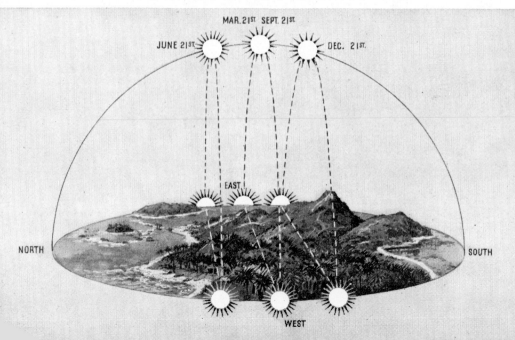

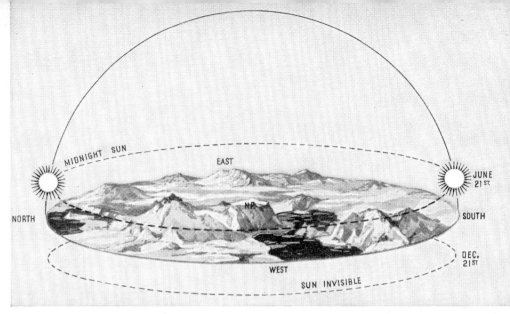

FIG. 6. *At the Poles, the sun travels round, and on a level with, the horizon at the Equinoxes, rising above it in summer and dropping below it in winter. For about four months of the year the sun is entirely above the horizon and for four months entirely below it. Its daily motion round the sky does not involve "rising" and "setting."*

five-and-a-half times that of water. But the average density of the surface rocks is less than three times that of water; consequently, the central "core" of the earth must consist of heavy material with a density approximately seven times that of water. Other considerations lead to the conclusion that this central core is composed of iron with an admixture of nickel and a small quantity of other metals.

The temperature of this central core is so high that any known substance would melt, but the pressure of the overlying rocks is so great that the earth as a whole is almost as rigid as steel. Nevertheless, under certain conditions portions of the mass may become liquid, or even "flow" without actual liquefaction.

The study of earthquake waves has added greatly to our knowledge of the structure and composition of the earth's interior. Careful records of such waves have shown that the earth consists of the following concentric "shells" around the central core (Fig. 7):

(1) a surface layer of sedimentary rocks, nowhere exceeding six miles in thickness, and in many places completely absent;

(2) a layer of crystalline rocks similar to granite, with a thickness of twenty-five to thirty miles, which is known as the *sial*, since these rocks are rich in *si*lica and *al*umina;

(3) a layer of heavier rocks, some 700 miles thick, which is known as the *sima*, since it is rich in *si*lica and *ma*gnesia;

(4) a transitional "olivine" layer of still heavier rock, with a dense metallic core at a depth of some 1,800 miles.

The total thickness of the sedimentary rocks and the *sial* and *sima* varies greatly in different parts of the earth. Mountain ranges have "roots" of *sial* extending far down into the *sima*. The continents, with their mountain systems, are floating like rafts in the heavier *sima*, even though the *sima* itself is not actually in a liquid state.

The conception of the continents as rafts of *sial* "floating" on the heavier *sima* led Wegener to develop his theory of Continental Drift, whereby he sought to explain, not only the conformity of structure and shape of opposing continental shores such as the eastern and western coasts of the Atlantic, but also the distribution of certain forms of life, living and extinct. As shown in Fig. 8, he assumed that the

9

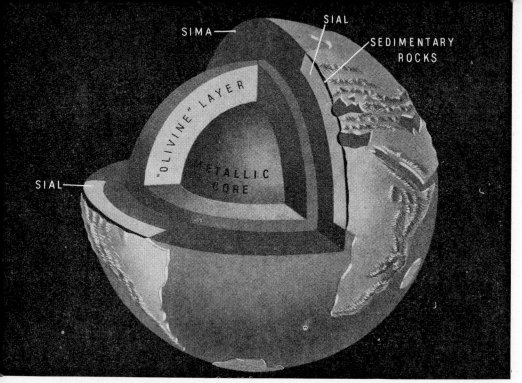

FIG. 7. *A pictorial section through the earth, showing the concentric shells of different types of rock surrounding the metallic core. The thicknesses shown are not in strict proportion.*

continents were originally grouped together in one land-mass, which he called *Pangœa*.

According to the theory, a portion of the land is supposed to have "drifted" away westward to form North America, while the major mass in the north formed Euro-Asia. The southern portion broke up and drifted apart to form the present conti-nental masses of South America, Africa and Australia, the plateau of Arabia, and the Deccan plateau in India.

The theory of Continental Drift may not be acceptable in its entirety, but it is of value to the geographer for the compre-hensive view it gives of the main structural features of the continents and oceans.

## THE TIDES

THE waters of the oceans rise and fall periodically in what are known as "tides." These are due principally to the attractive force between the earth and the moon and sun. Though the sun is sixty million times the size of the moon it is so much farther from the earth that its tidal influence is comparatively small.

At new and full moon the earth, moon, and sun are in a straight line, and the lunar tides are enhanced by the slight tidal effect of the sun. Such extra high (and low) tides are called "spring tides," a term which bears no relation to the season of spring. When the moon is at first or last quarter (half-moon) the lunar and solar effects are opposed to one another and the reduced tides which result are known as "neap tides."

Though the moon is said to revolve about the earth, it is truer to say that the moon and earth revolve about each other, their common centre of revolution lying very close to the more massive body, the earth. In point of fact, it lies about a thousand miles beneath the surface of the earth, which, therefore, performs a sort of "wobble" rather than a revolution. Fig. 9 shows how a tide is caused on one side of the earth by the pull of the moon and another on the other side by the earth's "wobble." The earth spins on its axis beneath these two tides, so that we may say, provisionally, that every point on the earth's surface encounters two high tides per day.

However, the moon, in consequence of its own motion, rises about three-quarters of an hour later each night, which means that the tides actually occur at intervals of about twelve and a half hours, while their times of arrival at different places on the earth are conditioned by the disposition of the continental masses. In the Antarctic Ocean, where there are no intervening continents, the tide moves freely from east to west in two long waves which measure some 6,000 miles from crest to crest, i.e. from one high tide to the next. Each of these tide waves, approximating to the theoretically ideal tide, sends one branch northward into the Indian Ocean and another northward into the Atlantic. The Pacific Ocean is so large that it has a tide-wave of its own.

As the Atlantic tide moves northward, the sides of the wave lag farther and farther behind the middle of the wave. The main bulge bends north-east toward the gap between Iceland and Norway, so that in Europe the tides approach from the west instead of from the east.

FIG. 8. *The world prior to Carboniferous times (300,000,000 years ago) according to Wegener, who named the single large land-mass "Pangæa." Note the position of the Equator.*

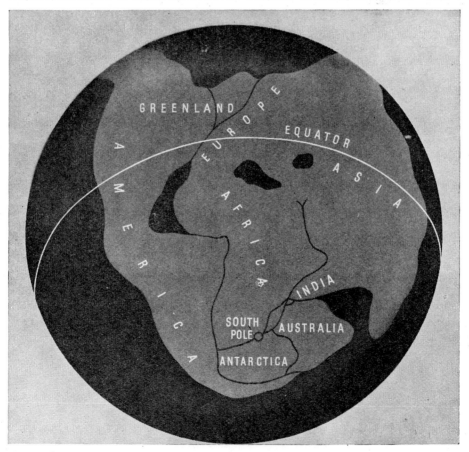

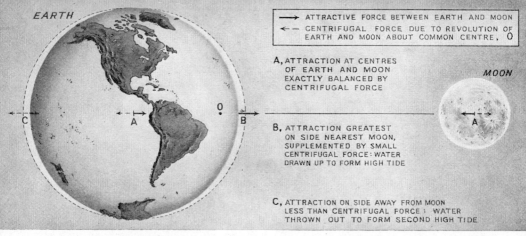

ATTRACTIVE FORCE BETWEEN EARTH AND MOON
CENTRIFUGAL FORCE DUE TO REVOLUTION OF
EARTH AND MOON ABOUT COMMON CENTRE, O

A, ATTRACTION AT CENTRES
OF EARTH AND MOON
EXACTLY BALANCED BY
CENTRIFUGAL FORCE

B, ATTRACTION GREATEST
ON SIDE NEAREST MOON,
SUPPLEMENTED BY SMALL
CENTRIFUGAL FORCE: WATER
DRAWN UP TO FORM HIGH TIDE

C, ATTRACTION ON SIDE AWAY FROM MOON
LESS THAN CENTRIFUGAL FORCE: WATER
THROWN OUT TO FORM SECOND HIGH TIDE

FIG. 9. *How the tides are caused. The attraction between earth and moon tends to draw these bodies together, but is opposed by the centrifugal force which operates outwards from their common centre of revolution* (O). *These two forces are exactly balanced at the centres of the earth and moon* (A), *thus maintaining a constant distance between the two bodies.*

In the Atlantic the interval between successive high tides approximates to the "ideal" period of 12 hours 25 minutes; in the ocean off Southern Asia and in the Caribbean Sea there is only one high tide per day; on the Pacific shores each alternate high tide is only partly developed.

Not only are there great variations in the times between high and low tides, but there are also great differences in the range of the tide, that is, in the height between high and low tide. In the open ocean the range of tide is so small as to be scarcely noticeable, but as the tide-wave approaches the coast it increases in height, and on open coasts the average range is from five to ten feet. Local circumstances cause great variations in the tidal range; Liverpool, for example, has a range of 29 feet, Cherbourg 16 feet, and islands of the central Pacific only 2 feet. At St. Malo the tidal range is sometimes as great as 40 feet.

Enclosed seas, such as the Mediterranean and the Baltic, have hardly any tide; semi-enclosed seas like the Caribbean have a tidal range of less than 2 feet.

The highest tides are experienced in certain funnel-shaped estuaries where the advancing wave of the tide is progressively compressed between converging shores, forming a huge breaker which rushes up the estuary at considerable speed. In the Severn estuary this phenomenon is called the *bore*, on the Trent it is the *eagre*, and on the Amazon it is known as the *pororoca*.

In the Bay of Fundy the tide may rise to a height of almost 50 feet, and the tide-wave advances with startling and even dangerous rapidity. Among the noteworthy effects of this phenomenally high tide are the so-called "reversing" falls of the St. John River. At low tide the river bed slopes steeply to the sea, causing rapids in the lower course below Saint John; at high tide the water in the Bay of Fundy may be 10 or 15 feet higher than the river, and the bore rushes up the estuary to form inward-flowing rapids.

Narrow straits connecting seas which have high tides at different times are subject to strong currents which alternate in direction as high tide reaches first one end and then the other end of the strait.

The potential energy of the tides is sufficient to supply all human needs, but it is doubtful if it will ever be economically advantageous to develop tidal power on a really large scale.

The Severn estuary provides one of the world's most advantageous sites for such a scheme, and detailed plans have been drawn up whereby some two thousand million kilowatt-hours of electricity could be generated, the equivalent of a million tons of coal a year. The project would involve the building of a barrier some two-and-a-half miles long to impound the water at high tide. With the fall of the tide electricity would be generated by water flowing from the basin through the turbines.

# STRUCTURE OF CONTINENTS

THE major surface features of the earth are the result of long epochs of mountain building, denudation, and deposition. In the 2,000 million years or more since the earth first took shape at least nine major periods of mountain building have occurred. The mountains formed during the first six of these periods have been almost entirely obliterated, leaving only minor traces on the present surface of the land; but the last three—known as the Caledonian, the Hercynian, and the Alpine periods of folding—have been of major importance in determining the structure and form of the present continents.

## Building and Rebuilding

The Alpine period of folding began a mere seventy million years ago and is now in its final stage of weak vertical movements of the crust. All the large mountain ranges of the present time belong to this period of folding, not because the folding was more intense than its predecessors, but simply because it is the most recent. From twenty to fifty million years have not been sufficient for Nature to destroy her own handiwork, as she has almost succeeded in doing in the case of the older formations.

Evidence that earthquakes and volcanoes are concomitants of the process of mountain building is seen in the map showing these phenomena (Fig. 10).

The primeval core of Europe is the so-called Baltic Shield, which has been a stable land mass during the whole period of life on the earth. On the north-western borders of the Shield are the Caledonian remnants of Scandinavia and the highland areas of the British Isles; to the south the remnants of the Hercynian folding are seen broken and re-uplifted in the block plateaux of Bohemia, the Black Forest, the Vosges, central France and the Meseta of Spain, and in the east-west ridges of Brittany, Cornwall, Devon and south-west Ireland.

Southward again are the Alpine folds whose form has been largely determined by the position of the stable Hercynian remnants, which were themselves fragmented by the convulsions accompanying the Alpine folding.

The lowlands which seem to bind these structural elements together as a matrix are in reality a mere veneer of sedimentary rocks and unconsolidated sediments derived from the wastage of the highlands.

In Asia the stable blocks are distributed around the periphery. In the north (pages 126, 127) are the ancient peneplains of the Baltic Shield and the Angara or Siberian Shield; in the south (Fig. 221; page 230) are the plateaux of Arabia and India. To these must be added the Chinese tableland on the east. Each of these ancient blocks is buried, partly or completely as the case may be, by sedimentary rocks.

The block of peninsular India similarly extends below the very thick recent deposits of the Indo-Gangetic Plain to the foot of the Himalayas; the Siberian block is covered with recent sediments in the west and with very ancient rocks in the east. Though it is the surface rocks which exercise immediate control over the activities of men, it is necessary in this, as in many other cases, to look to the underlying rocks if we wish to understand fully the setting in which human society has developed.

## All Stages Represented

The Central Asian belt of mountain ranges, plateaux and basins, which lies between the Angara block to the north and Arabia and India to the south, has had a complex geological history. The most northerly ranges, on the southern border of the Angara Shield, belong to the Caledonian system; the central ranges, from the Altai to the Kuen-Lun were first folded in Hercynian times, though they have also been subject to more recent uplift. South of the Kuen-Lun, the Himalaya, Arakan Yoma and allied ranges are mainly of Alpine date, while the East Indies probably represent a mountain chain still in process of formation.

The festoons of islands (Fig. 10) and peninsulas of the Pacific coast of Asia are undoubtedly due to the Alpine movements.

It seems clear that Asia, like Europe, has "grown" by the continued accretion of fold mountains around the nuclei of the ancient stable masses.

North America comprises three main structural elements: the ancient stable block of the Laurentian or Canadian Shield (Fig. 111), now covered by deposits in its south-western parts; the Hercynian area of the south-eastern quadrant represented by the Appalachians in the east, but completely hidden by sedimentary rocks in the Mississippi basin; and the "Alpine" folds of the Rockies in the west (pages 160, 161).

Africa is unique among the continents in its block-like structure and in the almost complete absence of fold mountains—the only accretion it has received since the earliest geological times is the extension of the Alpine fold system in the Atlas region. While other continents were being subjected to periods of mountain formation, Africa remained a relatively stationary block, though it was subjected to periods of uplift and warping which caused the plateau to be subdivided into a series of shallow basins (pages 212, 213).

The Great Rift Valley of Africa (Figs. 16, 141) owes its origin to vertical movements, but geologists are not agreed as to the exact mode of its origin. Some hold that the valley was formed by subsidence between parallel faults, others that it is a narrow strip of the crust held down by blocks overriding on either side.

# THE OCEANS

THE ocean basins are not merely parts of the land surface which have been submerged; they are fundamentally different from the continents in structure and in geological history. The continents have grown by accretion through the ages; they have been alternately uplifted and partly submerged beneath shallow seas; their surface features have been remodelled by denudation and deposition.

The ocean basins, on the other hand, are relatively permanent and stable features of the earth's surface. There is strong evidence that, while the sedimentary rocks of the continental surface were being deposited in the shallow seas or the narrow

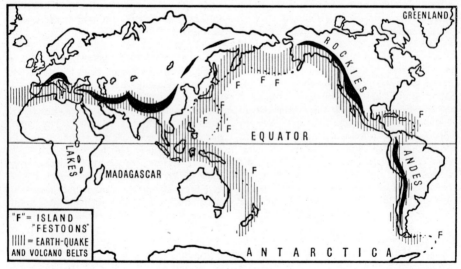

FIG. 10. *The earthquake and volcanic regions of the world. Note the so-called "Ring of Fire" encircling the Pacific. The heavy black masses show the great fold-mountain systems*

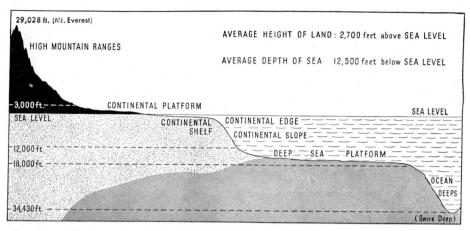

FIG. 11. *Diagram of a section of the earth's surface, showing proportions at different levels.*

troughs adjacent to the continents, the vast expanses of the ocean floor remained through long geological eras free from the deposition of rock waste and undisturbed by the processes of mountain building. The fundamental difference is shown also in the types of rocks. Whereas the continents are rafts of sial floating on the heavier sima, the oceanic basins consist almost entirely of sima.

Certain important aspects of the land surface and of the ocean are illustrated in section in Fig. 11.

(1) The average profile of the land surface is concave, while the form of the ocean bed is predominantly convex. This difference springs mainly from the fact that the land surface profile has been determined by denudation and deposition, while the ocean bed, being outside the range of these agencies, maintains the form imposed upon it by earth movements.

(2) There are two predominant levels of the earth's solid surface—the continental platform between sea level and 3,000 feet above it, and the deep-sea platform, between 12,000 feet and 18,000 feet below sea level. The first comprises approximately 70 per cent of the land surface and the latter 60 per cent of the ocean bed.

(3) The greatest height of the land (Mt. Everest, 29,028 feet high) is less than the greatest depth of the sea (the Swire Deep, off the Philippines, 34,430 feet).

These extremes of elevation represent only a small proportion of the total surface, only 4 per cent of the land being over 12,000 feet in height, and only 7 per cent of the ocean floor being more than 18,000 feet deep.

(4) The Continental Shelf continues the gentle slope of the land surface beneath the sea to the Continental Edge at a depth of about 600 feet, beyond which it is succeeded by the comparatively steep Continental Slope, by which the sea bed drops to the deep-sea platform. Further trough-like depressions occur in the Ocean Deeps.

The Pacific is possibly the oldest surface feature of the earth; it has even been conjectured—probably erroneously—that it is the hollow formed when the substance of the moon was supposed to have been torn out of the earth.

The floor of the Pacific basin has a step-like character which seems to bear some relation to the systems of fold mountains by which it is encircled. A west-to-east section shows a series of backward-sloping steps which probably owe their origin to major crustal folds in process of formation. In the north-west Pacific two such steps are discernible; an inner one whose edge is marked by the festoons of islands from the Kuriles through Japan, Formosa and the Philippines to the East Indies; and an outer one marked by the Bonin, Mariana, Guam, and Pelew Islands. From the edges of these steps the sea bed plunges steeply to the greatest deeps known.

In the south-west Pacific a submarine platform extends eastward from Australia at a depth of less than 6,000 feet. From it rise the islands of New Guinea and New Zealand (pages 260, 261), and off its north-eastern fringe are the step-like ridges from which rise the islands of Melanesia, forming an inner festoon, and Micronesia, forming an outer festoon. From the outer festoon, the platform drops steeply to great ocean deeps. Beyond these the bed rises gently as a mid-Pacific platform terminating on the broad ridge which bears Easter Island and the Galapagos Islands. From there it drops to the trough of the next "wave," represented by the exceptionally deep sea off the coast of southern Peru, beyond which the Andes rise as the crest of another earth wave.

The islands of Micronesia rise abruptly from the mid-Pacific platform as separate volcanic cones or as groups of cones connected by submarine ridges. In many cases the volcanic cones are fringed or even completely masked by coral reefs.

Volcano islands occasionally appear above the surface during an eruption of a submarine volcano (Fig. 13), persist for a time, and then subside. If the rate of subsidence is slow, the growth of a coral reef surrounding the island may keep pace with it, so that when the island itself has disappeared the reef remains as an "atoll" enclosing a lagoon (Fig. 12).

The Atlantic is in many respects fundamentally different from the Pacific. The latter is a circular basin fringed by young fold mountains running parallel to the coast and at no great distance from it. The Atlantic, on the other hand, is an S-shaped trough which seems to have been formed, in the main, by fracturing. Its opposing shores show a remarkable similarity both of form and structure, and the land forms of its hinterland are ancient fold mountains, plateaux, and their intervening plains.

The Pacific, rimmed by high mountains, receives comparatively few large rivers, whereas the rivers flowing to the Atlantic drain a large proportion of the adjoining continents. Indeed, though the Atlantic is only half the size of the Pacific, the area of the land surface which drains to it is more than twice that draining to the Pacific.

These differences account, in some measure, for the historical differences in the development of human society in the regions fronting the two oceans. The deeply-indented transverse coastline of the Atlantic basin, together with the ease of access from the sea to broad fertile plains and, by river highways, to the remote continental interiors, favoured the economic and social development of the regions contributory to the basin.

The most remarkable feature of the Atlantic basin is undoubtedly the great medial S-shaped up-swelling known as the Dolphin Ridge in the North Atlantic and as the Challenger Ridge in the South Atlantic. In the north the Atlantic is separated from the Arctic Ocean by a submarine ridge which runs from Greenland via Iceland and the Faroes to Scotland.

All these submarine ridges have a noteworthy effect on the distribution of warm and cold waters in the Atlantic. For example, the ridge through Iceland considerably restricts the flow of cold water in depth from the Arctic into the Atlantic, while per-

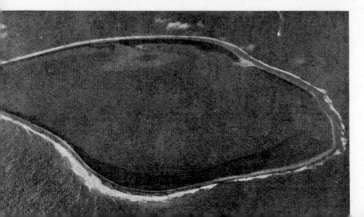

Fig. 12. *An air view of Clipperton Island, a true atoll in the North Pacific. The original island has become submerged, leaving its coral reef to enclose a shallow lagoon. Such reefs may support palm trees and other vegetation. Access to the lagoon is usually afforded by small gaps in the reef.*

FIG. 13. *The birth of an island. Belching forth steam and sulphur, this island suddenly appeared in the Pacific Ocean about 200 miles south of Japan, in 1946. Trembling and rocking as fresh convulsions forced it upwards, it rose 50 feet in the first month.*

mitting the flow of warm surface water from the Atlantic to the Arctic.

The islands of the Atlantic fall into three categories: (a) continental islands, such as the British Isles and Newfoundland, which rise from the continental shelf; (b) those which rise from the median S-shaped ridge, (e.g. the Azores and the Cape Verde Islands); and (c) true oceanic islands which, like St. Helena, rise abruptly from the ocean floor.

In its structural form the Indian Ocean combines both "Atlantic" and "Pacific" features. Features of the "Atlantic" type include the Kerguelan Ridge, which extends from the Antarctic to India, with a branch connecting Madagascar and India, and the absence over the greater part of the ocean of abrupt slopes and isolated deeps. "Pacific" features are seen in the fringing folds of the East Indies, with the abrupt

slopes to great deeps close inshore; in the isolated deeps to the west and south of Australia; and in the paucity of large rivers draining into the ocean.

The Arctic Ocean (pages 290, 291) is almost land-locked, its connexion with the Atlantic being partly broken by the submarine ridge through Iceland. A second ridge running from north-east Greenland through Spitsbergen divides the ocean into two basins, the Greenland Sea, and the Arctic Sea which surrounds the North Pole. There is thus a double barrier to the passage into the Atlantic of the very cold waters from the Polar regions.

The Antarctic Ocean (page 300), on the other hand, is open on all sides to the neighbouring seas, and there are no barriers to the movement of its cold waters to the Pacific, Indian and Atlantic Oceans. It has no natural geographic boundaries.

17

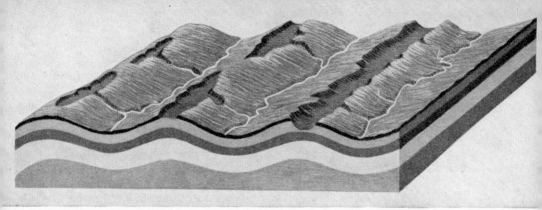

FIG. 14. *Diagram showing simple fold mountains as exemplified in the Jura (Alpine system). Note that weathering of the rocks has already begun along the crests of the anticlines.*

# MOUNTAINS

MOUNTAINS play a dual rôle in the development of human society. On the one hand their characteristic features combine to make them areas of scanty population; the steep slopes and harsh climatic conditions are unfavourable for agriculture; the rugged relief hinders communication, the spread of culture, and the establishment of central government; and the resulting paucity of population delays the full development of whatever resources the mountainous region may contain. On the other hand, the economic resources of the populous plains often owe their ultimate origin to the neighbouring mountains. The rock waste from the mountains provides the alluvium which builds up the fertile plain; the heavy rains and melting snows of the mountains feed the rivers on which human activities on the plains so largely depend; and the mountainous regions have often acted as rearing-grounds for virile peoples who have conquered and revitalized the peoples of the plains.

In modern times, however, the more frequent tendency has been for the more highly organized peoples of the plains to move upwards into the mountain zone in order to exploit the resources of timber, metals and water-power. The Germans, for instance, penetrated the mountain fringe of Bohemia in search of metals, thus establishing the alien fringe of Sudetenland which was in recent years so potent a cause of international strife.

*Types of Mountains.* Mountains may be divided into four main types in accordance with their mode of origin:

(1) Fold Mountains. (2) Block Mountains. (3) Residual Mountains. (4) Volcanic Mountains. (Figs. 14 to 17.)

(1) *Fold Mountains* are formed by the folding and crumpling of the rocks of the earth's crust, usually by lateral pressure. Practically all the great mountain ranges which exist at the present day—the Rockies, the Andes,. the Alps, the Himalaya, etc.—are fold mountains which were formed in comparatively recent geological times—say fifty million years ago.

FIG. 15. *Complex folding of the Alps, due to immense lateral pressure. See text.*

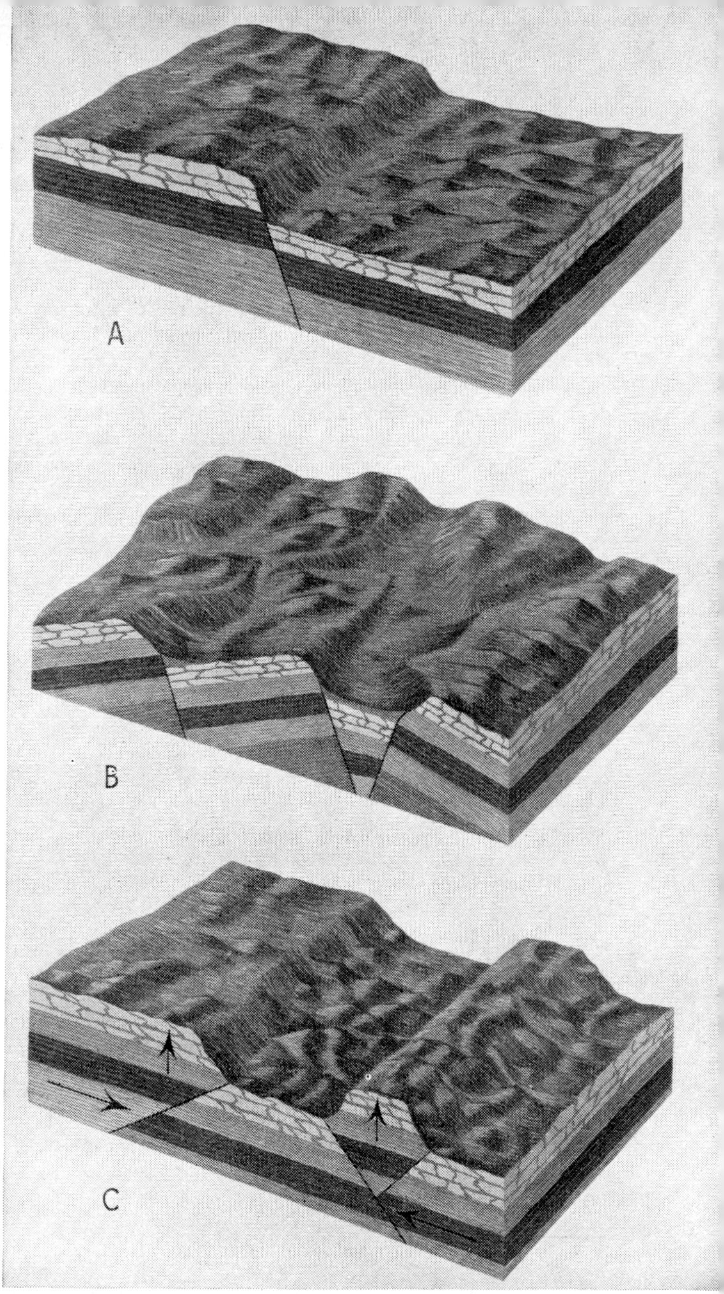

FIG. 16. *Types of block mountains.* (A) *Normal fault, causing a fault-scarp.* (B) *Step-faults on the left, trough-faults on the right, the latter causing a "graben" or rift valley.* (C) *Reversed faulting due to compression; faulted blocks pushed upwards, forming "horsts." Note that a rift valley may be caused either by downward normal faulting of a median block, or by reversed faulting thrusting up the blocks on each side of a median mass. Block mountains usually retain a plateau-like surface.*

Many degrees of complexity exist among the fold mountains of the world. The Jura Mountains are an outstanding example of simple folds, in which the anticline or arch (Fig. 14) forms the ridge, while the syncline or trough forms the valley. Erosion has so far succeeded only in wearing away the crests of the anticlines.

The complex history of a fold mountain system may be illustrated by the evolution of the Alps (Fig. 15). Some hundred million years ago the stable block of Africa was separated from a stable "European" block to the north by a deep "Mediterranean" trench, into which rivers poured vast quantities of sediment. Though the sea which occupied this trench was probably never very deep, many thousands of feet of *shallow-water* sediments were deposited in it, for the sea bed was continually sinking, possibly because of the constantly increasing weight of sediment laid upon it. Then the "African" block began to move slowly northward, crumpling up the sedimentary rocks of the trough in great folds which were overthrust upon each other and over the base of the "European" block to the north. It has been calculated that by this movement the distance between the two blocks was short-

19

ened by something like a thousand miles, and the titanic forces involved were able to twist masses of solid rock just as a child may tangle a bunch of ribbons.

The process of folding continued intermittently over a very long period, and as the mountains were raised up, their summits were being worn down by weathering.

In most mountain ranges, however, denudation has proceeded so far that the anticlines have been almost completely worn away and new mountains have then been carved out of the synclines, which are more resistant than the anticlines, since the rocks tend to be compressed in the synclines and stretched in the anticlines. Snowdon is a striking example of such synclinal mountains (Fig. 38.)

Mountain ranges are in course of time worn down to the roots to form *peneplains*. These may, however, be uplifted bodily, though, of course, very gradually, and so start on a second cycle of existence as mountains. The Appalachians of North America provide an excellent example of such a "rejuvenated" mountain system.

(2) *Block Mountains* are formed by vertical movements of blocks of the earth's crust along fault lines (Fig. 16). In some cases a block has been left standing up while the surrounding portions of the crust have subsided. Bohemia and the central plateau of France are of this type. An upthrusted block is sometimes called a "horst."

In other cases, block mountains are formed by the tilting of a fractured block, as in the case of the Sierra Nevada (U.S.A.), which consists of a single tilted block some 500 miles in length. Other types of block mountains were formed by lateral pressure from opposite directions, as in the case of the San Gabriel Mountains in California.

The form of the block mountains is, of course, modified by denudation, both during and after their formation, but they generally retain the plateau-like surface which distinguishes them topographically from fold mountains.

(3) *Residual Mountains*. Elevated regions may be so deeply dissected by weathering and river action that only the remnants stand out as mountains. The Catskill Mountains of New York State are an excellent example of such "residual" mountains, as they have been carved out of nearly horizontal strata by erosion alone. As noted above, raised peneplains composed of intensely folded rocks may also take on a new lease of life and be carved into residual mountains. Thus the Highlands of Scotland are residual mountains which have been carved out of a tilted block of land which was itself the uplifted remnant of a former mountain range.

In arid regions in which the uppermost layers of rocks are approximately horizontal, weathering unaccompanied by river action gives rise to the "*mesa* and *butte*" type of scenery (Figs. 72, 110).

(4) *Mountains due to Volcanic Action.* It is a well-known fact that the temperature in a mine or bore-hole increases at the rate of about 1 degree for every 60 feet of descent. If this increase is maintained, it is obvious that the temperature within, say, a score of miles of the surface will be sufficiently high to melt the rocks. On the other hand the pressure of the overlying rocks will be so great as to maintain the rocks in an effectively solid state, as is proved to be the case by examination of the behaviour of earthquake waves.

### Molten Rock

But with any temporary release of pressure, as, for example, by fracture, the overheated rock becomes molten and is squeezed upwards through joints, beddingplanes, or any other lines of weakness. If this molten rock reaches the surface it will form volcanoes or lava flows; but even should it fail to reach the surface it may profoundly modify the surface features. It is, therefore, convenient to include in this section not only actual volcanoes, but also all those land-forms which are due to the upwelling of molten rock.

*Bathyliths* are huge oval-shaped masses of granite or similar (igneous) rocks found in the central cores of many mountain ranges. The rocks of which they are composed could have solidified only at great depths and under great pressure, and the fact that they are now found at the sur-

Fɪɢ. 17.  *Sectional diagram of a volcano.  The slope of the cone varies according to the size of fragments ejected and the degree of fluidity of the lava.*

face is an indication of the vastness of the quantity of overlying rock which must have been removed by denudation. As the rocks of which the bathyliths are composed are very resistant to weathering, the course of former mountain ranges may often be marked by lines of bathyliths, such as those which form the parallel granite ridges of Brittany.

*Laccolites* are mushroom-like masses of formerly liquid rock whose upwelling has lifted the over-lying strata. As in the case of bathyliths, the overlying rock may be worn away, leaving a dome-shaped highland of granite rocks fringed by the remnants of the uplifted sedimentaries. Dartmoor is a granite laccolite fringed by beds of limestone and other rocks which formerly extended over the granite.

*Volcanoes.* The essential feature of a volcano is the vent in the earth's crust through which liquid lava, hot gases and ashes are poured out on the surface. The volcanic cone is a secondary feature, built up by the lava and ashes ejected from the vent, as shown in Figs. 1 and 17.

The form of the volcanic cone depends upon the type of material ejected. Steepsided cones, with an angle of slope of 30 to 40 degrees, are always of the explosive type, which from time to time hurl into the air great clouds of dust, ashes and rock fragments. Volcanoes of the non-explosive type erupt by the effusion of lava, which solidifies to form a flat cone. The most striking examples of this latter type are Mauna Loa and Mauna Kea (Fig. 189), on the island of Hawaii. At its base on the bed of the Pacific, at a depth of 16,000 feet, the cone of Mauna Loa has a diameter of over 100 miles; from this base it slopes up very gradually to a height of

14,000 feet above sea level, the total height of the cone being thus 30,000 feet.

Most volcanoes are intermediate in type between the purely explosive and the purely effusive; their cones are therefore built up of layers of both lava and ashes, and the angle of slope varies.

*Fissure eruptions.* The most impressive effects of volcanic activity are to be seen, not in the picturesque cones, but in vast lava flows which have welled up from fissures in the earth's crust. Iceland has frequently experienced such eruptions during the last 200 years. In 1783, for example, molten lava poured out of a fissure 20 miles long and streams of lava several miles wide "flooded" the surface of the land to a distance of 50 miles from the vent.

In past ages fissure eruptions of this type have built up extensive lava plateaux. The Columbia-Snake lava plateau, which covers an area of 200,000 square miles of north-western U.S.A., was built up by successive layers of lava which together have a thickness of over 4,000 feet. Valleys were filled and the hills submerged, and only the highest mountains left standing out as islands above the congealed flood of lava.

Another lava flow of comparable extent, though of much older date, is that of the "trap" lands of the north-western Deccan in India. In the British Isles the most notable example is the lava flow which formerly joined northern Ireland to Scotland, and whose remnants now form Giant's Causeway (Fig. 19) and Fingal's Cave on the Island of Staffa.

*The Distribution of Volcanoes.* Volcanic activity at the present time is almost restricted to two well-defined zones. One is the so-called Pacific Ring of Fire, which includes the Andes, Central America, the Rockies, the Aleutian Isles, Japan, the Philippines, the New Hebrides and New Zealand; the other includes the East Indies, Malaya, Burma, East Africa and the Mediterranean, crossing the Atlantic via the Azores and the Canary Islands, to link up with the island arcs of the West Indies (Fig. 10).

It will be noted that these volcanic regions coincide in the main with the areas subject to earthquakes, and that they are also regions in which mountain-building movements of the earth's crust occurred in recent geological times.

*Effects of Vulcanicity.* Soils formed by the weathering of volcanic ashes and lava are often of such great fertility as to attract a large agricultural population. It is, however, to the vulcanicity of far distant geological ages that we must look for the most notable effects on human activities.

Here and there the sites of ancient volcanoes have proved of considerable strategic importance. It has often happened that in the last stage of activity the pipe of the volcano has become choked with lava which on cooling has formed rock more resistant to weathering than the fragmentary material of which the cone was formed; consequently, this volcanic "plug" has remained standing out as a prominent crag which may have been utilized as the site of a fortress. Towns on or around such volcanic plugs include Edinburgh and Stirling, and Le Puy, with its conical rock, on the central plateau of France (Fig. 18).

FIG. 18. *Le Puy, Haute-Loire, France. This is one of a line of volcanic plugs and extinct volcanoes which runs from north to south across the Auvergne plateau of central France. Some of these plugs are formed of solidified lava, while others have been built up by deposits of volcanic ash. Their shapes, therefore, vary considerably.*

FIG. 19. *Columns of basalt forming the Giant's Causeway, N. Ireland. The lava sheet formerly extended to the Scottish coast, where similar columns are found in Fingal's Cave.*

# ROCKS, MINERALS AND SOILS

ONE of the determining factors in the geography of any region is the types of rock of which it is composed; the geographer must, therefore, be familiar with the characteristics of the different kinds of rock in so far as these are related to and influence human activities.

Rocks may be classified into four main groups according to their mode of origin: (1) Igneous. (2) Sedimentary. (3) Organic. (4) Metamorphic.

(1) *Igneous rocks* are those which have consolidated from a state of fusion, and include Volcanic, Plutonic and Intrusive rocks. Their characteristics vary according to the chemical composition of the original rock magma and with the conditions under which they solidified.

*Volcanic* rocks are formed from lava which cooled on the surface of the earth.

They include pumice, certain glassy rocks such as obsidian, and basalt—the dark, heavy, fine-grained rock of which the Giant's Causeway is formed.

*Plutonic* rocks are those which solidified far down in the earth's crust under great pressure. These conditions favoured the growth of crystals, and the typical plutonic rocks, such as granite and syenite, are coarsely crystalline.

*Intrusive* rocks were formed from liquid magma which forced its way through or between the upper layers of surface rocks. Masses of intrusive rocks which break across the strata are known as dykes, while those which were intruded between the layers are known as sills.

(2) *Sedimentary* rocks are those whose constituents are derived from other rocks, transported by wind, water or ice, and

FIG. 20. *Rock structures favourable to the accumulation of oil. Note concentrations of oil in the porous sandstone and the "sealing" of oil pools by surrounding impervious rock.*

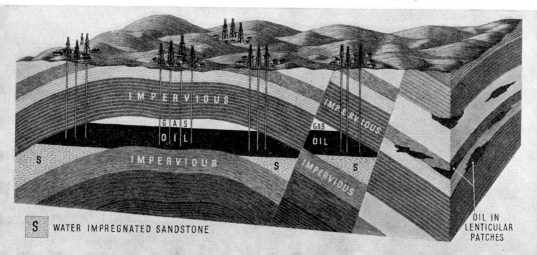

deposited in lakes, seas, or on the surface of the land. They include sandstones, shales and clay.

(3) *Organic* rocks are derived from the remains of plants or animals. Limestone and chalk consist largely of such remains, though some of the calcium carbonate of which they are formed was deposited as the result of chemical action.

(4) *Metamorphic* rocks are those which have been changed from their original condition by heat or pressure. They include marble (an altered limestone) and slate (an altered shale).

### Ores and Minerals

The constituent substances of which the various rocks are composed are called *minerals*, and these are generally classified, according to their chemical composition, as oxides, sulphides, carbonates, silicates, and so on. Those from which metals can be extracted are further termed *ores*. Gold is the only metal to be extensively mined in the pure state, though several other metals are known to occur in a pure form in commercially useless quantities.

The percolation of water through the cracks in the rocks often results in the removal of certain minerals by solution. These may be deposited again in crystalline form when the water evaporates, the deposition tending to occur upon existing crystals of the same composition. Thus, a valuable mineral which was formerly scattered through the rocks over a large area may become concentrated in a few rich deposits. Such deposits may be found in cracks and fissures, where they are known as "veins" or "lodes," or they may occur as nodules or sheets (seams) embedded in the rocks. Copper, lead and zinc ores are often found in lodes, iron and manganese ores in seams.

Coal is the product of the decayed vegetation of swamp-forests which in the remote past extended over large parts of the earth's surface (Figs. 21 and 22). The decaying vegetation first accumulated to form layers of peat. Then the land subsided and the peat was buried under thick layers of sediment. Compression of the peat by the overlying sediments

produced coal, while the sediments themselves were converted into sandstones or shales or clays according to their composition.

The world's most important coalfields date from the Carboniferous period, about 250 million years ago, but in North Germany, India, South Africa, Australia, and the New England States there are coals of much more recent date. Ancient coals have sometimes come into contact with molten rock which has converted them into a crystalline form of pure carbon known as *graphite* or "plumbago."

The origin of petroleum is still uncertain, but it is possibly the product of the decay of minute forms of animal and vegetable life which accumulated on the bed of the sea in various geological ages.

Buried under masses of later sediments, this organic matter was subjected to great heat and pressure, and the resulting distillation produced oil and gas. Frequently these passed upwards and outwards from the "source" rocks, in some cases escaping to the surface, where evaporation and oxidation reduced them to viscous or solid bituminous substances. Such are the asphalt which occurs in the famous "lake" in Trinidad, and the "tar pits" of Rancho La Brea, near Hollywood, U.S.A.

Sometimes, however, the oil and gas have been trapped in porous rocks which happened to be sealed by an impervious layer above, and in such cases the oil has been preserved for the use of man. A section through a typical formation of this kind is shown in Fig. 20.

### Types of Soils

On the surface of the earth the rocks are generally found to have become broken up into their constituent minerals, and are mixed to a greater or less degree with the products of vegetable and animal decay. These surface deposits are called *soils*, and are often classified according to the proportions of sand and clay in their composition, the following types being commonly recognized:

*Sandy soils*, which contain more than 60 per cent of sand and less than 10 per cent of clay; *loamy soils* containing

FIG. 21. *Fossil forest of the Carboniferous period, Victoria Park, Glasgow. These tree trunks, turned to stone instead of coal, were living plants 300,000,000 years ago.*

FIG. 22. *Remote source of our main coal supplies. Reconstruction of a Carboniferous forest in the Geological Museum, London. Note the giant dragonfly in the centre of the picture.*

approximately equal proportions of sand and clay; and *clayey soils*, or *marls*, of which the chief constituent is clay.

Sandy soils, being light and porous, are easily worked, even in wet weather, and warm up quickly in spring; they are, however, often deficient in plant food, and subject to rapid drying-out in summer. The disadvantages may be overcome by the addition of manure.

Clayey soils hold much water and are, therefore, heavy and difficult to work in wet weather; on the other hand, they are usually rich in plant-food, and with the addition of lime and manure can be made suitable for cultivation.

Loamy soils combine the advantages of sandy and clayey soils, and, therefore, constitute the best agricultural land.

From the point of view of the origin of the bulky constituents soils may be classified as residual, alluvial, glacial, volcanic, and wind-borne.

Residual soils are those which have been formed *in situ* from the underlying rock by the normal processes of weathering.

Alluvial soils consist of an intimate mixture of tiny particles derived from many different types of rock, and are deposited by rivers.

Glacial soils consist chiefly of stiff clays, stones, and large boulders, and are deposited by glaciers.

Volcanic soils are derived from the dust and ashes of geologically recent eruptions, and are often of exceptional fertility.

Wind-borne soils are found on the leeward margins of arid regions, where dust and wind-blown sand have accumulated. An important soil of this type, known as *loess*, occurs chiefly in the basin of the upper Hwang-Ho in north China, where the deposits attain a thickness of several hundreds of feet and occupy an area of thousands of square miles (Fig. 214).

The loess contains myriads of tiny vertical "cracks," which represent the casts of vegetation which grew during the intervals between dust storms.

Each of the major climatic regions of the earth is characterized by a particular type of soil, though other kinds of soil common to all regions may exist side by side with it.

In the *Equatorial Forest Regions* the characteristic soil is *laterite*, which may be red or greyish according to whether the parent rock is rich in iron or alumina. The heavy rainfall has leached out almost all the soluble salts, and the soil has acquired a granular, porous structure, which allows surface water to percolate rapidly downwards.

In the *Coniferous Forest Regions* the typical ashy-grey soil is called *podsol*. The surface of the podsols is composed of a spongy brown layer of partially decomposed vegetable matter which by its slow decay produces humic acids.

In the *Grassland Regions* the soils are typically dark brown or black, and are characterized by their great depth and their richness in mineral salts. The black earth or *chernozem* which forms the amazingly fertile agricultural belt of southern Russia represents the finest development of the richly productive grassland soils.

## Test Yourself

1. (a) What difference would the captain of a ship notice in docking at Gdynia in the Baltic and at Liverpool?
   (b) What natural source of energy, other than river flow, might be utilized for the development of electrical power? Explain how this might be done and at what places in England it would be most economical to attempt it.
2. (a) How has the Atlantic Ocean and its coastlines contributed to the development of our commercial civilization?
   (b) In what different ways can mountains be said to influence the development of human society?

*Answers will be found at the end of the book.*

## CHAPTER II

# NATURE AS SCULPTOR

ENUDATION is the name given to the complex process by which rocks are disintegrated and the land surface continuously remodelled.

The process of denudation consists of the interplay of several natural agents, but for convenience we shall consider them separately.

*Rain* as an agent of denudation acts both mechanically and chemically. Its mechanical action is most notable in regions subject to recurrent heavy downpours. In such regions the loose surface soil may be washed away by the direct impact of the raindrops. Where the original surface was strewn with boulders these have in many cases formed a protective cap beneath which earth pillars have been preserved (Fig. 23).

Chemically, rain breaks up the rocks by both hydration and solution. Hydration is the process of chemical combination of water with other substances. Many of the constituent minerals of rocks become hydrated in contact with water and, as the resulting compounds have greater volume than the original mineral, expansion and consequent disintegration occur.

The solvent action of rain water is due chiefly to the fact that in passing through the atmosphere it dissolves small quantities of carbon dioxide, thus becoming a very weak acid which is able to dissolve limestone and chalk. Where thick masses of limestone or chalk have been dissolved away the insoluble residue may accumulate to form a cultivable soil of considerable depth. The "clay-with-flints" which caps a large part of the English chalk lands is a residue of this type.

In tropical regions the solvent and chemical action of rain water is at a maximum, and over large areas the mineral contents of the soil consist only of the insoluble residue of the surface rocks.

*Frost* is the most powerful of all the "static" agencies of denudation. Its action is due to the fact that when water freezes its volume increases by 10 per cent, causing an expansive pressure of many thousands of pounds per square inch on the sides of water-filled crevices in the rock.

Repeated freezing and thawing widens and deepens the crevices so that angular fragments are continually broken away and even the hardest rocks disrupted. The *screes* so typical of steep mountain sides are the accumulation of angular fragments split from the parent rock, while the pinnacles and crags above owe their sharpness of outline to the same disruptive action.

*Alternations of heat and cold* are among the principal causes of the denudation of rocks in desert regions where the days are very hot and the nights cold. The resulting alternation of expansion by day and contraction by night sets up strains in the rock

*Fig. 23. Remarkable formations resulting from rapid erosion by rain. Earth pillars in the Italian Alps near Bolzano.*

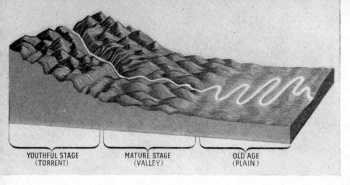

FIG. 24. *Three stages of river development exhibited at different parts of the course of one river. Such a river continues to erode and widen its valley and to smooth out its course until the final stage of old age is reached.*

which cause "exfoliation"—the flaking off of the outer "skin" of the rock—sometimes with a loud report.

*Wind* plays only an indirect part in the denudation of the rocks. Alone it is able to achieve little, but armed with angular particles of rock it becomes a powerful sandblast, eating away the softer parts of the rocks exposed to its action. In desert regions the rocks are often etched into strange shapes reminiscent of human figures or of castellated walls.

In the drier parts of the temperate grasslands, where ploughing has broken up the protective sod, wind erosion has had catastrophic effects. In the so-called "dust bowl" of western United States, for example, many thousands of square miles of land have been rendered completely useless to man by great dust storms which have swept away the soil (Figs. 126, 204).

The processes of "atmospheric weathering" outlined above would, if they acted alone, eventually bring the whole process of denudation to a standstill through the formation of a protective mantle of derived material around the parent rock. The products of weathering are, however, usually carried away as fast as they are formed, thus exposing fresh surfaces to the atmosphere.

The chief *transporting agents* are running water, the sea and ice. Each of these is in itself a powerful instrument of further denudation, using the fragments produced by weathering as abrasive material with which to erode the land surface. Each is also an instrument in the building up of new land forms, and the work of water and ice as denuding, transporting and land-building agents must be considered as inter-related processes.

## WORK OF RIVERS

RIVERS are Nature's most powerful agents in modelling and remodelling the earth's surface. Their action is a dual one: fast flowing streams carve out valleys and carry away the rock-waste formed by weathering, while slow-flowing streams deposit their burden of silt, thus building up new land or filling up seas and providing the material of which new mountains are built.

The course of a river, like the life of a man, may be divided into three stages—youth, maturity and old age.

The *youthful stage* (Fig. 25, A) is seen in the mountain torrent, leaping over its rocky bed in a narrow, V-shaped valley. Here the force of the stream is so great that not only are coarse particles carried in suspension, but even large boulders are rolled along the bed. Thus armed, the torrent is a

powerful erosive agent, and as most of its abrasive power is directed downwards, the cross-section of the valley remains narrow and V-shaped.

The *stage of maturity* (Fig. 25, B) is seen in the rather slow-flowing river swinging in wide curves from side to side of its broad, flat-bottomed valley. Here the energy of the stream is so reduced that normally it can transport only the finer particles of rock-waste, and cannot rapidly deepen its valley; indeed, most of its energy seems to be expended in carrying its load of sediment and in widening its valley.

The *stage of old age* (Fig. 25, C) is represented by the river in its lower course, meandering sluggishly across a broad plain which it may itself have built in times of flood by the deposition of successive layers of silt. A good example of a river in this stage of its life is shown in Fig. 32.

These three stages may often be seen in a single river between its source and its mouth, as shown in Fig. 24.

Where there are irregularities in the profile the river is inevitably engaged in smoothing them out. When, for example, a layer of specially resistant rock outcrops across the middle course of a river, a rapid or a waterfall results. As in the case of Niagara (Figs. 26 and 122), undercutting causes the fall to retreat progressively upstream until the resistant layer is completely cut through and the irregularity of the profile eliminated.

Lakes, too, are only transient features in the course of a river; sediment deposited by the river tends to fill them up and at the same time the lower lip of the lake basin is worn away by the erosive action of the stream. Under this double attack the lake will cease to exist in a comparatively short space of geological time (Figs. 27 and 28).

*Rejuvenation of Rivers.* Old rivers may sometimes undergo rejuvenation if there is a renewed uplift of the land. If the uplift is slow, the river may even start to cut down in the meanders it formed on the low-lying plain, producing deeply entrenched meanders like those of the Wye and Moselle valleys. When the rate of uplift is greater, deep gorges and canyons may be formed, especially in an arid area, since the vertical erosion of the river will outpace the weathering action which tends to widen the valley. The stupendous canyon of the Colorado is a good example of this process.

*River Capture.* A river may become considerably larger by capturing an additional supply of water from the head-streams of a neighbouring river. In its youthful stage a river not only deepens its valley but its source eats its way farther and farther back into the highland, where it may encounter the tributaries of less vigorous rivers and drain their water away. The less vigorous rivers are thus said to be "beheaded." A whole series of rivers in Northumberland—beheaded in succession

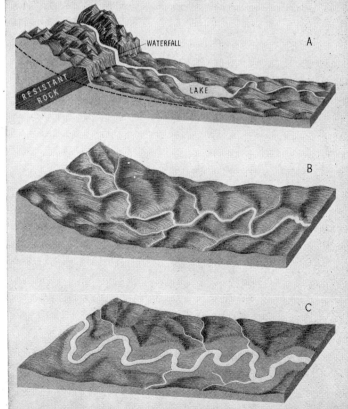

Fig. 25. *Illustrating* (A) *a river in its youthful stage. Note the waterfall at the outcrop of resistant rock in the river bed, and the lake. These are both temporary features. A river* (B) *in the stage of maturity, all irregularities, such as waterfalls and lakes having been smoothed out, and an approximate balance achieved between erosion and deposition. Finally,* (C) *a river in the stage of old age in which there is no downward erosion. The river expends its energy in meandering over the plain which it has itself built up by depositing silt during flood periods. Compare with Fig. 32. Rivers in youthful stages are utilized by advanced communities, but it is the rivers of maturity and old age which have had the greatest influence upon civilization.*

by the River Tyne—is shown in Fig. 30.

*Patterns of River Systems.* The patterns of river systems vary with their stages of development and with the structure and geological history of the land surface which they drain.

Rivers which develop on an evenly sloping surface will, if the rocks are uniform in character, assume a *dendritic* pattern, as illustrated in Fig. 31. Those which develop on an anticline consisting of alternately hard and soft rocks, such as we find in the Wealden district of south-east England (Fig. 83), result in the *trellised* pattern shown in Fig. 29 (Bottom). Fig. 29 (Top) shows how the original streams began to flow down the sides of the anticline, but both the rivers and the weather combined to remove the surface rocks and eventually exposed the hard and soft series beneath. Valleys running at right-angles to the original streams then developed in the newly-exposed softer rocks.

The Rhine is an example of a river which does not conform to any simple pattern. Some millions of years ago the Rift Valley between Basle and Mainz was occupied by a shallow sea which was drained to the south-west by a river flowing through the Belfort Gap towards the present Rhône. Gradually this sea was filled up with sediment and at the same time earth movements reversed the slope of the land, tilting it down towards the north, and diverting the Rhine northward over a low plateau. Then the plateau itself was raised up, but so slowly that the Rhine and its tributaries were able to maintain their course by rapid erosion of their valleys. Thus came into existence the Rhine Gorge between Bingen and Bonn, and the picturesque incised meanders of the tributary valleys of the Moselle and Lahn.

*Seasonal Variations of Rivers.* The volume of water in a river may vary considerably, according to the physical and climatic conditions over its basin. Rivers fed mainly by melting snow have their maximum flow in spring and early summer; those fed by very heavy summer rainfall, as in monsoon regions, have their maximum flow in late summer or in autumn. In Western Europe, where there is little snow and a fairly regular distribution of rainfall throughout the year, the rivers have a comparatively regular flow, though floods may occur at irregular and unpredictable intervals.

Where river basins are large enough to include a variety of physical and climatic conditions the lower course of the main stream may show a remarkable regularity of flow, as the flood period in one tributary may coincide with low water in others. Thus, the lower Amazon has a comparatively regular flow as it is fed partly from the Andes, partly from the Guiana Highlands, which have their maximum rainfall in the northern summer, and partly from the Brazilian plateau where the rain falls

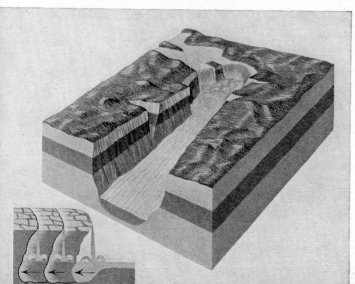

FIG. 26. *Block diagram of Niagara Falls. The uppermost layer of rock is a thick bed of hard jointed limestone which periodically collapses, causing a recession of the Falls. Since the end of the Ice Age, some 15,000 years ago, the Falls have been cut back to form a deep gorge seven miles long. This progressive retreat will continue until the hard rock is cut through and all the irregularities of the river bed are eliminated.*

FIG. 27. *That a lake is a temporary feature of the landscape is exemplified in Derwentwater, England, where silting up by the in-flowing river is clearly seen.*

FIG. 28. *Borrowdale, in the English Lake District, with Derwentwater in the distance. This former lake has been completely filled with sediments deposited by the river.*

for the most part in the southern summer.

The upper Rhine, which is fed largely by the melting snow and ice on the Alps, has its maximum flow in early summer; but its tributaries, the Moselle, the Main and the melting snows on the mountains round their source, giving floods in spring and low water in summer. Under natural conditions the growing-season is very short and a co-ordinated system of irrigation works is

FIG. 29. Above: *The "trellised" pattern of river drainage develops from the simple drainage of an anticline.* Below: *It matures when the crest of the anticline has been denuded away and rocks of varying hardness outcrop at right-angles to the original streams.*

Neckar, drain regions which have heavy rain in winter, so that their high-water period corresponds roughly to the low-water period of the upper Rhine. Consequently the lower Rhine has a remarkably even depth of water—a characteristic which has been of great importance in the development of the river as a highway of commerce.

The influence of river regime on human activities and the course of history is well illustrated by the contrast between Mesopotamia and Egypt. The Tigris and the Euphrates derive their flood water from the necessary for any considerable degree of prosperity. This in its turn necessitates a strong central government, but the mountainous region which provides the flood waters has also been the home of warlike people who have from time to time descended as a human flood on the rich plains and destroyed the political or economic unity on which the prosperity was based.

The Nile, on the other hand, derives its flood waters from the heavy summer monsoons of Abyssinia and is itself protected by vast stretches of flanking desert. The floods reach Egypt in the height of summer

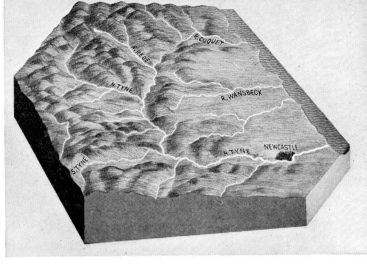

FIG. 30. *An example of river capture from the R. Tyne, Northumberland. The Tyne has successively beheaded four streams, and is on its way to behead a fifth—the Coquet. The Rede and N. Tyne were originally tributaries of the Wansbeck. The former courses of the S. Tyne and other streams can easily be traced. This process is explained fully on page 29.*

and sufficient water is retained in the soil to allow, even under conditions of natural flooding, for the cultivation of cool-weather crops. Hence, basic production in the lower Nile valley has been less dependent on a strong centralized government, and political fluctuations have not had such tragic results as in Mesopotamia.

*The Value of Rivers to Man.* Smoothly-graded rivers in stages of maturity and old age have profoundly influenced the activities of Man in all ages. The earliest civilizations arose on the alluvial river-plains of Egypt, Mesopotamia, India and China, where irrigation is easy and where the fertility of the land is periodically renewed by films of mud deposited by the flood waters. Navigable rivers have facilitated

FIG. 31. *Examples of the "dendritic," or tree-like, pattern of river drainage (page 30).*

the expansion of peoples and the opening up of new territories; thus the Anglo-Saxon and Norse conquests of England proceeded largely along the river-ways; the rivers of North America facilitated first the French expansion and later the westward advance of the American colonial people. The importance of rivers in the development of commerce is indicated by the fact that nearly all the great cities of the world are situated on or near the mouths of navigable waterways.

Rivers in their youthful stages are, in general, useful to Man only in the more advanced stages of society, when he has learnt to utilize water-power and to build large reservoirs to conserve the surplus water. Thus, the deep, youthful valleys of the southern Pennines in England were almost devoid of settlement until the Industrial Revolution led to the use of water-power for the early textile factories. In modern times the existence of large rivers in a youthful stage of development may be a great national asset capable of providing hydro-electric power on a vast scale. Modern large scale projects of river control aim at diverting the youthful river's energy and harnessing it to the service of Man in a variety of ways—the generation of hydro-electric power (Figs. 122, 125), improvement of navigation, the control of floods and the irrigation of arid lowlands.

Two outstanding examples of such large-scale operations are the Tennessee Valley Authority (T.V.A.) scheme (p. 189) and the control of the Volga at the Kuibyshev bend.

A RIVER IN OLD AGE
Fig. 32. An air view of the windings of
the Manawatu River, New Zealand.

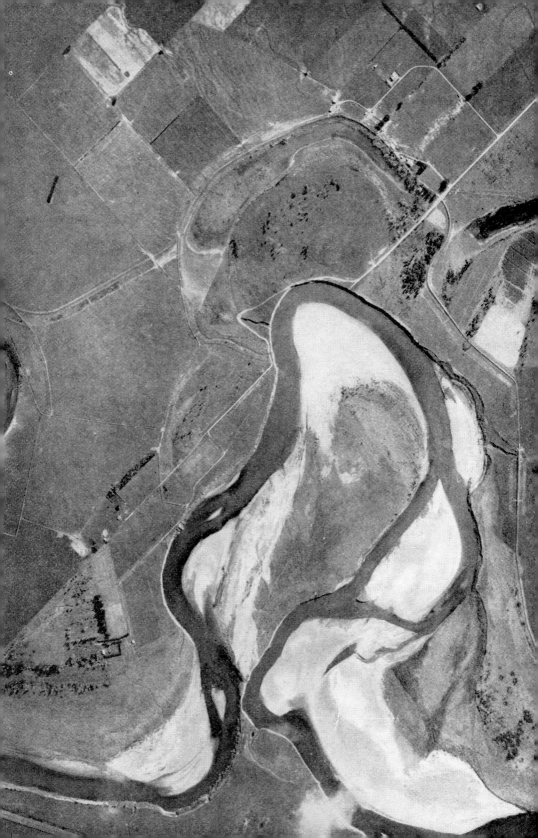

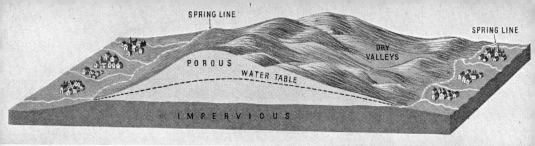

FIG. 33. *A common type of formation giving rise to permanent springs. See text.*

# UNDERGROUND WATER

OF the water which falls on the surface of the earth in the form of rain or snow, something like half evaporates, a quarter runs off in streams, and the remainder soaks into the soil and the upper layers of rock. The compactness of the rock at depths greater than, say, ten miles prevents the deep percolation of water, most of which is returned to the surface by means of springs, though much is drawn up by capillary attraction and passed into the atmosphere by evaporation and the respiration of plants.

Except where there are caverns and wide fissures, there are, of course, no pools or streams in the rocks: the water merely fills up all the small interstices between the rock particles, and water may form a considerable proportion of the total volume of a loosely compacted rock such as sandstone.

The level below which the rock is saturated with water is known as the *water-table*. Though the depth of the water-table varies with the type of rock, the amount of rainfall and the degree of evaporation, its contour generally follows that of the surface features, though with a lower angle of slope, as shown in Fig. 33.

Water percolates both downward and outward from the higher parts of the water-table, and where this cuts the surface a line of springs may occur. Where the pervious layer of rock is underlain by an impervious layer, as in Fig. 33, springs of a permanent character will occur at their junction, and provide suitable sites for villages.

*Artesian wells* are wells in which the underground pressure of the water is sufficient to cause the water to flow from a considerable depth up the shaft of a well or bore-hole, and even to flow out at the surface without the need of pumping. The conditions necessary for the existence of such wells are: *(a)* a pervious layer of rock with an outcrop in a region of fairly heavy rainfall; *(b)* an underlying impervious layer which prevents the water being lost by downward percolation; *(c)* an overlying impervious layer which prevents the seepage of water to the surface; and *(d)* a synclinal structure, or at least a downward dip of the water-bearing layer, so as to provide a sufficient hydraulic head.

The London Basin, shown in section in Fig. 34, is an outstanding example of an artesian basin. The water-bearing rock is the bed of chalk which is bent down in the form of a trough, and crops out as the Chiltern Hills to the north and as the North Downs to the south; below the chalk is the bed of Gault clay, and above the chalk is the thick deposit of London clay.

Another notable artesian basin occurs in the Great Plains district, east of the Rockies in the U.S.A. Here the chief water-bearing layer is the Dakota sandstone, and wells bored more than a hundred miles to the east of its outcrop yield strong artesian flows, which are of special value in a region so deficient in rainfall.

FIG. 34. *A section through the London Basin, showing the source of deep subterranean water.*

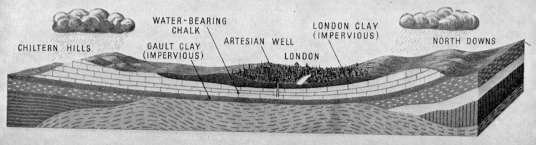

FIG. 35. *The Jenolan Caves, New South Wales. The limestone of these caves is of organic origin and, in association with coral reefs, was formed some 300 million years ago.*

One of the largest artesian basins is in Queensland and the neighbouring parts of New South Wales and South Australia. Here the water-bearing sandstone layer outcrops in the well-watered mountainous region near the coast, and dips westward under the impervious beds which form the interior plains, where it is tapped by many hundreds of deep artesian wells.

In the Sahara water-bearing sandstones are found at varying depths below the surface. Where such a layer outcrops at the surface natural oases occur, an example of which is shown in Fig. 73. Where it is near the surface, but fails to outcrop, shallow wells provide water which may be raised by primitive devices such as those shown in Figs. 102, 105, 212. In areas where there is a hydrostatic head artesian wells may be bored through the overlying rocks (Fig. 36).

In limestone districts, where the rock is exceptionally soluble in water containing carbon dioxide, underground water may dissolve out vast subterranean caves and channels, and it not infrequently happens that the river-drainage in such regions proceeds entirely below the surface.

As each drop of water hangs from the roof of a limestone cave it partly dries up before falling, and deposits a minute crystal of calcium carbonate on the rock. The next drop follows suit, and eventually a long crystalline pendant, resembling an icicle but usually wax- or rose-coloured, is formed. Such a pendant is called a *stalactite*. A similar deposit usually grows up from the floor of the cave at the spot where the drop falls, and is known as a *stalagmite*. A typical limestone cave, with stalactites, is illustrated in Fig. 35.

FIG. 36. *Relationship of wells and water-table in the Sahara. The water-supply of the Libyan and Egyptian deserts probably originates in the highlands 1,000 miles to the south.*

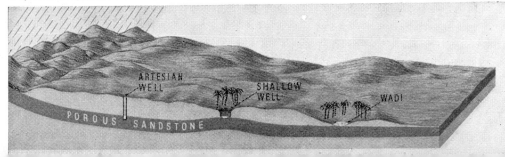

# PLAINS

FROM the point of view of human activity, plains are the most important of all the major features of the earth's surface. Comparison of the population and relief maps of the world will show that, while there are several large plains which for a variety of reasons are thinly peopled, all the large areas of dense population are plains, or at least regions of low relief. The reasons for the concentration of population on certain plains of the world are not far to seek. Under suitable conditions of climate they are of high productivity, and their slow-flowing rivers combine with the absence of land barriers to facilitate communications and trade. Even where the basic prosperity is due to agriculture, the density of population leads to the development of industries, and the concurrent growth of agriculture, industry and trade leads to still further expansion in all three directions.

### Types of Plain

Plains owe their origin to a variety of processes—river action, marine erosion, uplift of the sea bed, glaciation, etc.

Rivers form plains both by wearing down old land surfaces and by building up new ones. A land surface, like the rivers which drain it, may pass from the stage of youth, through maturity to old age, as shown in Figs. 24 and 25. The final stage of this long-continued process of denudation is known as a *peneplain*, to distinguish it from plains which have been built up by the deposition of sediment.

*Flood Plains* are formed by rivers in the stage of maturity when they can no longer carry the burden of rock waste which is passed on to them from the higher stretches of the river. With every flood the river overflows its banks, depositing a fresh layer of alluvium on the surface and thus building it up; but, even in times of normal flow, much sediment is deposited in the bed of the river and on its immediate banks. Thus the river raises itself above the surrounding plain at least as quickly as the flood plain itself is built up, so the process of flooding and the extension of the

flood plain have a tendency to continue.

*Delta Plains*. When a river enters a lake or the sea its velocity is checked and nearly all the fine sediment it has so far carried is at once deposited. Where there are strong tidal or coastal currents the deposits may be swept away from the river mouth, but in the absence of these the sediments often build up a delta which gradually extends farther and farther out.

In course of time the older parts of the delta dry out, and, if they are protected from floods and high tides, the fertility of the soil may enable them to support a dense agricultural population. The deltas of the Rhine, the Nile, the Ganges, the Yangtze-kiang and the Hwang-Ho are among the most fertile and productive regions of the world.

*Alluvial fans* are delta-shaped plains of gravel and mud deposited by rivers whenever their gradients are suddenly diminished. Such alluvial fans may spread and coalesce until they form a continuous plain at the foot of the mountains.

Examples of such plains are the Indo-Gangetic Plain, Mesopotamia, the lower Nile valley and the Po basin. In America the Great Plains of the Mississippi valley and the Pampas of Argentina owe their origin to a similar process.

### Reconstructed Plains

*Glacial Plains*. Some pre-existing plains have been so extensively re-modelled by glaciers and ice sheets that they have characteristics sharply distinguishing them from other plains.

Like rivers, glaciers are both erosive and constructive agents. Where the ice has been predominantly erosive the features of the former relief have been smoothed out, the drainage system destroyed, and the soil largely scraped away, leaving large areas of bare rock. Such is the region of the Canadian Shield (Fig. 111), with its innumerable lakes, poor, thin soil and scanty forest cover. Constructive work predominates near the outer margin of glaciation, where fertile plains may be built up by rock waste deposited by the ice-sheets.

FIG. 37. *Icebergs are "calved" from glaciers when the downward course of the ice is checked by its entry into the water, in which it rises by flotation and thus breaks off from the parent glacier. Iceberg formations are also shown in Fig. 193 and Fig. 201.*

# WORK OF ICE

GLACIERS and ice sheets are formed by the accumulation of snow over a long period; the pressure of the upper layers of snow, and alternate melting and freezing on the surface, convert the mass of snow into ice, which moves slowly down the valleys or spreads over the plains as an ice sheet (Figs. 119, 200).

During the Great Ice Age, which began about a million years ago and ended about 15,000 years ago, great ice sheets spread outwards from the Arctic regions and from subsidiary centres in all the mountainous areas in the north of Europe, Asia and America to cover most of the lowland north of 50 degrees in Europe and Asia and 45 degrees in North America. The modifications of the land surface caused by ice action in this period have had profound effects on the development of society in these regions.

In the mountainous areas the principal effect of former glaciation is seen in the over-deepened, U-shaped valleys (Fig. 39) which are of special importance from the point of view of human geography.

They often contain lakes which were formed either by the glaciers gouging out hollows in the valley floor or by the deposition of a barrier of rock-debris called a *moraine* across the valley floor.

Where such lakes are situated high above sea level, they are often used as sources of water-power for hydro-electric schemes, as in the projected plan of hydro-electric development in Scotland.

The flat valley floors generally have a thick covering of alluvium which was deposited either where the rapid streams from the surrounding highland received a sudden check on entry into the comparatively flat-bottomed valley, or in a lake which formerly occupied the valley. Such alluvial flats form rich agricultural land which would have been almost entirely lacking in the region but for the over-deepening of the valleys in the Ice Age.

Tributary streams from the "hanging valleys" (Fig. 40) often provide power for minor hydro-electric schemes.

The comparatively level shoulder between the mountain peaks and steep sides of the over-deepened valleys provides valuable summer pasture for the cattle of the Swiss peasants, whose main farm is usually on the level floor of the main valley (Figs. 49, 77).

*Passes formed by Glacial Action.* As the glaciers passed over the watershed between adjacent valleys they often scoured out deep trenches which remain after the disappearance of the ice as low passes through

39

the mountains. The Llanberis Pass (Fig. 39) and the Glaslyn Pass in the Snowdon district of N. Wales are excellent examples of such "through" valleys.

In other cases "through" valleys and passes owe their origin to the erosive action of rivers which formed the outlets of temporary glacial lakes held up between the edge of the ice and the highland. In the Chilterns, for example, there are several dry valleys which provide easy routes through the escarpment, and are today utilized by the main railway lines from London to the north-west.

*Effects of Continental Glaciation.* The effects of ice sheets which occupied large areas of lowland are, of course, on a more massive scale than those of valley glaciers, though here again the dual process of erosion and deposition may be seen.

In North America the region of greatest ice accumulation was in northeastern Canada. As the ice pressed southward from this region, it scooped away the soil, wore down the hills, and pitted the surface of the rock with innumerable depressions which are now occupied by groups of lakes (Fig. 111).

The rock-waste was carried southward by the ice sheet and deposited over the land surface as a thick layer of "drift," which completely obliterated the pre-existing surface features and built up the featureless plain of the prairies and the upper Mississippi basin. The "rock flour" of which the drift was mainly composed was derived from a great variety of rocks and is, therefore, extremely rich in plant food; consequently, the "drift plains" are among the world's most productive agricultural areas.

As the ice sheet melted and the edge retreated northward beyond the "Height of Land" which separates the Arctic drainage from that of the Atlantic, lakes were formed between the divide and the ice sheet. At a comparatively late period in the retreat of the ice, the only outlet for the vast system of glacial lakes whose remnants now form the Great Lakes was by the Hudson River, whose deeply eroded valley has been of the highest importance in the economic development of North America. It was, during the Ice Age, the funnel down which the water from the Great Lakes poured seaward and it has become, in our era, the funnel down which goods pour from the Middle West to the great port of New York (Fig. 109).

On the European Plain the surface features north of latitude 50 degrees are largely due to the effects of glaciation. To the north of the central belt of high land is a series of low plateaux, stretching from southern Poland, through Saxony to Westphalia and west of the Rhine (Fig. 81). These plateaux are composed largely of drift deposited by the ice sheet in its period of maximum extension and in the first stages of its retreat. As the drift dried out, much of the finely powdered rock-waste was blown southward in dust storms and

FIG. 38. *Snowdon and Glaslyn from Crib Goch, N. Wales. Such steep-sided, armchair-shaped hollows are known as corries. They mark the gathering ground of former mountain glaciers, where a pre-existing hollow was deepened and widened by the alternate freezing and thawing of accumulated snow. Rock waste was continuously borne away by the ice, leaving steep walls.*

FIG. 39. *The Pass of Llanberis, N. Wales, is an example of a* ∪*-shaped glacier valley. This valley, originally* ∨*-shaped, was "over-deepened" by the action of glaciers during the Ice Age.*

deposited on the southern margins of the plateaux, forming the extremely fertile soil known as loess (see page 26).

To the north of these plateaux lies a series of east-to-west valleys which mark spillways by which the water escaped along the edge of the ice in the successive stages of its gradual retreat northward. Many of these spillways are now occupied by parts of the Rivers Elbe, Oder and Vistula, and by their east-to-west tributaries, while the intervening parts which are unoccupied by rivers have been utilized for the construction of canals linking the various river basins. These canals were a major factor of the rise of Prussia to power.

Near the southern shores of the Baltic

the retreating ice sheet deposited a belt of sandy moraine stretching from Jutland through northern Poland to Latvia. In general, this is a region of low productivity, with considerable areas of forest and, especially in northern Poland, many lakes which occupy depressions in the surface of the moraine. The most striking feature of the landscape of southern Finland is the innumerable morainic lakes covering nearly a quarter of the surface (Fig. 41).

FIG. 40. *A typical hanging valley in Glen Lyon, Scotland. The main valley in the foreground has been "over-deepened" by a glacier, while the tributary valley (the level shoulder above the torrent) has remained at a higher level, since it was above the surface of the ice.*

FIG. 41. *The lakes which occupy a large part of the surface of Finland owe their origin to the ice sheet which covered the region in the Glacial Period. Some occupy hollows scooped out of the rocks; others occupy hollows in the irregular surface of the ground-moraine. Still others are dammed up by low sandy ridges or "eskers" which wind across the valleys, often forming irregular chains of islands such as those seen in the picture. Eskers were probably formed by sub-glacial streams whose channels became choked with sediment. Other notable examples of these formations are to be found in Ireland, Sweden and the U.S.A.*

# WORK OF THE SEA

THE erosive action of the sea is almost entirely confined to the narrow coastal belt where the water is so shallow that rock particles are moved by the waves. Apart from this marginal action the sea may be regarded as a protective envelope, shielding four-fifths of the earth's surface from the effects of weathering.

The repeated battering by storm waves (Fig. 42), exerting a force up to 2,000 lb. per square foot, is sometimes sufficient to shatter solid rock; such direct wave-action is, however, greatly magnified by the compression of air in hollows and crevices. With the advance of each wave against the rock face the compressed air forces its way along faults, joints and other lines of weakness, thus aiding in the disruption of the rocks.

The erosive power of the waves is, however, due mainly to the rock fragments with which they are armed. Hurled against the face of the rock by every incoming wave, these exert a powerful abrasive effect on the rocks, providing a constantly renewed supply of sharp-edged fragments as they themselves are worn away.

The rate of erosion varies with the hardness of the rock and with the exposure to storms, as will be seen by the examination of any sea cliff, especially where belts of alternating hard and soft rocks dip at a sharp angle; the softer beds and the lines of joints and faults form caves, chimneys and inlets, while the more resistant rocks stand

out as bastions, often with seaward extensions of reefs and "stacks" which mark the former position of the cliff (Figs. 43 and 44).

The line of retreat of a sea cliff is marked by a wave-cut platform which is submerged at high tide. Where such terraces occur above present sea level, they provide clear evidence of recent uplift of the land (or of sinking of the level of the sea) (Fig. 45). On the other hand, the continuation of such a "plain of marine erosion" far out under a shallow sea is indicative of a long period of gradually falling sea level followed by a rise.

*Deposition by the Sea.* The load of inshore rock waste consists mainly of sediment brought down by rivers, only a small proportion of the total being provided by wave action and by direct down-wash from the land. Practically the whole of this load is deposited close inshore, the largest fragments near the coast and the finer particles farther out on the continental shelf or in the "deeps" near the coast. Only the very finest particles are transported as far as the ocean deeps.

The material which is deposited inshore is redistributed by the process of longshore drifting, generally in the direction of the prevailing winds. It finds at least a temporary resting-place wherever there is comparatively still water.

Spits of sand and shingle often grow outwards in the lee of a headland, cutting off a stretch of calm water between them-

selves 'and the main coastline, as on the coast of south-eastern United States. In other cases, spits may stretch almost across the estuary of a river, thus hastening the formation of a delta, as at the mouth of the Vistula. By such processes the land lost by marine erosion is counterbalanced by new land built up by marine deposition. Thus we see "the hungry ocean gain advantage on the kingdom of the shore, increasing store with loss and loss with store."

*Types of Coast.* The geographer is interested in land forms mainly in relation to their effects on human activities. From this point of view coasts are best classified as coasts of *submergence*, which owe their dominant forms to the sinking of the land,

FIG. 42. *Huge Atlantic breakers beating on the rocky shores of the Scilly Isles.*

tures will follow the relief pattern of the original highland. Ranges running parallel to the coast will give the Dalmatian type of coast (Fig. 100). Where the ranges run athwart the coast, as in south-western Ireland, the inlets will penetrate far into the interior with regularly diminishing width and depth. Highlands which have been fractured and glaciated before submergence, such as those of Norway, Alaska and the South Island of New Zealand, give a fjord type of coast. Such "transverse" coastlines provide many excellent harbours, though the mountainous character of the hinterland often robs them of commercial value.

and coasts of *emergence* which are formed by the land's rising relative to sea level.

The dominant characteristic of submerged coasts is their irregularity. If a hilly or mountainous region is submerged, the valleys become deep, narrow, many-branched inlets, while the ridges stand out as islands and peninsulas which are obvious continuations of the unsubmerged hinterland. The trend of the coastal fea-

When a lowland region is submerged the resulting coastline is very deeply indented since the slight slope allows the sea to flow far up the shallow valleys; each tributary valley, no matter how insignificant its

FIG. 44. *Outcrops of alternately hard and soft rocks on the coast of Anglesey, N. Wales. The action of the sea tends to wear away the headlands and fill up the coves.*

FIG. 45. *Raised beach, or "wave-cut platform," on the coast of Islay, Scotland. The hills on the left represent a still higher beach, dating from Ice Age times.*

stream, becomes a subsidiary inlet, and each slight ridge a peninsula or island. Submerged coasts of this type are often of the highest value to man because of the productivity of the land and the ease of communication by both land and water. Many of the great ports of the world have grown up on such submerged lowlands, at the limit of ocean navigation of the drowned estuaries, e.g. London, Hamburg, Philadelphia, Baltimore.

*Coasts of Emergence* are characteristically unindented. The sea bed is smoothly contoured, since any hollows tend to fill up with sediment and any ridges to be worn down as elevation of the general level brings them within the range of action of the waves; the elevation of such an evenly contoured surface produces a straight, even coast.

On such a newly emerged coast the waves break a considerable distance out to sea, and there build up a barrier beach. In many areas men have acted upon the hint given by Nature, and accelerated the process by land reclamation, as in Holland (Fig. 82), Flanders and the delta of the Po.

Even where emergent shores border mountain ranges, they are characteristically regular in outline, as on the west coast of America between latitudes 40 degrees N. and 40 degrees S. Here the formation of fringing barrier beaches is prevented by the steepness of the slope of the sea bed, which continues that of the adjacent mountains. Consequently, good natural harbours are restricted to such structural breaks in the coastline as the Golden Gate of San Francisco (Fig. 124).

## Test Yourself

1. At what stage in the "life" of a river would you expect to find an increasing human population in its vicinity? Give reasons for your conclusions.

2. What connexion can be traced between the natural features of the area round the southern Pennines in England and the rapid development of this area with the coming of the Industrial Revolution?

3. From your atlas find examples throughout the world of submerged lowlands giving rise to large seaports, and try to discover what other factors have contributed to the growth and importance of such ports.

*Answers will be found at the end of the book.*

Fig. 46. *An airman's view of the weather. This infra-red photograph, taken at 20,000 feet, looks from England across the Channel towards France and Belgium. Fair weather cumulus cloud defines both coasts, growing to cumulo-nimbus over Belgium. In the distance a secondary depression is giving rain. Above the dense bank of grey nimbo-stratus can be seen a thick white layer of alto-stratus, giving place in turn to cirrus higher up.*

46

CHAPTER III

# UNDERSTANDING THE WEATHER

WE become so accustomed to the kind of weather that is our lot that we are hardly aware of the profound influence it has on our clothes and housing, our crops, our industries, our health, our mental and physical energy and on our way of living generally. Exceptional heat waves, days of severe cold, cloud-bursts or long spells of drought provide a topic of conversation and force on our notice the ever-present influence of weather, but the less spectacular day-to-day and season-to-season changes are, in general, taken for granted.

Should our duties or our pleasure take us to Egypt, India, California or the Congo, we should immediately be aware of a new set of conditions to which we should have to adapt our ways of living or suffer the consequences in discomfort, ill-health, or agricultural failure. Yet the weather in these parts is taken by the natives for granted and, by determining their choice of crops and by imposing on them certain habits and ways of life, imparts a character and individuality to the region which is a clear reflection of its climate.

### Raw Materials of Weather

If, therefore, we wish to understand the lives, habits, character and occupations of mankind in our own and other countries, it is a first necessity that we should understand their climates and weather.

The day-to-day changes of temperature, the occurrence of rain, snow, hail, sunshine, wind, fog and cloud, etc., are studied as weather in the science of meteorology. The raw materials for the study of both weather and climate are the observations and measurements made and recorded regularly by thousands of observers all over the world. These observations (non-instrumental) and measurements (made at reading stations with barometers, thermometers, rain-gauges, sunshine-recorders and hygrometers), are collected and co-ordinated by the meteorological offices and are published from time to time.

### Observing and Recording

But some backward parts and uninhabited regions do not yet provide a sufficient network of recording stations, and information from these parts is scanty. In these cases we must make intelligent guesses at the weather and climate from the samples described by travellers and explorers during their visits, from the analogy of other places which might be expected to have similar climates, and from the vegetation and the habits of animals and man, which may confidently be expected to provide a certain, though approximate, guide to the climatic conditions prevailing.

But the meteorologist is a scientist and is not satisfied merely to record: he is driven to understand. So the next step is to analyse the observations with a view to finding out why it is hot or cold, wet or dry, and how the weather is produced. From here it is but a step to foretelling when and where different types of weather will occur. Thus forecasting depends on explaining, which depends in turn on observing.

Though the weather has intrigued man for centuries it is only in the last fifty years that he has begun really to understand it; and his knowledge, growing at an enormous pace, is accelerated in wartime by the demands for precise forecasting for both military operations and for flying.

At the best equipped and most important meteorological stations observations are

47

taken at hourly intervals through the day and night and there are, in addition, self-recording instruments that make continuous recordings of temperature, pressure, humidity, rain, and so on. Other stations take readings at less frequent intervals, perhaps only once a day.

Rain-gauges and self-recording instruments may be set up in remote localities (e.g. a mountain top), where interesting and important phenomena may be expected; these may be visited at infrequent intervals, perhaps once a week.

Only the most completely equipped meteorological stations supply information for the daily forecasts, but the others supply valuable information for "post-mortems" on the weather and for the compilation of climatic data.

### An Ocean of Air

Let us now describe and consider the meaning and significance of the observations of each of the principal elements of weather made at a "first order" station.

(1) *Pressure.* We live at the bottom of an ocean of air, the atmosphere, whose weight subjects us to a continual pressure of 15 lb. per square inch. We are not aware of this pressure because it is equally balanced inside and outside our bodies, but should we ascend rapidly in an aeroplane, we quickly become conscious that the pressure outside us has been reduced, because the air in our ears and stomach presses outwards, causing a stuffy feeling in the ears and partial deafness, and, if we go high enough, a ballooning of the stomach.

The atmospheric pressure is measured by means of the barometer, in which the weight of a column of liquid (nearly always mercury) is balanced against the weight of the air. The pressure of the air, which is approximately the same as that of a column of mercury 30 inches high, is nowadays usually expressed as a force in the C.G.S. (centimetre-gram-second) system. Expressed in this way, the normal atmospheric pressure is 1,013,200 units or "dynes," or 1,000 millibars (mb.). Conversion from one unit to the other may be made thus: 1,000 mb. = 29·531 inches.

The level of the mercury rises and falls from day to day and from hour to hour, but a barometer at sea level hardly ever falls below 28 inches or rises above 31 inches and usually stands between 29 inches and 30·5 inches. These small variations are, however, of very great significance, for the atmosphere is very sensitive to small pressure differences and readily moves to equalize them, thus creating wind. It is necessary to read the barometer with very great accuracy, to one-thousandth of an inch in fact.

Before the barometer reading can be used by the forecaster and compared with the pressure at other places on his map it is necessary to calculate and make corrections for temperature of the instrument (for tube, scale and mercury expand by different amounts when warmed), for latitude (the force of gravity varies with latitude) and for height above sea level (for the weight of the air depends on its thickness, therefore a station 500 feet above sea level is relieved of the weight of 500 feet of air). A correction can be made on the assumption, which is only approximately true, even near sea level, that pressure diminishes 1 mb. for each 30 feet of ascent. Thus the pressure on Mt. Blanc (15,780 feet), is little more than half that at sea level. Low pressures like this give us headaches and the feeling of lassitude and nausea known as mountain sickness. In extreme cases they may even cause delicate tissues to break and let the blood out.

### How the Air is Warmed

(2) *Temperature.* The thermometers are kept in a screen or box standing on legs 4 feet above the ground. Its sides are louvred and it has no bottom, so that the thermometers are shielded from the direct rays of the sun, and the air is able to circulate freely. The reason for this will be clear when we understand the process by which the air is warmed and cooled.

Virtually all our warmth comes from the sun, but the sun emits energy of many kinds, all in the form of waves, but with different wave lengths. In order of increasing wave length these are: actinic, ultra-violet, light (from violet to red end of spectrum), infra-red, heat. This energy is

Fig. 47. *On calm evenings the cold air slides down the slopes, filling the valley with mist, which is dammed back by the belt of trees and, in the case of the garden, by the wall.*

only slightly absorbed by the air, which is non-resistant, especially to the long-wave heat rays; and so the air at great height, though subjected to strong sunshine, is not appreciably warmed up. But where the sun's rays fall on a solid object, a building for example, the energy is absorbed and the temperature of the object is raised. Thus the earth's surface, and objects on it, are warmed by the sun and re-radiate the energy as long-wave heat rays, which in turn warm the air in contact with them.

But radiation, by itself, is a very inefficient means of transferring the warmth from the ground to the air; working alone it could warm only the lowest six feet or so of air. The process is aided by convection and turbulence. The air warmed by contact with the ground expands and becomes lighter than the still cold layers above; it rises, carrying its warmth with it, and is replaced by colder air, to be warmed and to ascend in its turn. This is known as convection. Turbulence is the up-and-down

movement of air caused when its flow is disturbed by irregularities in the ground surface—hollows, hills, trees, buildings, etc.

Convection and turbulence together are thousands of times more effective than conduction and between them act quite efficiently in stirring up the air and distributing the warmth. Turbulence is clearly most effective in windy weather and so long as the wind blows strongly we cannot expect to get really hot days. Convection is more important in calm, usually anti-cyclonic, weather; but it should be noticed that it only works one way. It can carry heat upwards, but not cold; it can distribute the warmth of the day, but not the chill of the night time.

On a calm night the lowest air layers are chilled from the ground, and the chilled air lies stagnant, causing an inversion of temperature, i.e. a lower temperature at the surface than in the air a distance above it; and in winter brings risk of ground frost and fog. The cold, heavy, frosty air drains slowly into hollows and valleys, where the worst frost pockets occur (Fig. 47). Gardeners avoid such frost pockets for their fruit trees and more delicate plants.

Since the sun's energy is reissued to the air from the ground, the warmest air is to be found low down, while the air becomes colder and colder farther from the surface of the ground. On an average the rate of fall of temperature, known as the lapse rate, is about 3 degrees per 1,000 feet. This figure can be used as an approximate means of estimating the temperature to be expected on mountains or at heights where aeroplanes fly; but, as we shall see later, it is never quite true, and it sometimes happens, as has just been described, that the lapse rate is inverted near the ground at night. All this affects the stability of the air and its liability to convection.

At first it seemed natural to suppose that the temperature fell continuously towards a zero of cold in empty space. But experiments made with sounding balloons (Fig. 48) carrying recording thermometers soon showed that this was not so. At a height of about 7 miles above England the temperature, having fallen to about —60 degrees F., remained approximately constant and that figure even showed a tendency to rise again at greater heights. The height at which this happens over the equator is about 10 miles with the air temperature at about —110 degrees F., the air above this height being known as the stratosphere.

At night, when the earth is no longer receiving heat from the sun, its surface cools down and passes its heat back to the air and into space. Consequently the temperature falls until the warmth of the rays of the sun is felt again as it climbs above the horizon. Usually, therefore, the coldest hour (daily minimum) is about dawn and the warmest (daily maximum) is soon after midday; not at midday, because for some time after the sun reaches its highest point it is still pouring warmth into the earth faster than the earth can radiate it away. When the expenditure of heat by radiation from the earth exceeds the income deriving from the sun the temperature begins to fall. This is usually between 2 p.m. and 3 p.m.

So far we have assumed that the surface on which the sun's rays fall is flat, but we can see that it makes a big difference if there are mountains, hills, valleys or hollows. The east face of a hill gets the morning sun and its temperature rises quickly until by midday, perhaps, it passes into shadow and the temperature may begin to fall. Conversely the west face may have its daily maximum quite late in the afternoon, while the north-facing slope, perhaps in shadow throughout a winter day, will be generally cold and inhospitable (Fig. 49).

FIG. 48. *Release of a "radio-sonde." This balloon records and broadcasts weather data during its ascent into the stratosphere.*

FIG. 49. *Alpine valleys generally have flat floors and level benches where the soil is deep, separated by steep rocky slopes. Man chooses the sunny side for his fields, orchards and homes, leaving the dark north-facing side to the pine forests.*

A hill presents only one face at a time for the reception of sunlight, but radiates freely from all sides by night. Thus mountains always tend to be cold, and even if the sunny side is being strongly warmed, the warmed air is quickly carried away by the wind. On a high mountain you may suffer from sunburn on exposed skin and frostbite on enclosed feet at the same time.

The nature, colour and texture of the surface on which the sun's rays fall influence the amount of heat absorbed. Dark surfaces, peaty soils, tarred roads and black clothes are hotter by day than light soils, water surfaces, or white linen suits, which reflect some of the heat without absorbing it. Compacted soils are usually able to pass some of the heat they receive down to lower layers, but the lower layers of a loose sand remain cool, because of the insulation provided by the air spaces between the grains. The sun's heat is thus concentrated on the surface of the ground.

In cold weather iron feels cold to the touch, because the warmth of the skin is quickly conducted away, but wool, a poor conductor and a good insulator, feels warm. But an iron roof in hot sunshine quickly becomes unbearably hot, because very little heat is required to raise the temperature of most metals.

Rocks, soils, vegetation, and water differ greatly in colour, compaction, conductivity, and specific heat, and hence arise many minor differences in temperature, but the greatest contrast is that between land and water. All the properties of water make it slow to warm up and cool down. It is a good reflector and a good conductor, but above all, the layers mix freely, spreading the warmth of the surface down by day and in summer, and replacing the chilled surface water with the warmer water from below by night and in winter.

The air tends to take the temperature of the surface it rests upon and, for all the reasons given, the air temperature above the oceans is much warmer in winter and cooler in summer than above the land. If the wind blows from the sea to the land, the climate of the coast will be like that of the sea, and the more steadily and strongly the wind blows the farther inland will the maritime climate be experienced.

In Western Europe, where the westerly winds off the Atlantic prevail strongly, the marine effect is felt far into the heart of the continent. But in the eastern states of the U.S.A., where the wind generally blows from land to sea, the effect is very much less marked. Washington is in the same latitude as Lisbon, but it is 17 degrees colder in January and 7 degrees hotter in July. Thus it is clear that temperature is not entirely manufactured on the spot, but is imported to a large extent, and the direction from which it comes is important.

### Warmth of the Sun

The higher the sun rises in the heavens the stronger is its power for two reasons. Firstly, a pencil of rays of given cross-section is concentrated on a smaller area of surface, and, secondly, the rays pass through a lesser thickness of atmosphere and are less weakened thereby.

The sun's fiercest heat is felt, therefore, when the sun is directly overhead—at the equinoxes at the equator (Fig. 5), at the solstices at the tropics, and twice a year at places between. But it must be remembered that the day at the equator is always twelve hours long, while at the tropics on mid-summer day the sun is above the horizon for thirteen-and-a-half hours, reaching the overhead position at midday. So the tropic at midsummer receives more heat than the equator, and the temperatures rise higher than they ever do at the equator.

At the North Pole on June 21, the day is twenty-four hours long and the sun's angle $23\frac{1}{2}$ degrees throughout the twenty-four hours (Fig. 6). The amount of heat received should be considerable, but we have to recall that at this low angle the heat of the sun has to pass through a great depth of air and much is lost. Moreover, a great deal of the energy that reaches the surface is reflected back from the snow and cannot be used for warming the air.

(3) *Wind Direction and Force.* The observer looks at the wind vane and notices the compass point from which it is blowing. Unless he is equipped with an anemometer, which accurately measures the speed of the wind, he estimates its force on the Beaufort Scale (Fig. 50).

Although one would imagine that this scale can only be approximate (for different types of trees react differently according to stiffness, leaf cover, etc.), it is surprising how accurate such estimations can become.

### Air in Motion

The wind is, of course, just air in motion, and it moves because pressure in one place is higher than in another. But it does not move straight from high pressure to low, i.e. across the isobars (page 59), because it is acted upon by the rotation of the earth and deflected from such a course. In the northern hemisphere it receives a constant deflection to the right which finally causes the air to flow parallel to the isobars and at right angles to the pressure gradient. This is known as the geostrophic wind. This final arrangement conveniently enables us to ascertain the direction of the wind simply from the run of the isobars.

This relationship is not found at the surface of the ground, because friction with the earth's surface prevents the geostrophic force from exercising full power, so that the surface wind, though much more variable and unreliable than the wind aloft, generally blows at an angle of from 10 to 20 degrees to the isobars and towards the low pressure. But at heights of 2,000 feet, where the air is not impeded by friction, the geostrophic wind occurs, and, moreover, its force is proportional to the pressure gradient and can be estimated from the spacing of the isobars (Fig. 65). For instance, a difference of pressure of 1 mb. between two places 17 miles apart gives a wind of 25 m.p.h. at 2,000 feet. But at ground level it slows down to about 15 m.p.h. and blows in irregular gusts.

As a general rule, the force of the surface wind on land is three-fifths that of the

| Beaufort number | Description | Specification for use on land | Average speed in m.p.h. and symbol |
|---|---|---|---|
| 0 | Calm | Smoke rises vertically | 0 |
| 1 | Light air | Direction shown by smoke drift but not by wind vanes | 2 |
| 2 | Light breeze | Wind felt on face. Leaves rustle. Ordinary vane moved by wind | 5 |
| 3 | Gentle breeze | Leaves and small twigs in constant motion. Wind extends light flag | 10 |
| 4 | Moderate breeze | Raises dust and loose paper. Small branches are moved | 15 |
| 5 | Fresh breeze | Small trees in leaf begin to sway. Crested wavelets form on inland waters | 21 |
| 6 | Strong breeze | Large branches in motion. Whistling heard in telegraph wires. Umbrellas used with difficulty | 28 |
| 7 | Moderate gale | Whole trees in motion. Inconvenience felt when walking against wind | 35 |
| 8 | Fresh gale | Breaks twigs off trees. Generally impedes progress | 42 |
| 9 | Strong gale | Slight structural damage occurs. (Chimney pots and slates removed) | 50 |
| 10 | Whole gale | Seldom experienced inland. Trees uprooted. Considerable structural damage occurs | 59 |
| 11 | Storm | Very rarely experienced. Accompanied by widespread damage | 69 |
| 12 | Hurricane | Above | 75 |

FIG. 50. *The Beaufort Scale, employed for estimating and reporting wind force.*

geostrophic, and at sea, where friction is less, three-quarters. We can now understand the long-known rule known as Buys Ballot's Law, which states that in the Northern Hemisphere an observer standing with his back to the wind has the low pressure to his left; in the Southern Hemisphere he will have it on his right.

(4) *Humidity.* In the screen is an instrument known as the wet-and-dry-bulb thermometer (Fig. 52). When the observer takes the wet-bulb reading he will usually find that it is a degree or two colder than the dry bulb. This is not because the water is cold, for it quickly takes up the same temperature as the air. It is because evaporation is going on from the muslin; evaporation uses up heat and the heat is taken from the mercury bulb. The cause is the same as that which makes a wet bathing costume feel cold even on a hot day, especially if the day is dry or windy, or which makes

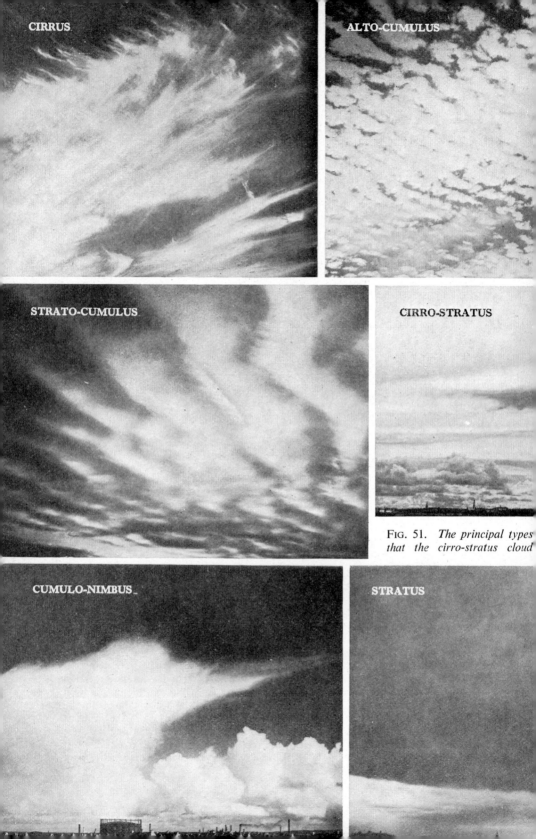

CIRRUS

ALTO-CUMULUS

STRATO-CUMULUS

CIRRO-STRATUS

FIG. 51. *The principal types
that the cirro-stratus cloud*

CUMULO-NIMBUS

STRATUS

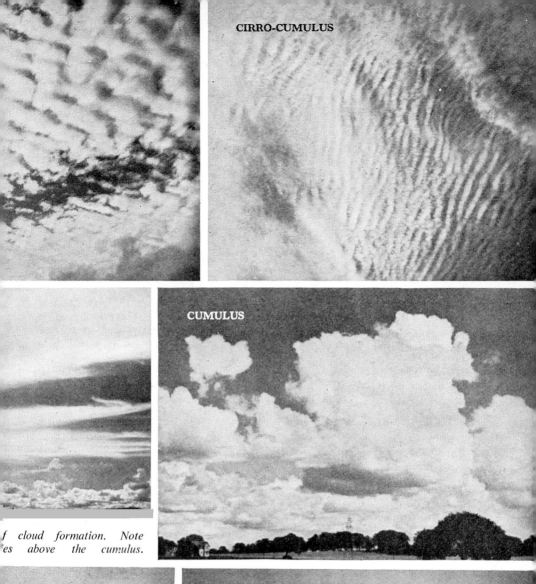

CIRRO-CUMULUS

CUMULUS

*f cloud formation. Note es above the cumulus.*

ALTO-STRATUS

the boy scout's finger feel cold on the windward side when he licks it and holds it up to detect a breeze.

Now, the drier the air, the faster the evaporation, the more heat is required, and the greater is the depression of the wet-bulb temperature below the dry-bulb. If both wet-bulb and dry-bulb readings are the same, no evaporation is happening and the only possible cause is that the air is fully saturated and can take up no more water vapour. The air is then said to have a relative humidity of 100 per cent.

Relative humidity can be defined as the ratio of the amount of water vapour present in the air to the greatest amount it is capable of holding at that temperature.

### Mist and Fog

There is always water vapour in the air and the hotter it is the more it can hold. It follows from this that if air is cooled down it eventually becomes saturated and the water vapour must condense as droplets of water which make dew (on blades of grass or cold surfaces like a tumbler of iced water), mist, cloud, or fog (in cold air), or hoar frost (if the saturation temperature is below freezing). The temperature at which this happens is known, naturally enough, as the "dew" point and is of the greatest importance in the formation of clouds and rain.

The fact that heat is used up in evaporation is a matter of vital concern for our comfort, for we keep our bodies cool in hot weather largely by the evaporation of sweat from the skin. Without sweat glands we could not endure temperatures above blood-heat (98·4 degrees F.); our body temperature would rise unchecked and cause heat stroke. But, provided he can go on sweating, a man can, and does, endure temperatures of 120 degrees or even 140 degrees—but only if the air is dry. In muggy weather, with a high humidity, the process does not work efficiently and we suffer severely from the heat.

For this reason, wet-bulb temperatures exceeding blood-heat are insupportable and must, if prolonged, result in death. Fortunately they do not occur; but wet-bulb temperatures of 80 degrees F. bring on heat stroke and 70 degrees F. seems to be as much as a white man can stand if he is to do any manual labour.

(5) *Visibility*. An important element the observer has to report upon is the distance at which objects can be seen, i.e. the visibility. At every station there is a list of objects—houses, trees, hills—at known distances away. By testing which he can see and which he can't he is able to assess the visibility or transparency of the air, which he reports according to the following code:

| Code figure | Distance | | Description |
|---|---|---|---|
| | Yards | Metres | |
| 0 | 27 | 25 | Dense fog |
| 1 | 110 | 100 | Thick fog |
| 2 | 220 | 200 | Fog |
| 3 | 550 | 500 | Moderate fog |
| 4 | 1100 | 1000 | Mist or haze |
| 5 | 2200 | 2000 | Poor visibility |
| | Miles | Kilo-metres | |
| 6 | 4⅜ | 7 | Moderate visibility |
| 7 | 6¼ | 10 | Good visibility |
| 8 | 18⅝ | 30 | Very good visibility |
| 9 | 31 | 50 | Excellent visibility |

Visibility depends on the amount of two kinds of impurities in the air, dust and water particles. The latter, as fog or mist, account for the lowest visibilities, but the former gives rise to haze. Neither is likely to occur when a fresh breeze blows, for the air is stirred and mixed so that fog is dispersed and dust is scattered through such a depth of air that it is too rarefied to impair the visibility badly. Calm anticyclonic weather encourages the dust to settle into the lowest layers. It also encourages temperature inversions in which the air cools below its dew point, forming low fog. Towns, especially industrial towns, create their own murky pall of dust and smoke which drifts slowly to leeward, contaminating the air and impairing visibility for many miles (Fig. 210).

(6) *Clouds*. When air is cooled below its dew point on the ground, fog is the result. More commonly the dew point is reached at some thousands of feet up and

the condensation causes cloud. To understand its origin it is important and necessary to understand a simple physical principle—that air, in expanding, becomes cool. We are familiar with the converse of this in the heating of the end of a bicycle pump where the air is compressed.

### How Clouds are Formed

Nearly all cloud is formed by cooling as a result of expansion, and the expansion is caused by the ascent of air which finds itself, at higher levels, subject to decreased atmospheric pressure. Now, since the decrease of atmospheric pressure is regular, the amount of expansion per foot ascended is regular, and the consequent cooling is regular—being 5·4 degrees F. per thousand feet (the adiabatic lapse rate). If moving air, i.e. wind, is forced up the slope of a mountain range 3,000 feet high, its temperature at the top will be 16·2 degrees F. lower than it was at sea level.

Let us suppose, for example, that a west wind is blowing off the Atlantic against the western mountains of Scotland. Suppose its temperature over the Atlantic is 50 degrees, and that its relative humidity is 83 per cent. This corresponds to a dew point of 45 degrees. It only needs to cool 5 degrees for saturation to be reached, so that cloud will begin to form just below a thousand feet.

There are two principal ways in which this ascent of air may occur; by an inclined ascent up a hillside, as just stated, or over another mass of air. The resultant cloud takes the form of a layer (stratus) with a flat base marking the level at which the temperature is at dew point.

The other form of ascent is vertical, or nearly so, and results from convection (page 49). Probably the convection is local and a small cloud is the result. As before, the base will be flat, but the top will be rounded and billowing with an outline that changes from minute to minute as the cloud "boils" up. This is known as a heap cloud (cumulus). These are the two fundamental types of cloud, but their variety is endless and they occur at various heights. The chief varieties are shown in Fig. 51.

(7) *Rain*. The observer has two duties to fulfil with regard to rain. First, he must measure the depth of rain that has fallen since the gauge was last read (usually twenty-four hours). Secondly, he must report whether rain is falling at the times of observation and what sort of rain it is—heavy, light or drizzle—and whether falling persistently or in intermittent showers.

Remember that the drops of water that form clouds are too small and light to fall, and that a cloud is nearly always formed in ascending air currents which buoy it up. It is only if the droplets grow together into large drops that they will become heavy enough to fall to the ground as rain. This requires a good thick cloud, and many meteorologists believe that it happens only when the cloud extends high enough to cause ice crystals to form. In any case, only drizzle is produced by thin clouds. Remember also that the drops, once formed, have to fall through unsaturated air and, unless they are large, may be evaporated during their journey from the cloud to the ground.

Only two types of cloud reach sufficient thickness to give rain, though drizzle may reach the ground from some of the others. These two are nimbostratus and cumulonimbus, and their rain-giving quality is implied in their names (*nimbus*,

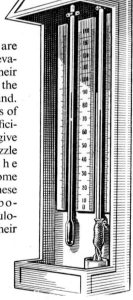

FIG. 52. *The wet-and-dry-bulb thermometer consists of an ordinary (dry-bulb) thermometer, which gives the air temperature, and a thermometer whose bulb is covered with a muslin bag connected by a wick to a reservoir of water. See page 53.*

FIG. 53. *A forecaster at the Meteorological Department of the British Air Ministry is seen here plotting reported weather on a large-scale synoptic map and drawing in the isobars and fronts.*

(8) *Snow and Hail.* These must be reported upon by the observer under the general heading of "precipitation" or "hydrometeors." When water drops are frozen they become ice pellets, or hail. This generally happens in cumulo-nimbus cloud where the drops are carried above freezing level in the uprush that is usual in the body of this type of cloud. The

rain). There are three principal causes of rain, corresponding to three different origins of rain-producing clouds.

(i) *Convectional, or instability, rain.* Powerful convection builds up large cumulo-nimbus clouds giving heavy showers of large drops, for only large drops can fall through the strong rising air currents which give rise to this type of cloud. This is the hot weather rain of summer thunderstorms, the rainfall of the tropics and of the interior of continents in summer.

(ii) *Orographic rain* is caused by the forced ascent of moist air up hill and mountain slopes, and the cloud formed is nimbo-stratus. Once the rain has begun, the heat liberated by the condensation may set up auto-convection and give rise to cumulo-nimbus.

(iii) *Cyclonic rain* is due to the ascent of warm moist air over a body of colder, heavier air along a front. This is probably the principal cause of rain in the belts of cyclonic climate, including Western Europe and much of North America.

pellet may fall down and be carried up again several times, and each time that it rises above freezing level it has a new shell of ice frozen on to it until it may grow to a considerable size, occasionally as large as a hen's egg. Such a missile may do very considerable damage; men and cattle have been killed by them in the tropics. Hail is commonest in spring, when the freezing level is still fairly low but when days are hot enough to produce the necessary powerful ascent.

If the water is still in the form of vapour when it gets to freezing level and condensation occurs at temperatures below freezing point, ice crystals of feathery texture in a great variety of beautiful forms are produced. These snow crystals are all hexagonal; that is, they have a six-sided symmetry. Bunches of such crystals may run together, forming large, loose flakes, especially if the snow is not far below its melting point. The colder snow of high latitudes is generally in the form of quite small flakes or of single crystals.

# FORECASTING THE WEATHER

THESE meteorological elements — pressure, temperature, wind, humidity, visibility, clouds, rain, snow or hail — having been recorded at the meteorological station, are sent by teleprinter, telegraph or radio to the forecasting stations and provide the basis for the weather report and forecast.

Ships far out on the ocean contribute by radio and help to fill in the blanks on the world map, and the aeroplane today makes an invaluable contribution. Meteorological flights are daily flown hundreds of miles out over the Atlantic, taking observations at all heights and sampling the weather that is coming to us. All this information from land, sea and air is received in a "shorthand" code of letters and figures, decoded and plotted on a map (Fig. 53) known as a synoptic map, because it presents all the facts to the eye at once. Each weather element is shown by a separate symbol or figure at the position of the station on the map; Figs. 63 and 64 provide the key.

The map looks very complicated and a great deal of practice is needed before one can visualize the state of the weather even at one station. To appreciate the weather conditions at some dozens of stations takes longer still, and is part of the training of every meteorologist. Visualization is made a little easier by drawing isobars, or lines joining together all places with the same pressure, reduced to the sea-level equivalent. (See page 48 and Fig. 65.)

## Special Difficulties

The meteorologist is now in a position to say what the weather was at the time of observation, but naturally interest centres on what it will be, i.e. on the forecast. Thus, in forecasting, the meteorologist must be able to say (1) where the weather will travel; and (2) what changes it will undergo in the process. It is as well to realize that this is difficult anywhere, and especially difficult in an area like the British Isles.

The especial difficulties attaching to the British Isles are consequent on their position on the western side of a continent in latitudes with the most variable weather in the world. British weather comes mainly from the west, off the Atlantic, where close observations are impracticable; it undergoes sudden changes on leaving the sea for a rather mountainous west coast. Also Britain is situated in a debatable ground between three weather systems (Fig. 66). The forecasts must therefore be of a general nature applying to a considerable area (e.g. S.E. England), where the weather may differ materially in places fifty or a hundred miles apart.

## Theory and Practice

It is an interesting exercise to tabulate the daily forecast and, beside it, write the weather as it happened. When this has been done for a month or two it will provide a more valid basis for criticism than a mere general impression; it is probably right much more often than you think.

The preparation of a forecast demands (1) a considerable theoretical knowledge of the behaviour of the atmosphere and (2) a considerable practical experience of what actually happens. The latter can only be acquired by practice, so let us turn to the former as a preparation for the interpretation of the weather maps.

It was stated above that the average decrease of temperature with altitude was about 3 degrees F. per thousand feet, but at the same time we were careful to point out that this is hardly ever true and that the lapse rate varies from day to day and from hour to hour. This has very important results on the stability of the air and on the consequent weather phenomena, especially clouds, rain and visibility. That is sufficient to show the fundamental importance of understanding what is meant by stability.

A marble lying at the bottom of a hemispherical bowl is stable, because if it is pushed to one side it rolls back and eventually settles where it was before. Turn the bowl upside down and balance the marble on the top and it is unstable; at the slightest disturbance it rolls off, gathering speed as it rolls; and it will not come back. Again, a cork floating on water is in stable equilibrium because it is lighter than the water on

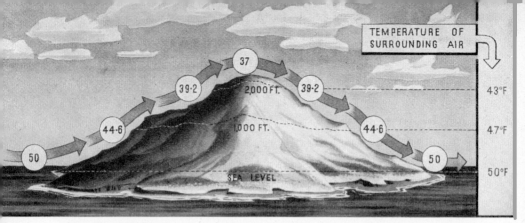

37

39·2     2,000 FT.     39·2          43°F

44·6     1,000 FT.     44·6          47°F

50          50          50°F

SEA LEVEL

FIG. 54.    *Here air is represented as flowing around and over the hills.    When it is forced upwards air expands and cools.    The rate of cooling is 5·4 degrees for each thousand feet. During its descent of the lee slope the air is compressed and warmed by a like amount.*

which it floats, but heavier than the air in which it sinks. Lift it in the air and drop it; it falls.  Push it under water and let go; it bobs up to the surface.

To apply this to the atmosphere is not so simple, because we have to consider air floating in air and the weight of air depends on (1) the pressure to which it is subjected (high pressure compacts and makes it dense, low pressure expands it and makes it rarefied), and (2) its temperature (hot air is lighter than cold).  Fortunately we can ignore the question of pressure, because the pressure varies so slightly from place to place that it has little effect on the density at a given height.  The distribution of temperature thus becomes the chief determinant of air density.

Now let us consider a mass of air which is being forced up a hillside and let us suppose that the lapse rate is the average one of 3 degrees F. per thousand feet and that the sea-level temperature is 50 deg. F. (Fig. 54).  The air, of sea-level density, rises to levels where the pressure on it is less, so that it expands and, as we saw on page 57, cools at a rate of 5·4 degrees F. per thousand feet.  Thus by the time it reaches 1,000 feet, its temperature has fallen to 44·6 degrees F., but the surrounding air is at a temperature of 47 degrees. The rising air is therefore colder and heavier, and therefore tends to sink as soon as it has the chance, which it will get when it crosses the divide.  The air is stable since it tends to move back to its original level.

Next let us consider the air over a tarmac

road on a hot summer afternoon and let us suppose that the air temperature over the fields on either side of the road is 65 degrees F. (Fig. 55).  The tarmac gets very hot and the air on it is heated much more than that over the fields; suppose it is at 70 degrees F.  It expands and becomes lighter than the surrounding air and begins to float upwards.  As it ascends it cools at the "adiabatic" rate (the rate for rising air) of 5·4 degrees F. per thousand feet, so that when it has risen to 1,000 feet, its temperature is 64·6 degrees F.

But if the normal lapse rate (the rate for still air) of 3 degrees per thousand feet applies to the air on either side, the air at 1,000 feet over the fields is 62 degrees F. The ascending air is still lighter than its surroundings and continues to ascend. The diagram shows that it reaches the temperature of its surroundings just above 2,000 feet. Here both the rising and surrounding air are at the same pressure as well as at the same temperature. Their density is therefore the same and the air has reached stability.

It will be seen that all this happens because the adiabatic lapse rate is steeper than the normal temperature lapse rate. But what happens when the lapse rate is not normal but is steeper than the adiabatic?  This could happen if the air aloft was very cold or the air at the ground was abnormally hot.  Both cases are met with, but the latter is more common, and in fact occurs on most hot summer days, especially in the lower layers of the air.

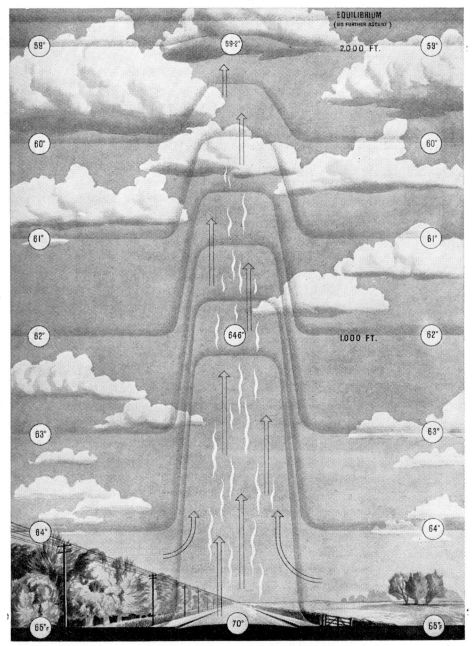

FIG. 55. *Free ascent. Air, having been warmed by the sun-heated surface of the road, rises of its own accord (convection) and as it rises it cools, as shown in Fig. 54. At some height which can be calculated (see text), the cooling brings the rising air to the same temperature as that of the surrounding air. When this occurs the ascent stops.*

In our diagram the lower layers of the air have been so heated by the sun that their lapse rate is steeper than the adiabatic up to 2,000 feet. Once convection has started, the rising air, instead of approaching the temperature of its surroundings, becomes still lighter and lighter, and its uprush is unchecked. Not until it reaches 2,000 feet, where the lapse rate is less steep than the adiabatic, does it begin to approach stability, and not until 2,100 feet does it at last attain to it.

From all this it is clear that hot air on the ground is very unstable and conduces to "overturning" of the air, with an exchange of upper and lower layers. On the other hand cold air on the ground, and especially inversions of temperature, are very stable and difficult to break up.

So far we have ignored a very important fact—that the rising air may cool to the dew point and form cloud. When this happens heat is liberated (the latent heat of condensation) and that heat passes into the air, delaying its further cooling, though by how much it is unfortunately impossible to say exactly, because that depends on the amount of water available for condensation, and that, in turn, depends on the temperature.

At high temperatures in the tropics the rate of cooling of rising saturated air is very slow and is likely to be less steep than that of the surrounding air. Thus, once cloud is formed the ascensional movement is unlikely to be checked for some time. The vigorous ascent is maintained and clouds build up to great height and give torrential rain. Cloud may thus be started by quite modest hills and may set up a chain of events which gives rain out of all proportion to the size of the hills, e.g. the monsoon rains on the Western Ghats of India. When the lapse rate is such that the air is stable while dry, but unstable when saturated, it is said to be conditionally unstable—that

FIG. 56. *Forced ascent causing orographic rain on the windward slope of mountains. The text explains how the air becomes much warmer on the leeward side, accounting for such hot dry winds as the "Foehn wind," to the north of the Alps in Switzerland, and the "Chinook," which melts the snow on the eastern slopes of the Rockies in Alberta.*

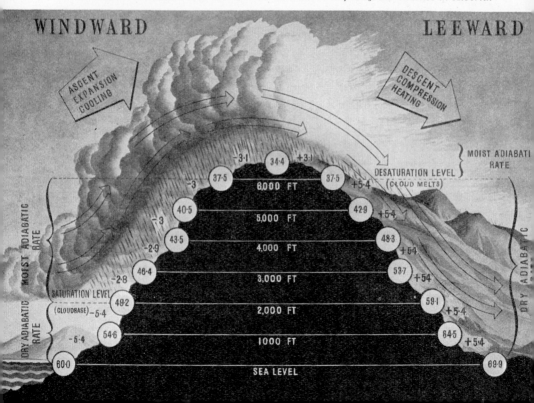

is, conditional on condensation occurring.

The reader is now referred to the maps in Fig. 66, B and C (page 74), where the large-scale causes of weather are explained by the general circulation of the atmosphere.

Differences of temperature produce differences of pressure, for warmed air expands and rises, other air moves in to fill the low pressure thus formed, and wind is the result. If the globe were stationary, the air, heated in the tropics, would rise and be replaced by air from higher latitudes. The heated air would move in the upper atmosphere towards the poles, where it would descend to replace the air moving along the surface towards the tropics.

But the rotation of the earth introduces complications by deflecting the wind to the right hand in the Northern Hemisphere and to the left in the Southern. So instead of having N. and S. winds blowing in towards the equator we have NE. and SE. winds, known as the Trades, which move in to fill up the low-pressure trough near the equator —a region of calms or light winds known as the Doldrums (Fig. 66, B and C).

The return current in the upper air meanwhile is making its way towards the poles, but has to contend with the centrifugal force which tries to throw it back again. Somewhere between 30 degrees and 40 degrees N. and S. the thermal gradient, that is, its driving force, loses its power and the air can proceed no farther. Consequently, an accumulation of air occurs here, giving rise, at the earth's surface, to a belt of anticyclonic calms (the horse latitudes). The air descending here flows outwards in both directions, equator-wards to reinforce the trade winds and pole-wards (though again deflected by the earth's rotation) to form the westerly winds. From the neighbourhood of the poles cold heavy air moves away, and meets the westerlies in a low-pressure belt about lat. 70 degrees N. and S. This is the generalized circulation as it would probably be were it not for a further complication—the distribution of land and sea.

We have seen that the air tends to assume the temperature of the surface on which it rests, and the longer it stays the more completely it does so. Any interference by air invading from another region, where different temperature conditions obtain, will upset the process. Consequently, the most uniform masses of air will occur where such invasions are infrequent, i.e. in the great world anticyclones from which air spreads outwards, such as the great "lake" of cold stagnant air that accumulates over Siberia in winter, and the spreading whirl of warm moist air that covers the North Atlantic throughout the year.

It is possible to draw a broad distinction between areas of divergence of air (anticyclones), with stable climates, and areas of convergence of air (low-pressure zones such as the Doldrums and the cyclonic belt), with unsettled weather and variable climates.

The two qualities that distinguish air masses are (1) their temperature, which depends largely on their latitude (*polar* or *tropical*) and (2) their humidity, which depends on the nature of the surface, land or water, on which they originate (*continental* or *maritime*). Other air masses, e.g. equatorial and monsoon, are also recognized, but they are not so clearly defined, the former being produced by the convergence of two similar masses (namely, the trade winds of the two hemispheres), and the latter being a massive stream of fairly uniform air which is a continuation, across the equator, of one of the trades.

### Air Masses and Fronts

*Polar Continental Air* (*P.c.*). This has its origin in the cold heart of continents in winter and in polar regions all the year round. The mid-winter temperature at Yakutsk is −47 degrees F.; at Winnipeg −4 degrees F. Colossal volumes of cold air are involved in the area in Eurasia and North America that is below freezing in January. The atmosphere is extremely stable and very difficult to disturb. Ascent of air is difficult to start and impossible to maintain; precipitation is therefore unusual and the climate is dry. In any case the amount of moisture present in air at these low temperatures is small and gives only light falls of snow, except when warmer and moister air enters from outside, as it begins to do when spring approaches.

Now let us follow this P.c. air as it moves away from its place of origin, e.g. Canadian air passing on to the North Atlantic over the east coast of the U.S.A. The lower layers are quickly warmed up, but the upper air is still intensely cold. So the lapse rate steepens, instability develops and the air ascends, forming cumulus cloud and perhaps cumulo-nimbus with short heavy showers separated by bright intervals. Its moisture reserves will have been added to in passing above relatively warm water. But should the polar air pass over warm land (e.g. Mexico), though instability develops and cumulus forms, it is not likely to possess sufficient moisture to produce rain.

*Polar Maritime Air (P.m.).* This arises over the cold seas in high latitudes and may often have started as P.c. air, modified on passing out to sea. It has many of the qualities of P.c. air but does not reach such depths of cold, the low layers rarely having freezing temperatures. But its humidity is higher, and this gives it great energy for the production of cumulo-nimbus and showers when instability develops. This happens as its lower layers are warmed as it drifts to warmer regions. It is thus very turbulent, stormy and bumpy. Visibility is good between the showers because of the washing out of impurities and because of the strong turbulence.

*Tropical Continental Air (T.c.).* The great mass of descending air that makes up the tropical (horse latitude) anticyclones has an inherent stability, but where it rests on land the surface layers become highly heated, especially in summer. The lapse rate is steepened by day and the air becomes very unstable. Convection results, but though winds and dust storms are produced the air is so dry that clouds and rain do not follow. This is the climate of the tropical deserts of the Sahara, Australia and, to a smaller extent, South Africa and the south-west of the U.S.A. and Mexico. Only when moist air enters does rain occur, as, for example, in tropical climates in summer. The air, however, is no longer T.c. but equatorial.

On moving to colder regions the lapse rate becomes less steep and the air more and more stable, but its heat is still a source of energy if it meets damp air.

*Tropical Maritime Air (T.m.).* Centres of tropical high pressure cover a large

FIG. 57. *Clouds and weather in a vigorous depression. Compare with Fig. 58 and page 67. The centre of the depression (lowest pressure) is at the tip of the "warm sector" over the North Sea. The cloud walls along the warm and cold fronts are 4-5 miles high but are greatly exaggerated in this diagram.*

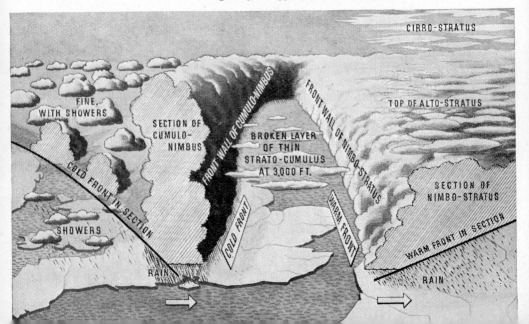

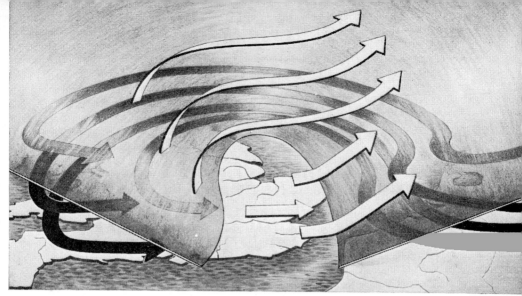

FIG. 58. *Air-flow in a depression. Warm air (white arrows) above the plane of separation rises gently over the cold air (black arrows) along the warm front and is jerked upwards at the cold front where the cold air turns and thrusts under it.*

area of the ocean and in summer form separate oval anticyclones separated by the low pressures that are generated over the heated continents. These anticyclones are the sources of mighty masses of warm moist air with a stable stratification.

From them air streams north-eastwards in the Northern Hemisphere as the westerlies, its lower layers cooling as it travels over colder water. Stable at its source, it becomes still more stable and difficult to disturb, an unpromising medium for convection. But as it cools, its heavy load of water vapour condenses either as sea fog, or, if mixed by turbulence, as low cloud of a stratus type. Drizzle or steady rain can be produced if the air is forced upwards by high land barriers.

As a general principle it will be noticed that cold air masses become more and more unstable as they leave their source region, while hot air masses become more and more stable. Thus cold air masses produce convection, heap clouds, and heavy showers; warm masses produce fog, layer cloud, and drizzle or light, steady rain.

We have seen that air masses spread from centres of divergence, the great high-pressure regions of the globe. Inevitably they come into conflict in regions of convergence, the great low-pressure centres, to which air masses of diverse origins are

attracted. The inflowing air has to escape upwards and if the masses differ in temperature, the warmer and lighter rises above the colder and heavier. The regions of their convergence are the stormy and rainy regions of the globe, the two chief being the Doldrum belt (or equatorial front) and the sub-polar Lows (or polar fronts) of both hemispheres.

*The Equatorial Front (Doldrum Belt).* Here meet the trade winds from both hemispheres, mainly T.m. air, hot and heavily charged with moisture. In general there is little difference between the two air currents; their surface temperature is 75 degrees to 80 degrees and humidity at sea level about 85 per cent. The wind speed falls off as they approach each other until, in the zone of their meeting, calms prevail. Here are the highest temperatures (about 80 degrees). This is the heat equator, and it does not necessarily coincide with the geographical equator. In fact, it migrates north and south of the geographical equator in the northern and southern summers respectively, with a lag of about three months behind the sun.

On the heat equator the air ascends, often violently, producing heavy rain often accompanied by thunder. Once cloud formation begins in the ascending air a great store of heat is liberated by the condensation

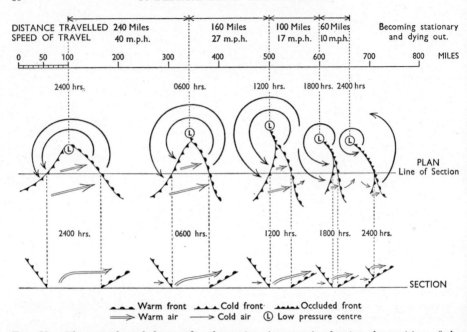

FIG. 59. *The growth and decay of a depression (see text), showing the position of the centre and the form of the fronts at six-hour intervals. In this example of a rather rapid occlusion the warm air has been lifted off the ground within twenty-hours by the cold front first overtaking and finally over-riding the warm front.*

and the ascent becomes more violent.

At sea the most favourable conditions for instability occur at night, which is the time of most rain and most frequent thunderstorms. But on land the midday heat of the almost vertical sun so strongly warms the surface air and steepens the lapse rate, that instability is set up in the afternoon, which is the rainy and thundery part of the day. The daily round of weather in the rainy season of equatorial and tropical climates is thus monotonously regular. The morning dawns fine and clear, the cool of night quickly gives way to the heat of day, by ten o'clock air begins to rise; cumulus clouds form and gather, building up, as the day wears on, into cumulo-nimbus. A few heavy splashes fall and then the view is blotted out by torrents of thundery rain. Towards evening the showers cease, the clouds shrink and subside, finally melting away and leaving the clear starry sky of the tropical night. The rain usually sets in between one and four o'clock in the after-

noon; at any particular place its onset is so regular and reliable that one's daily round of activities and appointments can be regulated by it. Hence the familiar phrase heard so frequently in tropical lands: "See you after the storm."

*The Polar Front.* The impact of air masses along the polar front is much more complicated because of the great contrasts between the masses involved, which may be P.m., P.c., T.m. and occasionally T.c. Let us consider first the effect of warm, moist, T.m. making a flank attack on a stream of cold dry P.c. The warm air must rise over the cold, even though some mixing occurs; condensation must result, and rain will be produced. The cloud will form along the plane separating the air bodies and this plane usually has a slope of about 1 in 100. The type of cloud will be in accordance with the height of this plane at each point, from cirrus, five miles up, to nimbo-stratus almost down to "the deck" near the line where the front is at the ground. From the nimbo-stratus rain will fall, heaviest near the front. The rain will fall through the polar air from the tropical air aloft, its area forming a wide strip.

Next consider the case of P.m. air making a flank attack on a stream of T.m. air. The cold air must thrust its way under the warm, displacing it upwards, more violently than in the preceding case. The plane separating the two air bodies is more steeply sloping, usually about 1 in 50. The more violent and more nearly vertical movement gives rise to cumulus and cumulo-nimbus clouds from which heavy showers of rain or hail fall. Thunder may occur.

### Depressions

Now let us turn to the condition in the North Atlantic Ocean where P.m. air is in conflict with T.m. (Fig. 66, c). The two streams may be flowing side by side, but in opposite directions. They do not mix, but remain clearly distributed; the surface that separates them is not vertical but is much more nearly horizontal; it usually has a slope of about 1 in 100, with the warm above the cold. Such an arrangement cannot persist; wave motion is set up along the separating plane where the warm air brushes over the cold, just as the surface of water billows up when a wind blows over it. At the apex of each of the northward bulges of warm air the pressure is relatively low. This is the first stage in the development of a depression; it rapidly grows: the tongue of warm air thrusts northwards and the tongues of cold air on either side thrust southwards.

Now let us consider what happens to the air-flow. From being parallel streams flowing in opposite directions the warm and cold masses begin to flow in a circular form, but not quite in a horizontal plane. The warm air has to rise over the tongue of cold air to the east and in doing so it reproduces the weather conditions described in Fig. 58.

The cold air, on the other hand, thrusts under the warm air on the west side of the warm tongue. In doing so it reproduces the weather conditions associated with a cold front, forming a narrow strip of squally rain (Fig. 57). Thus the succession of weather in a vigorous depression seen by an observer over whom the system passes from west to east with the centre to the north of him is as follows:

(A) *Phenomena Associated with a Warm Front:* 1. Appearance of cirrus cloud, matting up to cirro-stratus; a "watery sky" with haloes round the sun or moon, which constitute one of the most certain prognostics of rain to come.

2. The cirro-stratus gives way to alto-stratus, "ground-glass sky," through which the outline of the sun is diffused; drizzle may begin towards the end of this stage.

3. Cloud becomes thicker, darker, and heavier (nimbo-stratus); steady rain falls, heavy as the warm front approaches.

(B) *Phenomena Associated with the Warm Air Mass of the Warm Sector:* Mild weather; stratus cloud; south-west wind; no rain, or drizzle only.

(C) *Phenomena Associated with a Cold Front:* Sudden shift of wind to west or north-west, cumulus or cumulo-nimbus cloud, heavy clearing showers with bright intervals between.

(D) *Phenomena Associated with Cold Air Mass:* Cold invigorating air, turbulent and bumpy; good visibility and mainly blue sky; clouds of heap type, due to instability, build up by day, but decay towards evening.

### Occlusions

When the isobars are plotted on the weather map the depression at once shows itself as a system of closed isobars with low pressure in the centre. The relation of the fronts and air masses to the isobars in Fig. 65 should be carefully studied. The isobars are usually bent at the fronts, often quite sharply at the cold front. Since the wind direction is related to the isobars we should expect the sudden change of wind that occurs as the front passes.

The diameter of a vigorous depression may be about a thousand miles, and if it travels at a speed of 25 m.p.h. it would take nearly two days to pass over; but they vary in size and in speed of movement. Depressions of this type often pass over the British Isles or up the English Channel.

FIG. 60. *Tornado in Nebraska, U.S.A.* Left: *Cone forming in cloud.* Centre: *Fully-developed cone reaching the earth.* Right: *Cone striking a house, which appears to explode.*

But many have begun to decay by occlusion, as illustrated in Figs. 58 and 59. The warm front loses some of its speed by the warm air having to climb over the cold; the cold front advances more rapidly and finally overtakes the warm front, at first near the apex of the warm salient and later farther south where the warm sector was wider.

The warm sector shuts up like the blades of a pair of secateurs and the warm air is squeezed upwards off the ground. The cold air behind now comes against the cold air in front and what happens depends on their relative coldness. If the cold air in front is colder than the cold air behind, the "warmer" cold air behind rises over it. This is known as a *warm occlusion.* This does not mean that it gives warm weather, but rather *warm front* weather. The alternative arrangement gives a *cold occlusion* with *cold front* weather.

### Tropical Storms

Over certain parts of the oceans in the tropics violent storms are experienced, giving winds of great force and torrential rain. The pressure in the centre of the storm is very low, perhaps 900 mb., and the pres-

FIG. 61. *Damage done by a tornado in Texas, U.S.A. A swathe of destruction has been cut where the "cone" touched the ground. The houses in the background are quite unaffected. Fortunately, these prairie tornadoes are short-lived and the area devastated is usually quite small.*

sure gradient is very steep. But the area affected is not great, being perhaps two hundred miles across, and the storm moves relatively slowly. It is therefore easily avoided by aircraft and fairly easily by fast ships. In the centre there may be a small patch of fine weather with blue sky (but with a very heavy swell on the sea) known as the eye of the storm. Round this the winds blow in an anti-clockwise swirl in the Northern Hemisphere (clockwise in the Southern) at 70 m.p.h. or more. They are known as hurricanes in the Caribbean, as typhoons in the China seas, and as cyclones in the Indian Ocean. They die out quickly if they pass on to the land, but are capable

of causing great havoc along the coast.

The prairie tornado, probably the most spectacular and destructive of storms, fortunately covers a very narrow track and is short-lived. Not uncommon in the prairie states of U.S.A., they are chiefly encountered in early summer, usually in the afternoon, but have been known in every month of the year (Figs. 60 and 61).

A cone or pipe of inky black cloud extends down from a heavy cumulo-nimbus and where it touches the ground destruction is terrific. Thunder and lightning often add to the terror, and torrential rain sometimes falls. In the centre the atmospheric pressure is approaching a vacuum

(perhaps half the normal, but no barometer that has been in the centre has survived the experience). Here the effects are explosive; the air inside a house expands to fill the vacuum, bedclothes and curtains are sucked up the chimney, corks and contents are sucked out of bottles, the walls may collapse outwards as if by an explosion within. The rush of air into this "vacuum" produces winds of 100 m.p.h. or more, which transport houses, trees, haystacks, etc., sometimes for miles.

The storm is always associated with a deep V-shaped depression caused by the meeting of tropical air from the Gulf of Mexico with polar continental air from the north-west. They travel east or north-east at a speed of 20 to 40 m.p.h. and cut a narrow swathe of destruction as far as they go. But though the devastation is complete, and Kansas expects ten tornadoes a year, the area actually affected is small. It is a fairly general practice to insure against tornado damage, the risk to life being about one in a million in Kansas if you live to be a hundred. It is easy to run out of the way provided you run in the right direction—north-west or south-east and not north-east or south-west (the direction of travel of the storm).

*Waterspouts* are similar to tornadoes, occurring over the sea or inland lakes. A good deal of water is sucked up, as is proved by the rains of small fish and frogs that are reported from time to time, often at some distance from the waterspout. But this is not the main source of the rain that accompanies the spout; such rain is always fresh, even over the sea.

*Dust Devils.* Similar vortices produce the whirling columns of dust, known as dust devils, that dance across sandy desert regions during the heat of the day. The air is too dry to give any rain.

### Lightning and Thunder

The electric power expended on a single good flash of lightning is enough to light all the lamps in London for a few seconds, and hundreds of flashes are produced in a single storm. Thunderstorms are occurring somewhere or other on the earth at every moment of the day. Buitenzorg, in Java, which appears to hold the record for frequency, has thunder 250 days in the year.

The principal source of this power seems to be the building up and breaking down of raindrops on whose surface resides the electrical charge. In this way the positive charge (on the drop) and the negative charge (in the air) are redistributed in the cloud and around it (Fig. 62). The difference of electric pressure mounts rapidly until the resistance of the air breaks down and the flash passes.

This breaking up and reunion of drops occurs in clouds of the cumulo-nimbus type, in which powerful currents of air are ascending. When the rising current is strong enough to carry the cloud to heights of four or five miles a curious "anvil" of cirrus cloud sprouts from the top of the cumulo-nimbus—a sure prediction of thunder (Fig. 51).

### Preparing a Forecast

The up-currents in a thunder cloud are terrifyingly powerful: 50 m.p.h. or more. Aircraft avoid them; if caught, as they may be by night, they may have a rough passage and may even be broken up.

The heat of the flash expands the air explosively, producing a loud crack, such as we hear when lightning strikes nearby. But if it strikes far away, we hear the noise from the near end of the spark followed by the noise from the rest of its length; and, since sound takes nearly five seconds to travel a mile, the noise may last for some time. Echoes from ground and cloud cause it to last longer still and give the crash, rumble or growl of near or distant thunder.

Now that we have seen something of how different kinds of weather are made we are in a position to return to our weather map (Fig. 65), and prepare our forecast. In the last twenty-five years, a revolutionary change has come over our methods. Previously the pressure system was the basis and forecasts were made according to the weather expected, in cyclones, anticyclones, wedges of high pressure and the like. Today, while these terms are still in use, it is recognized that the pressure systems are symptoms of air masses and fronts; the air mass is now the unit and

ANVIL OF CIRRUS

TORRENTIAL RAIN    HEAVY RAIN    RAIN

Fig. 62. *Thunder cloud. Ferocious up-currents, exceeding twenty-four feet per second (see text), prevent rain from falling from left-hand half. Rising water-drops here concentrate a positive charge. In the right-hand half rain carries the positive charge to earth, leaving the cloud negatively charged. Lightning flashes from the positive to the negative.*

basis of forecasting. The first duty of the forecaster is thus to identify and to separate the air masses on his map, which he does by their characteristics of temperature, relative humidity, cloud type, hydro-meteors (rain, hail, snow), visibility and (when available) their lapse rates. In general the high pressures will be the areas under the influence of an air mass and the low pressures will be the regions of their conflict.

Very much simplified, the problems to be solved are now as follows:

(1) How the air masses and the fronts dividing them will move, taking their weather with them.

(2) What changes will occur in the weather as a result of *(a)* the development or occlusion of fronts, growth or decay of "highs," "lows," etc.; and *(b)* the passage over different types of country, sea or land, high land or low, etc.

For the solution of all these problems there is an answer based on theory, but the safest guide is the past behaviour of the weather and the movements observed from the weather maps of the preceding days.

Below are a few simple rules for forecasting British weather from the weather map, but it cannot be over-emphasized that forecasting is not a simple process.

### Sixteen Rules

1. A depression moves: (i) *From* an area where pressure is rising *to* an area where pressure is falling. (ii) In the direction of the strongest winds in the system. (iii) In a direction parallel to the isobars in the warm sector (if not occluded). (iv) Along the general path that it has followed in the previous hours.

Although most depressions travel from west to east, there are numerous exceptions and each one must be treated on its merits.

2. The rate of movement of a front perpendicular to its own length may be estimated from the distance between adjacent isobars. Warm fronts move rather more slowly than such estimates indicate, cold fronts rather faster, this difference leading

**STATION MODEL**

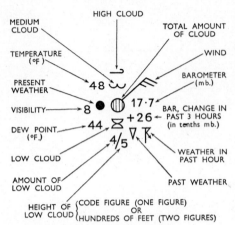

FIG. 63. *The weather conditions at each station are plotted thus. Each element has its standard position.*

to occlusion. The position of the fronts can thus be estimated for any time ahead up to twenty-four hours.

3. Secondary depressions revolve anticlockwise round primary depressions.

4. V-shaped isobars round a low pressure trough indicate strongly convergent winds and violent over-riding along a front with exaggerated cold-front squalls.

5. Depressions, once they become occluded, slow down, become stationary, and die out.

6. A depression is deepening if the fall of pressure in front of it is more rapid than the rise behind.

7. A depression is filling up if the fall of pressure in front of it is less rapid than the rise behind.

8. Thundery tendencies require careful watching, especially in the summer.

9. An anticyclone between two cyclones, generally in the form of a high-pressure wedge, usually consists of a tongue of polar air and moves with the depressions.

10. Other anticyclones are more stable and less mobile, and their weather is that of the air mass concerned, but their nature and behaviour are best judged from their record on previous charts.

11. Cold anticyclones, most frequent in the later winter months, often consist of polar continental air. Much stratus cloud is common, and frost and fog are characteristic, especially at night.

12. Warm anticyclones, most frequent in

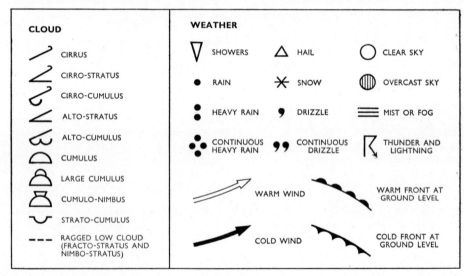

FIG. 64. *A selection of the weather symbols standardized at the meeting of the International Meteorological Organization at Warsaw, 1935, and now used throughout the world.*

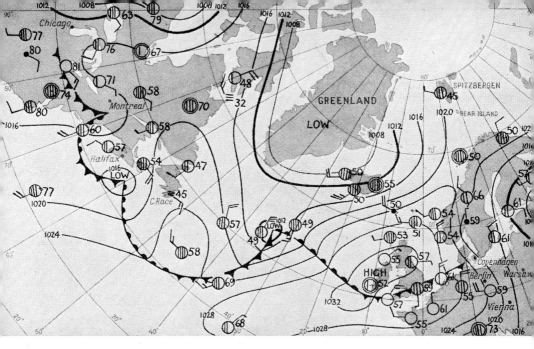

Fig. 65. *A polar front in July. The wavy line of warm and cold fronts traces the line of contact with the earth's surface of the undulating plane of separation between relatively cold (P.c. and P.m.) air to the north and relatively warm (T.m.) air to the south. The northward-pointing salients of warm air are the centres of a family of depressions separated by southward bulges which are seen to be wedges of high pressure (travelling anticyclones), one of which is crossing Britain. A vigorous depression can be observed coming in from the Atlantic Ocean south of Greenland. Another weather map is shown on p. 352.*

the summer months, often consist of tropical maritime air. Fine weather, little wind and high temperatures are usual. Sea fog may occur by day and land fog at night, especially in autumn.

13. Apart from occasional drizzle, rain does not occur in anticyclones.

14. Humid winds, especially from the west, precipitate rain on windward slopes.

15. Local factors of relief, soil, etc. influence the weather locally, but are too complex to be treated here.

16. Do not expect too much from your forecasts until long practice and experience have shown that you can make them with reasonable accuracy.

## Test Yourself

1. Why have the Trade Winds and the Doldrums ceased to be of vital importance to the world's commerce?

2. (*a*) Explain the difference between fog and cloud.
   (*b*) What kind of weather would you expect in Britain in July with the presence of an anticyclone?

3. If, on a day-long hill-climb where alternative tracks are available, you wish to enjoy as much sun as possible, which face would you ascend and which descend, and why? Which face would you avoid?

*Answers will be found at the end of the book.*

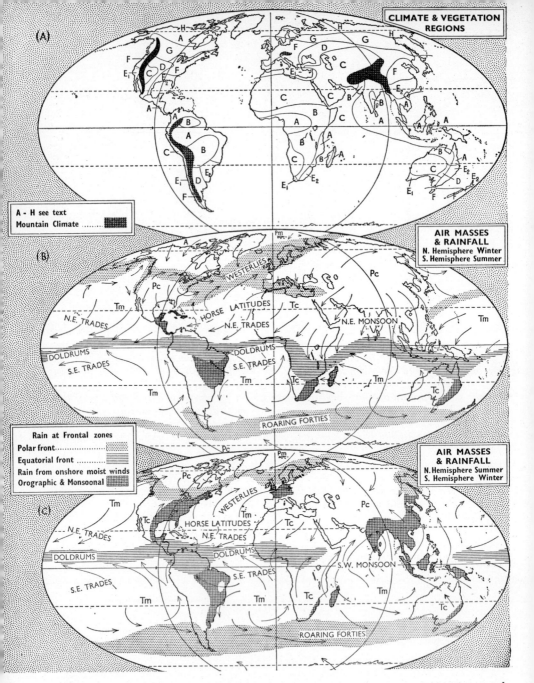

FIG. 66. *The winds make the weather. In the anticyclones, where the winds blow downwards and outwards, rain is unusual; the land is desert and the sea very salt. Such are the anticyclones over the tropics of Cancer and Capricorn, source regions of warm tropical air (T.c. and T.m.). Cold air (P.c. and P.m.) is dispersed from the anticyclones over the poles and the high-latitude continents in winter. Converging air masses must escape upwards; this causes rain. Onshore moist winds also cause rain.*

## CHAPTER IV

# CLIMATE AND LIFE

IN our introduction to the science of meteorology we have been studying the weather—the day-to-day changes of temperature, the occurrence of rain, snow, hail, sunshine, wind, fog and cloud, etc. The average conditions of these elements constitute the study of climate in the science of climatology. As in all processes of averaging, the extreme or exceptional conditions are averaged out and disappear, but nobody would be satisfied with a description of the climate of, say, Britain, that omitted to mention the liability to severe frosts in April and May, when the average temperature of these months is 15 or 20 degrees above freezing point.

### What is Climate?

Such occurrences, even when abnormal, must find mention in the climatic description of a place, for their power for good or ill over mankind in general and over fruit-growers in particular is vital and may be catastrophic. Climatic description must take cognizance of the exceptional as well as the normal, of the expectable extreme as well as the mean.

But though the average conditions that the climatologist studies are made up of very varied weather (resulting from a great variety of causes), climatology is none the less an interpretive science, depending ultimately on a knowledge of first causes as much as does the science of meteorology. Average conditions depend, in the main, on prevailing causes and these are well understood.

In any case, a miscellaneous collection of apparently unrelated facts, such as would together constitute the climate of a place, is difficult to remember unless the underlying causes are understood. We shall try, therefore, to sift out the broad principles of the general plan of climates, so that, when we find these well-understood causes in operation, we shall be able to make intelligent anticipations of the climatic conditions likely to prevail in any place.

Climate, as we have seen, is usually defined as the average weather conditions experienced at a place, and a full description of the climate would involve a detailed study of the weather and everything that bears upon it.

Some elements, such as the duration of daylight at different seasons (which is fixed by the latitude) and the temperatures and rainfall, are clearly of more importance than others, such as the duration of sunshine, visibility, humidity, etc. Classifications of climate, which, of course, are devised only for our convenience, consequently pick on the most significant elements, usually winds, temperature and rainfall, and adopt these as the criteria for definition. But we shall find that the other elements usually go with these and that no insoluble difficulties are experienced.

There appears, at first sight, to be a bewildering variety of climates, but a recurring pattern can be discerned if we close our eyes to local minor variations and concentrate on the major and essential features.

When this is carefully done, we cannot fail to perceive their intimate dependence on (1) the main pressure and wind belts and (2) the distribution of land and sea. Since each of the prevailing planetary winds consists of a mass of air of uniform and well-known characteristics, the type of weather associated with it in any place is, in broad generalization, expectable

### Types of Climate

But the pressure and wind belts vary in accordance with the seasons, whereby there originate seasonal contrasts at any given place, and these become more strongly contrasted in higher latitudes. If we bear these controlling factors in mind, we can anticipate the average weather, which constitutes climate, and can conveniently classify the principal climatic types as shown in the following summary, which should be studied in conjunction with Fig. 66, A.

**A. Equatorial.** (Broad-leaved evergreen forest.)
Little or no seasonal variation.
Air Mass. Doldrum front of trade winds.
Temperature. Hot all the year. Humid.
Rain. Wet (more than 60 inches). No dry
season.
Weather. Daily rhythm. Frequent thunder.
Vegetation. Broad-leaved evergreen forest.
Example: Akassa (Nigeria). 4 degrees N. 6
degrees E.

| J. | F. | M. | A. | M. | J. | J. | A. | S. | O. | N. | D. | |
|----|----|----|----|----|----|----|----|----|----|----|----|---|
| 78 | 79 | 80 | 80 | 79 | 77 | 76 | 76 | 76 | 77 | 78 | 79 | Temp. (deg. F.) |
| 3 | 7 | 10 | 9 | 17 | 19 | 10 | 9 | 19 | 25 | 11 | 7 | Rain (inches) |

**B. Tropical.** (Savanna.)
Marked wet and dry season.
*Winter.*—Dry Season.
Air Mass. Tropical continental.
Temp. Hot. Very hot before and after rains.
Rain. Little or none.
Weather. Wind and dust. Dry.
Veg. Grass withers, trees shed leaves.
*Summer.*—Wet Season.
Air Mass. Doldrum front of trade winds.
Temp. Hot, humid, like equatorial.
Rain. Very heavy showers.
Weather. Daily rhythm. Thunder with rain.
Veg. Savanna, i.e. grassland with trees.
Growth rapid in this season.
Ex.: Kayes (Senegal). 14 degrees N. 12
degrees W.

| J. | F. | M. | A. | M. | J. | J. | A. | S. | O. | N. | D. | |
|----|----|----|----|----|----|----|----|----|----|----|----|---|
| 71 | 81 | 89 | 94 | 96 | 91 | 84 | 82 | 82 | 85 | 83 | 77 | T. |
| 0 | 0 | 0 | 0 | 1 | 4 | 8 | 8 | 6 | 2 | 0 | 0 | R. |

**C. Desert.** (Scrub or no plant cover.)
No wet season.
Air Mass. Tropical continental in low latitudes.
Polar continental in high latitudes.
Temp. Hot in low latitudes. Summer hot and
winter cold in high latitudes.
Rain. Very rare showers.
Weather. Cloudless, dusty, great daily tem-
perature variation.
Veg. Nil or open scrub. (Except with
irrigation.)
Ex. 1: Cairo. 30 degrees N. 31 degrees E.

| J. | F. | M. | A. | M. | J. | J. | A. | S. | O. | N. | D. | |
|----|----|----|----|----|----|----|----|----|----|----|----|---|
| 55 | 57 | 63 | 70 | 76 | 80 | 82 | 82 | 78 | 74 | 65 | 58 | T. |
| ½ | 0 | 0 | 0 | 0 | 0 | 0 | 0 | 0 | 0 | 0 | 0 | R. |

Ex. 2: Astrakhan. 46 degrees N. 48 degrees E.

| J. | F. | M. | A. | M. | J. | J. | A. | S. | O. | N. | D. | |
|----|----|----|----|----|----|----|----|----|----|----|----|---|
| 19 | 21 | 32 | 48 | 64 | 73 | 77 | 74 | 63 | 50 | 37 | 26 | T. |
| ½ | ½ | ½ | ½ | 1 | 1 | ½ | ½ | ½ | ½ | ½ | ½ | R. |

**D. Continental.** (Prairie or Steppe.)
Marked hot and cold season.
*Winter.*—Dry season.
Air Mass. Polar continental.
Temp. Below freezing.
Precipitation. Occasional light snow.
Weather. Calm, reliable. Rare blizzard.
Veg. Grasses, dormant or dead.
*Summer.*—Wet season.
Air Mass. Tropical continental or mari-
time.
Temp. High for latitude, very hot by day.
Rain. Heavy while it lasts.
Weather. Thundery showers in afternoon.
Veg. Grass in spring (dies in summer).
Ex.: Kiev. 50 degrees N. 31 degrees E.

| J. | F. | M. | A. | M. | J. | J. | A. | S. | O. | N. | D. | |
|----|----|----|----|----|----|----|----|----|----|----|----|---|
| 21 | 23 | 31 | 45 | 57 | 64 | 67 | 65 | 57 | 56 | 34 | 24 | T. |
| 1 | 1 | 2 | 2 | 2 | 3 | 3 | 2 | 2 | 2 | 2 | 1 | R. |

**$E_1$. Mediterranean.** (Evergreen woodland and
shrub.)
Marked seasons.
*Winter.*—Cool wet season.
Air Mass. Front between polar continental
and either tropical maritime or
tropical continental.
Temp. Mild. No month averages below 43
degrees F.
Precip. Heavy but infrequent. Snow rare.
Weather. Cyclonic. Bright between depres-
sions.
Veg. Evergreen woodland and shrub. Trees
and shrubs grow continuously, especially
in spring.
*Summer.*—Hot dry season.
Air Mass. Tropical continental.
Temp. Hot, very hot at midday.
Rain. Rare. Very dry.
Weather. Sunny, very little cloud.
Veg. Evergreen, but inactive during hot dry
weather.
Ex.: Algiers. 37 degrees N. 3 degrees E.

| J. | F. | M. | A. | M. | J. | J. | A. | S. | O. | N. | D. | |
|----|----|----|----|----|----|----|----|----|----|----|----|---|
| 53 | 55 | 58 | 61 | 66 | 71 | 77 | 78 | 75 | 68 | 62 | 57 | T. |
| 4 | 4 | 4 | 2 | 1 | 1 | 0 | 0 | 1 | 3 | 5 | 5 | R. |

**$E_2$. Humid Sub-tropical.** (Forests.)
No cold season, no dry season.
*Winter.*—Cool season.
Air Mass. Polar continental or polar front.
Temp. Mild. No month averages below
43 degrees.
Precip. Moderate showers.
Weather. Variable, often cyclonic.
Veg. Slow growth of evergreen forest, some
deciduous forest; dormant.

*Summer.*—Hot and rather moist.
Air Mass. Tropical maritime.
Temp. Hot.
Rain. Heavy showers, sometimes torrential.
Weather. Trade wind; occasional hurricane.
Veg. Vigorous growth of evergreen forest.
Ex.: Sydney. 34 degrees S. 151 degrees E.

| J. | F. | M. | A. | M. | J. | J. | A. | S. | O. | N. | D. | |
|----|----|----|----|----|----|----|----|----|----|----|----|----|
| 72 | 71 | 69 | 65 | 59 | 55 | 53 | 55 | 59 | 64 | 67 | 70 | T. |
| 4 | 4 | 5 | 6 | 5 | 5 | 5 | 3 | 3 | 3 | 3 | 3 | R. |

**F. Cool Temperate.** (Deciduous forest.)
No dry season.
*Winter.*—Cold season.
Air Mass. Polar front, polar continental or polar maritime.
Temp. Averages above freezing, but often falls below, especially at night.
Precip. Frequent, not heavy, except on high coasts; snow in early months of year.
Weather. Cyclonic. Very variable.
Veg. Forest sheds its leaves.
*Summer.*—Warm season.
Air Mass. Polar front (less often than in winter). Tropical maritime or polar maritime.
Temp. Warm. Rarely hot.
Precip. Cyclonic; afternoon thunder.
Weather. Rather variable; long fine spells.
Veg. Broad-leaved trees grow full leaf cover in spring, shed in autumn.
Ex.: Paris. 48 degrees N. 2 degrees E.

| J. | F. | M. | A. | M. | J. | J. | A. | S. | O. | N. | D. | |
|----|----|----|----|----|----|----|----|----|----|----|----|----|
| 37 | 39 | 43 | 49 | 56 | 62 | 65 | 64 | 58 | 50 | 43 | 38 | T. |
| 2 | 1 | 2 | 2 | 2 | 2 | 2 | 2 | 2 | 2 | 2 | 2 | R. |

**G. Cold.** (Coniferous evergreen forest.)
Long summer days, long winter nights.
*Winter.*—Cold, especially in interior.
Air Mass. Polar continental.
Temp. Below freezing.
Precip. Light snow.
Weather. Crisp, cold, calm; occasional blizzard.
Veg. Coniferous evergreen; inactive.
*Summer.*—Hot, especially in interior.
Air Mass. Polar continental or polar front.
Temp. 60 degrees or 70 degrees.
Precip. Short showers, depression rain sometimes.
Weather. Convectional showers (afternoon).
Veg. Coniferous evergreen; active growth.
Ex. 1: (Continental) Orenburg (U.S.S.R.). 52 degrees N. 55 degrees E.

| J. | F. | M. | A. | M. | J. | J. | A. | S. | O. | N. | D. | |
|----|----|----|----|----|----|----|----|----|----|----|----|----|
| 3 | 6 | 17 | 38 | 58 | 66 | 71 | 67 | 55 | 39 | 17 | 6 | T. |
| 1 | ½ | ½ | 1 | 1 | 2 | 2 | 2 | 1 | 1 | 1 | 1 | R. |

Ex. 2: (Maritime) Trondheim (Norway). 63 degrees N. 10 degrees E.

| J. | F. | M. | A. | M. | J. | J. | A. | S. | O. | N. | D. | |
|----|----|----|----|----|----|----|----|----|----|----|----|----|
| 26 | 26 | 31 | 39 | 46 | 54 | 57 | 56 | 49 | 41 | 34 | 29 | T. |
| 3 | 3 | 2 | 2 | 2 | 2 | 3 | 3 | 5 | 4 | 4 | 3 | R. |

**H. Arctic.** (Tundra.)
No warm season. Long winter night.
*Winter.*—Eight to eleven months long.
Air Mass. Polar continental and Arctic.
Temp. Below freezing.
Precip. Fine, light snow.
Weather. Anticyclonic; some blizzards.
Veg. Tundra. No activity in winter.
*Summer.*—Very short. ("Midnight sun." See Fig. 6.)
Air Mass. Polar continental, polar maritime or Arctic front.
Temp. Not far above freezing. Sub-soil frozen.
Precip. Light rain or sleet.
Weather. Unsettled by depressions.
Vegetation. Brief spell of rapid growth of grasses and flowers.

Ex. 1: (Continental) Sagastyr (Siberia). 73 deg. N. 124 degrees E.

| J. | F. | M. | A. | M. | J. | J. | A. | S. | O. | N. | D. | |
|----|----|----|----|----|----|----|----|----|----|----|----|----|
| −34 | −36 | −30 | −7 | 15 | 12 | 41 | 38 | 33 | 6 | −16 | −28 | T. |
| 0 | 0 | 0 | 0 | 0 | ½ | ½ | 1 | ½ | 0 | 0 | 0 | R. |

Ex. 2: (Maritime) Spitsbergen: 78 degrees N. 14 degrees E.

| J. | F. | M. | A. | M. | J. | J. | A. | S. | O. | N. | D. | |
|----|----|----|----|----|----|----|----|----|----|----|----|----|
| 4 | −2 | −2 | 8 | 23 | 35 | 42 | 40 | 32 | 22 | 11 | 6 | T. |
| 1 | 1 | 1 | 1 | ½ | ½ | ½ | 1 | 1 | 1 | 1 | 2 | R. |

Each of these climates has been labelled with a vegetation sub-title, but before we trace this relationship more closely, it will be as well to study the elements of ecology.

The science of ecology (from the Greek word *oikos*, meaning house or home) seeks the relationship between organisms and their environment. It is not a simple, satisfactory science, for the environment is a very complex thing and is constantly changing. If we stand back and take a broad view, if we close our eyes to some of the apparent contradictions and local peculiarities, it is possible to see a close general relationship between natural vegetation and the climate in which it grows. The soil exerts only a minor influence, and it is true that the best criterion of climate and the best basis for a classification is the natural vegetation which the climate favours.

FIG. 67. *A eucalyptus tree in Victoria, Australia. This tree, characteristic of Australia, has leaves which turn their edges towards the sun, to minimize loss of moisture through evaporation.*

flocks and herds, draining the swamps, building his towns, and penetrating to all corners of the earth.

The works of man thus appear to be most unnatural, but if we take a broad view, we shall see that what he has done has not usually been in opposition to nature, but in co-operation with it; he has not controlled his environment so much as learnt to make the best of it for his purpose. Crops are still grown mainly where the climate suits them best, industries arise where the locating factors are most favourable, forests and fisheries give employment and wealth where nature provided them.

Animals, owing to their mobility and their independence of action, are less closely bound by natural conditions; they may, for instance, avoid the rigours of winter by migrations on a large scale. Their ecology is therefore less straightforward. Man, and especially civilized man, has freed himself from the trammels of his natural surroundings to such an extent that his present distribution, his characteristic behaviour, and his modern activities seem to bear little relationship to his environment and to be hardly at all controlled by it. Further, his activities have profoundly changed the face of the earth and often hopelessly obscured the simple natural relationships, clearing the forest for his cultivation, grazing the grasslands with large imported

But by using his intelligence to direct his destiny man is progressively liberating himself from immediate dependence on nature and in this respect is becoming increasingly an unnatural animal. Human geography and the distribution of man cannot therefore be treated in the same fashion as the geography of plants. And even in the geography of the plant kingdom we shall find it simpler to ignore, at first, the ravages and changes wrought by man in his efforts to shape his environment to his will.

Ultimately, however, if a true picture is to be presented of the world as the home of man, we cannot evade the issue, but must recognize, not only the directing influence of the environment, but also the disturbing creations of man's hand and the products of his mind and heart. Inanimate elements, natural forces, plants, animals, and man, with his creative and destructive powers, produce a tangled web of interactions in which only the broadest patterns can be detected; and the patterns are constantly changing and evolving to present new shapes and designs to the eye of the beholder.

The only hope of understanding the pattern lies in disentangling the threads and tracing each from its simple origin to its confused and tangled end. Let us begin by studying the influence of climate on vegetation.

The vegetation of any region may be said to have two characteristics, species and habit; broadly, these are conditioned by heredity and environment respectively. The spread of a species is limited by its ability to establish its seeds and to propagate its kind; consequently it is a relatively slow process unless assisted by man. A species that originates in, shall we say, Australia, such as the eucalyptus tree (Fig. 67), will not have the opportunity to spread beyond that continent. In a less isolated land mass the opportunities for dispersal are greater, but in the face of unfavourable natural obstacles of uncongenial climate or soil, the spread is restricted. And the younger the species the less will be the areas it has had time to colonize, other things being equal.

But the actual species of plants that make up the flora are of less importance to the geographer than their general habits of growth, which are imposed upon them by their environment and especially by the climate, for such habits may be shared by quite unrelated groups of plants. Thus, the vegetation of all the equatorial forests has the same general appearance and affords the same general type of human environment, though the species of trees, creepers

FIG. 68. *A typical mangrove swamp in the Solomon Islands. The tangled, spreading aerial roots growing in soft mud are washed by the tide. There is no other vegetation in the swamp, and the mangrove trunks spring straight upwards towards the light.*

FIG. 69. *Mother with "Joey" in her pouch. The kangaroo is a strong-legged jumping marsupial of the Australian grasslands.*

and undergrowth are quite distinct in the Amazon, the Congo and the East Indies.

Man can and does transfer useful plants from one area to another of the same type, as is the case with wheat, probably a native of the Euphrates-Tigris basin, which has been established in the temperate grassland climates of North and South America, Africa, and Australia. Maize, a native of America, has similarly helped to provide

a prolific food crop in the sub-tropical climates of all the continents.

Plants which are characterized by similarity of habit are collectively called a formation, and afford a proper basis for geographical description.

Broadly speaking, all vegetation can be classified into (1) forest, in which trees predominate; and (2) grassland, in which herbaceous plants predominate. There are, of course, gradations of open woodland with grass and of grassland with trees. Forests require much more water (generally rain) than does grass, though it is not possible to say just how much is required; that will appear as each type is considered. It is not a simple matter of amount, for seasonal distribution is also important. Both types degenerate with increasing aridity, forest dwindling to (3) scrubland, and grass, in which bare patches appear between the plants degenerating through poor steppe, into (4) desert.

### Social Unit

Each formation to be described may be regarded as a social unit in which plants, animals and man help and hinder one another, until they gradually shake down into a kind of equilibrium condition or "climax." A change introduced at any point, e.g. the desiccation of climate, the introduction of an alien animal such as the rabbit, or the felling of trees by man, sets in motion a whole chain of readjustments until eventually the scene settles down again towards a new and different equilibrium.

Pages 76 and 77, together with Fig. 66, A, show the distribution of the chief climatic and vegetational regions. These we shall describe in greater detail, and show how man has made use of each and has modified it in the process, but first we must consider the distribution and spread of the animal groups that inhabit them (Fig. 70).

It has been pointed out that animals are less at the mercy of their environment than plants and that, by virtue of their mobility, they can spread more rapidly from their place of origin. A limit is, however, often set to their diffusion by natural geographical barriers such as the sea, deserts, and, to a less extent, forests and mountains.

Everybody knows that in the isolation of Australia a very peculiar and individual marsupial fauna has grown up, primitive in the evolutionary scale. The young (kangaroos, for example) are born very immature and helpless and are carried by the mother in a pouch (Fig. 69), where they attach themselves to the teat and live like that for months before leaving this safe and comfortable refuge.

The young will also return to the pouch when frightened, even when they are quite large and have lived an independent existence outside it for some time. In form and habit they imitate the placental mammals of the other realms (the carnivorous marsupial Tasmanian wolf looks very like a real wolf and behaves in the same way). They are, in fact, adapted structurally to their environment and mode of life in much the same way, and we shall be able to recognize forest, grassland and desert types among the marsupials as well as among the placental mammals.

The degree and effectiveness of the isolation and the length of time (geological ages) for which the realm has been isolated explain the peculiarity of the fauna. This explains why the Nearctic and Palæarctic realms have close resemblances in many respects, for though the Atlantic separates them today, they were joined in quite recent geological times (Fig. 8).

### Checks to Migration

Australia and Papua, on the other hand, have been separated from Asia from very remote times in geological history. Fig. 70 shows the major zoo-geographical realms and the frontiers between them. These frontiers consist of effective geographical barriers—seas, mountains and deserts—which have fairly successfully checked migrations and the invasion of one area by the fauna of another.

There is no doubt that many animals could be transported to and established in other regions to which they are not native, as useful domesticated animals have been. The sheep and cow, introduced by man, thrive in all the temperate grasslands of the world and the rabbit has found a congenial home in Australia, where it has become a

serious pest. The American grey squirrel has similarly overrun Great Britain.

Many interesting cases occur of discontinuous distribution and are often difficult to explain. The large running birds are widely separated, ostriches in South Africa, rheas in South America, emus and cassowaries in Australia. It is generally believed that their common ancestor originated in the Indian region (where they are found fossilized) and that they spread and differentiated subsequently, each in his own region, the links having died out in the intervening areas.

Tapirs, elephants, camels and opossums are other examples of discontinuous distributions. Often the explanation seems difficult unless one adopts the theory of Continental Drift (page 9), or postulates a land bridge which has been subsequently severed, as, for example, one between Australia and South America used by the opossums. Compare, too, the postulated connexion between Nearctica and Palæarctica mentioned above.

### Man's Adaptability

Man is the most universally distributed animal on the earth. By virtue of his adaptability in matters of clothing, shelter, and diet he is able to inhabit all climatic regions, from the margin of the ice-cap in Greenland to the forests of the equator and the Sahara Desert, and he can live from sea level to the high puna of the Bolivian Andes at 20,000 feet above it. Having mastered the seas, mountains and deserts, he is stopped by no geographical barriers and he has adapted himself to nearly every environment. His diet varies from fruit and grain to meat and fish; in fact, with the possible exception of the pig, he has the most catholic taste of all the animals. His control over his environment introduces an entirely novel factor in geographical distribution which we shall consider next.

Regarded by the zoologist, all mankind belongs to a single species (*Homo sapiens*), just as all dogs belong to a single species (*Canis canis*). We know what an assortment of mongrels are produced by the interbreeding of dogs; there is also a great variety of mixed-breed men (Fig. 224). By

**POLYNESIA**
No Mammals except Bats, Flying Foxes; many Birds and Fishes; few Reptiles.

**FAUNAL REGIONS OF THE WORLD**

HOLA
NEARCTIC REALM
NEOTROPICAL REALM

Tropic of Cancer
Equator
Tropic of Capricorn
Ar

**FIG. 70.** *Reading from left to right:* (1) Musk-ox, cougar, porcupine, grizzly bear, raccoon, skunk, musk-rat, gopher, prairie dog.

(2) Chamois, roedeer, yak, ox, rat, mole, goat, mouse.

(*a*) (*Common to both* (1) *and* (2) ). Seal, polar bear, sheep, reindeer or caribou, walrus, bison, elk, wolf, marmot, glutton, lemming, lynx, field-mouse, fox, otter.

(3) Howling monkey, spider monkey, sloth, condor, humming bird, macaw, toucan, marmoset, alpaca, llama, vicuña, tanager, boa, puma, guanaco, ocelot, jaguar, chinchilla, guinea pig, capybara, iguana, rhea, tapir, cavey, alligator, coral snake, peccary, curassow, tree frog, lung-fish.

(4) Chimpanzee, jackal, oryx, eland, gnu, vulture, hartebeest, gorilla, lion, rhinoceros, elephant, giraffe, baboon, zebra, buffalo, leopard, hyena, civet, springbok, secretary bird, ostrich, hippopotamus.

(5) Squirrel, panther, macaque, gibbon, long-tailed monkey, orang-outang, nylghau, gazelle, elephant, rhinoceros, deer, leopard, zebu, buffalo, tiger, wild dog, striped hyena.

(6) Cockatoo, bird of paradise, koala, parakeet, kangaroo, wallaby, Tasmanian wolf, emu, lyre bird, wombat, brush turkey, phalanger, bandicoot, duck-billed platypus.

careful selection of mates we can produce a thoroughbred dog, and if we applied the same principles to human beings we could, theoretically, produce pure racial types.

Geographical separation, together with personal preference or repugnance has set limits to the extent of inter-breeding between markedly dissimilar races of men, but where two races have been brought into close contact, especially if there is no race prejudice, a large mixed-breed population eventually results, as, for example, the *mestizo* of South America, produced by crossing Spaniards (Mediterranean) with the native Indian (Amerind).

### The Rise of Man

Man is an animal who has risen above the beasts by the use of his hands, tongue and brain. By the use of his hands he has been able to strengthen his meagre equipment for defence, first by the use of chipped stone tools, in due course often mounted in wooden hafts (lower and upper palæolithic cultures), and very much later by the development of the rubbing and grinding technique, as a supplement to that of chipping, for the making of stone implements (neolithic culture). Some stones found to soften with heat came to be hammered (copper culture) and then cast (full bronze age). Later still iron, needing greater heat (a draught furnace) for its treatment, gave men better axes, swords and ploughshares (early iron age). With the use of charcoal for reducing iron ore came the further discovery of steel. The part played by fire in this evolution is one of many hints as to the earliness of this vastly important and useful servant of man.

### Major Natural Regions

Man's upward climb is described in detail in Section IV. Here we are concerned with the major natural regions, determined by climate, defined by vegetation, characterized by animal associations, and profoundly influencing the activities of man. Despite much alteration and interference, exploitation and development, these natural regions remain the fundamental elements of geographical description.

*The Tropical Rain Forest* (including what is sometimes called Equatorial Forest and Monsoon Forest). This is found wherever the temperature is high, over 70 degrees throughout the year, and where rainfall is heavy, over 60 inches a year, occurring all the year round.

### Nature Uncurbed

Vegetation runs riot; its exuberance is impressive and even awe-inspiring. Trees grow to a great height (100 feet or more), some taller than others, so that the forest, seen from above, has no regular top level like the canopy of our own oak or beech forests. Their trunks and branches are interlaced and intertwined with creepers and lianas with long, thick, rope-like stems (Figs. 68, 71, 134, 202).

Beneath is a dense tangle of lower growing shrubs and bushes, so thick that the forest is impenetrable without hacking one's path with axe or machete. Down here is a pale sickly light coming through the dense green canopy of leaves and branches aloft. Since there is no season of cold or drought to check growth, most of the trees are evergreen, and since there is little or no seasonal rhythm, leaves, flowers, and fruits grow, expand, ripen, die, and fall at any time of the year.

### Life in the Forest

Trees are of great variety—hardwoods like ebony, mahogany and greenheart, cow trees (which grow to 200 feet), palms in great variety, rubber trees, etc. Characteristically, there is nothing like a pure stand of any kind of tree; they are scattered through the forest so that their commercial exploitation is difficult and expensive.

Grasses and ground-carpet plants have little chance, but, where the forest has been cleared or thinned, lower growing plants such as bananas can be grown and form one of the most important food and commercial crops. Movement on the ground being so impeded, many of the animals that inhabit the forests are arboreal. There is a great variety of apes and monkeys, with long, loose limbs, prehensile hands and, often, prehensile tails, admirably adapted for climbing. Even the carnivores, the jaguar for example, and some of the snakes,

FIG. 71. *This remarkable photograph of a clearing in the Selvas of the Amazon, taken by Dr. A. Hamilton-Rice, shows the Tropical Rain Forest from the air. Robbed of leaf litter, the soil is exposed to heavy rains, which percolate through it, quickly destroying the concentration of its chemical constituents and so depriving it of its fertility.*

like the boas, are good climbers, for their prey is likely to be found in the trees.

Many of the birds climb rather than fly, for strong powers of flight are no great advantage in dense forest. Their diet is mainly fruit and nuts and some (e.g. parrots) have strong nut-cracker beaks. Crocodiles and hippopotamuses inhabit the rivers, and there is a rich profusion of insects, butterflies (often gorgeously coloured), and beetles.

Towards the margin of the forest, where it begins to pass into the savanna, the trees are more spaced, open glades appear and ground vegetation (e.g. grasses) and ground animals such as elephants, rhinoceroses and tigers enjoy more favourable conditions. Many of the trees are here deciduous, for the dry season is lengthening; in the monsoon forests of Burma and India, teak and sal are valuable hardwoods.

*Man in the Tropical Forest.* The forest environment is an enervating and depressing one. Nature provides food easily, but not liberally, so that food-gatherers cannot be numerous. The forest is difficult to clear for cultivation and quickly reclaims territory won by man unless his efforts are unrelaxing. But it yields certain products of value, especially to the white man: hardwood, rubber, quinine, oil-palm, bananas.

Though at first these were simply collected, it has been found profitable to concentrate cultivation in plantations cleared of the natural vegetation. The most suitable areas for such plantations are on or near accessible coasts, and the main development is in Ceylon, the East Indian and West Indian islands, West Africa, etc. Native labour is at present employed under the direction of white managers, who are generally only temporary residents, enduring, rather than enjoying, the enervating climate and the isolation of exile.

*Tropical Grasslands* (*Savannas*). (Fig. 150.) Farther from the equator, about 10 degrees N. or S. in the lowlands, the rains fail in the winter and a dry season comes in, increasing in length towards the deserts of the tropics. The rains of the summer are heavy, very heavy, but the drought of winter prevents the growth of forest, which must have water at its roots all the year. A few trees occur, but they are scattered or grouped in small clumps, and are typically umbrella-shaped, with a flat crown of leaves, which are shed in the dry season.

Other vegetation consists of coarse grasses growing to a height of over 6 feet in the wet season, but withering and dying down in the dry, when the scene is brown, dusty, and desolate. The grasses grow in clumps, not forming a close turf, and some are cultivable, e.g. guinea corn, sugar cane, and bamboo.

Over these extensive grassy plains in Africa roam vast herds of buffalo, zebra, wildebeeste, and antelope in great variety; less gregarious are the giraffes and rhinoceroses. All of these are herbivores and most are admirably adapted, with long thin legs, for great speed, by which they escape their enemies. It happens that most of the large areas of tropical grassland are in the nature of flat or undulating plains, over which they have full opportunity to exercise their great speed. The giraffe and ostrich in Africa, kangaroo and emu in Australia, are, each in its own peculiar way, built for speed; so are Africa's lions and other carnivores which hunt down these herbivores for their prey.

*Man in the Tropical Grasslands.* At first a hunter, here man is generally now a stock rearer or cultivator. The stock are mainly cattle of poor quality and they are exposed to many parasite and tick-borne diseases; large areas are made unusable by the tsetse fly.

Cultivation of maize, millets, etc., is carried on in patches cleared by burning the grass and bush in the dry season; the crops grow during the rains and are harvested early in the dry season. A combination of stock-rearing with cultivation of small patches of land for food and fodder is common; but some pastoral tribes, such as the Masai, scorn cultivation. Crops are generally the women's work, while the men look after the cattle and, at one time, did the fighting.

The savanna offers few attractions to the white man, for the crops that can be grown and the stock that can be kept do better in cooler lands, which are also more attractive to live in. Their economy is, therefore, still mainly native.

The high-level savannas with cooler climates offer an exception, and parts of Kenya, Tanganyika, Brazil, etc., are looked

FIG. 72. *The Kalahari Desert, S.W. Africa, crudely sculptured by sun, rare rain storms, and wind which has winnowed the sand from the bare, stony desert in the foreground.*

FIG. 73. *A typical oasis in the Sahara, with palm trees clustering round a pool.*

upon as suitable for white colonization, but there is much difference of opinion on the subject. Here are plantations of coffee, tobacco, sisal, and maize.

*Deserts.* Large areas of the world in the heart of great land masses, or sheltered by high land from rain-bearing winds, get very little rain and, since all plants need water, have scanty vegetation or none at all. Sources of water other than rain, e.g. underground supplies or rivers entering the desert from wetter areas outside, give rise to oases where trees may flourish (Fig. 73) and crops may be grown, but in the complete desert there is no sign of life—tree, shrub or grass (Figs. 148, 158).

Weathering breaks up the rock into fine sand which is blown about by the wind; huge areas are therefore covered with undulating, shifting sand dunes. Other areas are swept clear of sand, the ground consisting of bare rocks or coarse rock fragments (Fig. 72).

On the fringes of the desert, where rain is almost adequate, scattered tufts of grass or scrub begin to appear. Gradually the desert passes into savanna or sagebrush, or acacia-brush, or salt-brush or steppe. The annual amount of rain needed to prevent desert cannot be defined with precision; the air is dry and evaporation is rapid, so that even as much as 20 inches of rain in hot deserts may not be enough to maintain plant growth. In colder climates 10 or 15 inches may be enough to produce a cover, albeit thin, of grass or scrub.

The conditions in deserts are clearly unfavourable for animal life. Even the camel, which is inseparably associated with deserts, really belongs to the marginal scrublands, though it has feet adapted to travelling over sand, and can make long journeys without food or drink (Fig. 74).

*Man in the Desert.* The only places of permanent habitation are the oases, where sedentary groups cultivate the date palm, fruit, and crops such as maize, barley and wheat. These oases may be within the desert, drawing supplies of water from underground sources, or they may be terminal oases where rivers, fed from regions of heavier rainfall or melting snow on mountains, lose themselves in the desert. In the latter case and in some of the former, the water is distributed over the fields by canals.

A different mode of life is that of the nomadic Arab engaged mainly in transport and trade by camel caravan (Fig. 74). With his greater freedom and independence the nomad considers himself superior, and the temptation is strong to exact tribute from the sedentary cultivator or to plunder his accumulated wealth.

The desert offers little to the white man except minerals. In the Atacama Desert in northern Chile there are rich deposits of nitrates, and in the islands off Peru accumulations of guano. These provide quick-acting and highly-soluble fertilizers; their preservation in the deserts is, of course, due to the absence of rain, which anywhere else would dissolve them. As part of her national plan Russia now utilizes, with the aid of irrigation, the agricultural resources of Turkistan to produce cotton, tobacco, fruit, etc. (Figs. 96 and 97).

*Temperate Grasslands.* In Eurasia the steppe lies to the north of the desert; in the Americas similar grasslands—the prairies of Canada and the U.S.A. and the pampas of Argentina—lie east of the desert, farther from the mountains that rob the desert areas of rain. Rain is too scanty for trees, which are further discouraged by strong desiccating winds and, no doubt, by prairie fires. They may grow locally, especially along watercourses.

### Great Cornlands

Winters are severe in the Northern Hemisphere and the winter precipitation, which is slight, is in the form of snow; winter is milder in the narrower continent of South America, with light winter rain.

More rain falls in early summer and the grass grows strong and green; it withers and dies down in the heat of midsummer, although the rain then is actually as heavy as in spring. Flat or gently undulating land characterizes all these regions and in the natural state they present a picture of miles of waving grass, over which wild cattle, bison, sheep and antelopes range freely, travelling in great herds, northwards in summer and southwards, towards warmer climate and better grass, in winter.

Rodents and burrowing animals, jerboas, marmots and prairie-dogs, coneys and jack-rabbits live in large colonies underground; some of them escape the cold and foodless winter by some degree of hibernation, but most of the birds are migrants. Wolves and other carnivores prey on them, though these are more properly animals of the forests and their margins.

*Man in the Temperate Grasslands.* At first, probably, a hunter, man attempted cultivation near rivers and herding as a supplement. This became the dominant mode in some regions and was characteristic until a hundred years ago, and still survives in large parts of Central Asia. But the demands of the industrial population for foodstuffs and raw materials have brought about a revolution in land use, which has been made possible by railway and overseas communications.

The revolution has proceeded in two directions, first by an intensification of stock-rearing, as in the cattle ranch and the sheep range, and second by the ploughing up of grass for crops such as wheat, oats, maize, flax, etc. The latter is the more productive method and has gradually encroached upon the cattle pastures, as, for example, in the Argentine. Sometimes it has gone too far, and unsuitable land has been ploughed with appalling results in soil erosion and loss of fertility (Figs. 126, 204).

The conditions that suit good grass also suit cereals, which are cultivated grasses, and the enormous production of grain from both prairie and pampas (Fig. 121), produced by relatively small numbers of men making full use of machinery, has made possible the maintenance of teeming urban industrial populations thousands of miles away.

*Mediterranean Evergreen Trees and Shrubs.* Round the shores of the Mediterranean Sea, in Europe, North Africa and Western Asia, is found a very characteristic type of climate with very hot, dry summers, when the weather is like that of the deserts that lie to the south, and mild wet winters when the weather is a mild variety of the Western European type, with fairly abundant rain, largely derived from depressions. The winters are not cold enough to put the vegetation to rest and some growth goes on.

### Avoiding Drought

In spring and autumn both temperature and rain are favourable for quite vigorous plant growth, but the summer is hot, dry and dusty, with clear skies and strong sun. Vegetation must economize the scanty water available at its roots and all plants are adapted for this purpose, having, for example, tough leathery leaves or spines and extensive roots (Fig. 101). Bulbous plants are numerous and they avoid the drought by dying right down in summer. Grasses are at a disadvantage, their place being taken by low-growing herbs and small bushes and shrubs.

Trees are numerous but are scattered and are seldom worthy of being called forests. They are evergreen, but with a greyish, dusty look, quite unlike the bright

FIG. 74. *A camel caravan on the march near El Kantara, Algeria. The one-humped camel is used in the hot deserts, but its home is the marginal scrublands.*

fresh green of our beech or oak woods. Evergreen oak, cypress and stone pine are the most characteristic, together with the gnarled and stunted olive, laurel and myrtle.

Wild sheep, surviving in Sardinia, goats and asses have found sustenance in these regions and there is a variety of small animals, but little remains of the native fauna.

The Mediterranean lands provide the only large region of this type, but there are narrow strips on the west margins of the other continents in latitudes of 30 degrees to 40 degrees N. and S., and they have the same general appearance. The chaparral of California, the mallee scrub of South and West Australia are very like the *maquis* of the Mediterranean; the regions of Cape of Good Hope and central Chile are similar.

*Man in the Mediterranean Climate.* This environment, though not over-generous, brought out the latent ability for organization among cultivators of ancient times. With care and foresight they were able to harness orderly climatic conditions with strong seasonal contrasts and to build up an early progressive and prosperous civilization. Today its limitations are as marked as its advantages; the European Mediterranean land is over-populated and the rural standard of living is low. Cultiva-tion of cereals (wheat and barley) and fruit (vine, orange, lemon, peach, etc.) is the chief occupation.

Grass is poor, cattle are unimportant; the goat is better suited to the rough kind of grazing available, but is very destructive of trees which protect the hillsides from the heavy winter rains and consequent wash-ing away of soil. The "Mediterranean" regions of Italy, Sicily, Spain, California and the Cape district of South Africa are the chief suppliers of citrus fruit. The olive tree is characteristic and the fruit yields an oil which is universally used for cooking, taking the place of animal fats used in our climate.

The sunny reliable climate with mild winters makes the Mediterranean and California excellent holiday resorts.

*Humid Sub-tropical Forests.* On the eastern sides of continents in latitudes that correspond to the Mediterranean climates there is rain all the year and plant growth goes on uninterruptedly, though less vigorously in the cool winter season. The native forests here almost rival those of the tropics into which they grade insensibly, while pole-wards they pass imperceptibly into the cool temperate forests. They provide some hardwood timber, and when cleared, the land is productive of such crops as sugar, tobacco, tea, coffee, maize

Fig. 75. *Tundra is the name given to the bleak, treeless plains, which, in Europe, Asia and N. America, separate coniferous forest and Arctic ice. The cold climate prevents the cultivation of food-crops or pasture, and the few inhabitants live by hunting and fishing. The woman is gathering cotton-grass in the tundra of Yakutsk, U.S.S.R.*

and rice. Inland, and beyond the mountains, the climate is drier and warm grasslands occur, as in Tennessee, the "downs" of New South Wales, the Veldt of South Africa and the Pampas of Argentina.

*Man in the Sub-tropical Forests.* South China has been cultivated for centuries and the forest cleared on lowlands and slopes to support a dense population on an agricultural basis. The Indians of the south-eastern forests of N. America combined an essentially hunting and collecting economy with the cultivation of corn (maize), beans, and squashes (pumpkins) in clearings made by "ring-barking" the trees. Under the European settlers this area became famous for cotton and tobacco grown on the "plantations."

### European Influence

In New South Wales, Natal, and Uruguay primitive native economies have yielded to European influence, though at a later date, and their great productive capacity is being realized in the cultivation of a variety of sub-tropical crops and the raising of cattle and pigs for dairy and meat. The interior grasslands have become great granaries and raise large crops of maize, wheat, linseed, etc., and support vast flocks of sheep and herds of cattle. On the whole, the development of these climatic opportunities in the Southern Hemisphere has not progressed very far or fast, and the density of rural population is rather low, but the potentialities of these lands are immense and there is ample room for the population to increase.

*Temperate Broad-leaved Forest.* On the west sides of continents between latitudes 40 degrees and 60 degrees and stretching as far into the interior as there is 20 or 25 inches of rain the natural vegetation is forest of deciduous trees such as oak, beech, maple, sycamore, etc., often occurring as nearly pure stands of one kind of tree. The kind of tree is usually determined by minor differences of soil or ground water, oak on the heavy clays, beech on the lighter soils, while on the acid, sandy soils the trees are often pine, fir and larch, anticipating the *taiga* (page 123) of the cold, wet, acid soils which are found farther north.

There is relatively little carpet of ground vegetation, though the more open forests have low-growing bushes and trees such as hazel, alder and holly. The pale green light under the dense canopy of beech woods in summer scarcely permits anything to grow, and the forest is open and unobstructed between the tall, grey-green boles. In autumn the leaves fall, and the branches remain bare throughout the winter.

The forests die out eastwards in the heart of the continents, but reappear farther east where the rainfall increases again. Here they extend far to the south, for there is no dry season on eastern margins, and the forest merges into the tropical forest, becoming thicker and more luxuriant as the tropics are approached. Many beautiful trees occur, such as maple, hickory, and the tulip tree. Undergrowth increases in lower latitudes, lianas appear and bamboo often makes impenetrable brakes.

The animals of the temperate deciduous forest, with its more open nature, are not so tree-bound as those of the tropical forest. Birds and climbing animals such as squirrels and martens are numerous enough, but ground fauna like wild boars, elk, deer, weasels, badgers, bears, wolves and foxes abound. Since winter food is scanty, many of the birds are migrants, but travelling distances to supplies of abundant food are too great for the animals, which are therefore resident. They may store food, like the squirrels, or hibernate, like the dormouse, or make do with the nuts, roots and grasses left from autumn.

*Man in the Deciduous Forest.* Few large continuous stands survive today: most of the forest has been cleared for cultivation, for which, except in the wettest and roughest parts, both soil and climate are excellent. At first a hunter, man here in time learned from other peoples the art of cultivation, and now, since these are the most highly developed regions of the world, he is, in the main, an industrial worker and town dweller. It is to be noted that the deciduous forests did not yield much in the way of cultivable food plants; these had to be introduced.

The forest still yields valuable timber of a hard type—oak, beech, maple, hickory, etc.—and forest industries give employment to many. Agricultural practice varies enormously with the stage of economic development; much of it is of the peasant type, for the land does not lend itself to the large-scale production of uniform cash crops that is characteristic of the grassy plains. Even in the most highly developed regions farming is balanced, both stock and crops being reared, and, though cash crops are grown, the farmer derives much of his subsistence from the land he cultivates.

## Natural Advantages

The cyclonic climate, stimulating by its variability but without unendurable extremes, combined with complex historic factors, made a part of this region one of the most highly developed in the world, even before the industrial age. The presence of the world's best coalfields helped to ensure for Western Europe and eastern North America an early start and rapid development in industry, and to maintain their predominance in technical advance.

*Coniferous Forest.* The coniferous trees are well adapted to endure the long cold winters, the short but warm summers and the scanty rainfall of high latitudes and continental interiors and at high altitudes on mountain slopes. Their leaves are narrow and thick-skinned, which makes them very economical of the scanty water in summer, and allows them to survive the long winter without wilting, when ground water is not available because frozen. They retain their leaves all the year round and can make use of any spells of warmer weather in spring and autumn for the assimilation of food. Spruce, fir and pine are the chief types and they often occur in mighty stands all of one kind (Figs. 95, 118). Larch and silver birch (which is not cone-bearing) are also abundant and extend to the very polar limits of tree growth.

On the west coast of North America, in British Columbia, Washington and Oregon, trees of coniferous type dominate the forests in cool temperate climates which elsewhere would have deciduous forest. The reason for this is bound up with their geological history and post-glacial colonization. Because they grow under exceptionally favourable conditions they attain enormous size; sequoias and Douglas firs are the giants of the coniferous evergreen family.

Wolves, gluttons, bears, elk (moose) and wapiti are characteristic animals, but there are numbers of small animals with beautiful and valuable fur, such as ermine, sable, skunk, and beaver. Birds, reptiles, and amphibians are less numerous than in the deciduous forest to the south, and the soil population is scanty, especially earthworms, which elsewhere fulfil such a useful function by turning over the soil and increasing its fertility.

*Man in the Coniferous Forest.* These regions are only scantily populated. The long severe winters discourage settlement and only the hardiest crops can grow when the forest is cleared. Man here was for long a hunter and the trapping of animals for their fur is still the way of life for many in Canada and Siberia.

## Exploiting Water-power

But the chief commodity produced today is the soft-wood itself, for timber and wood-pulp, for which there is an insatiable demand in the more highly developed regions in lower latitudes. Water power is used in great quantities both by saw mills and pulp mills; consequently, the best conditions for exploitation are found where rapids and waterfalls occur, e.g. along the St. Lawrence in Canada and in the glaciated regions of Finland.

Cutting is done in the winter; the logs wait for the thaw to raft them downstream to the mills (Fig. 112). The cultivation of hardy cereals and the keeping of dairy cattle (stall-fed in winter) give occupation where the forest has been cleared. The cold waters often abound in fish, and fishing gives employment to great numbers in Norway, Scotland, Newfoundland and Alaska.

*Tundra.* The hardiest trees cannot grow unless the summer months reach temperatures of 50 degrees F., so the coniferous forest becomes stunted polewards; trees grow smaller and more scattered and eventually give way to tough, shrubby bushes and tufty grass, sedge, lichen and mosses. The soil is frozen for most of the year, only the top layers thawing in the long days of the cool summer. Drainage is bad and ice-cold water stands round the roots. The scene is desolate and monotonous. Only on better-drained slopes is it relieved by the colour of flowering plants, such as Iceland poppy, thrift, geum and. willow herb, and by cotton-grass (Fig. 75).

The tundra provides food for reindeer (caribou), musk ox, arctic fox and wolf, but many of these migrate to the forests in winter. Birds such as ptarmigan, buntings, and owls visit the tundra in summer, but emigrate on the approach of winter. Insects are numerous and mosquitoes emerge in swarms in summer to torture man and beast.

*Man in the Tundra.* Life is very hard; the population is very sparse and the people primitive. Hunting (caribou, seals, walrus, etc.) and fishing are the main sources of livelihood, except for scattered mining settlements, such as the coal mines of Spitsbergen (Fig. 199). The summer is too short and cool for crops to be raised or stock to be kept, though domesticated reindeer have recently been introduced.

On the borders of the tundra in Western Siberia and Arctic Europe, reindeer herding is important, and there are ports such as Archangel, Murmansk, and Petsamo.

*Ice Deserts.* Regions such as the Antarctic continent (Fig. 200), the ice-cap of Greenland and the islands of the Arctic Archipelago, where the snow lies throughout the year, cannot support life and are uninhabited except for visitors from the sea, penguins, walrus and polar bear.

*Mountain Associations.* The decrease of temperature with altitude on mountains, like that with increasing latitude, results in a rather similar succession of vegetation zones. But the rainfall conditions offer no parallel. Rain generally increases with altitude up to a height of 5,000 to 6,000 feet, and then decreases again, so that the summits of high mountains are generally rather dry, though there is always enough precipitation to give a snow cap above the snowline.

On the high Andes in Ecuador, in the Himalaya and the mountains of East Africa the tropical forest gradually gives way to sub-tropical (about 3,000 feet), then to

FIG. 76. *An Aymara Indian piping to his llama on the Bolivian plateau. The llama is related to the camel and is widely used as a beast of burden in this upland region.*

FIG. 77. *Near Davos, in Switzerland. Snow-covered in winter, the higher grasslands, or "alps" provide rich summer pasture. Most of the milk is made into cheese.*

temperate broad-leaved (about 5,000 feet), then to coniferous (about 10,000 feet), which passes by dwarf forest into steppe desert (Fig. 76) and then to mountain tundra, which extends to the snowline.

In the Alps the broad-leaved forest reaches about 3,000 feet and the coniferous to about 5,000 feet, but is higher on the warmer south side.

It should be noticed that the vegetation zones on mountains are much more closely spaced, which lends great variety to the mountain habitat for plants, animals and man.

*Man in the Mountains.* The rapid changes of temperature that occur up the slopes of mountains result in rapid changes of vegetation type and accordingly of human occupations. Man can therefore move readily from one zone to another. He may be a farmer in the valley in spring and autumn, a pastoralist, tending cattle on the Alpine pastures in summer (Fig. 77), and a craftsman in wood-carving in winter. Life is varied, but it is also arduous and sometimes hazardous, breeding a hardy, adaptable and independent type of man.

*Land Utilization.* The history of man in his social organization (hunter-collectors — hoe-cultivators — plough-cultivators—and city-dwellers) is reflected in progressively efficient methods of land utilization. Population densities in intensively cultivated lands, such as the monsoon lands of China and India, sometimes reach 500 per square mile, but the modern tendency is towards low rural densities and high urban concentrations.

If we look at the present distribution of population throughout the world, we shall notice the following points:—

1. The scanty population of high latitudes and high mountains.

2. The great barrier of deserts from the Sahara, through Arabia and Tibet to Mongolia, broken seriously only by the long oases of the Nile and Euphrates-Tigris valleys.

3. The empty deserts of the Southern Hemisphere.

4. The generally low density in equatorial and monsoon forests, except in places along approachable coasts.

5. The higher densities on higher lands

in the tropics, especially in the Americas.

6. The existence of three great areas of high density: Europe, North-east America, and the Monsoon Lands. The high density in the last is in the main dependent on intensive agriculture. That in the other two is mainly urban and industrial, for these are regions where the manufacturing and marketing aspects of the commercial age have reached their highest development.

The production of food crops and agricultural raw materials is now on an intensified scale, with machinery partly replacing man-power. The density in the wheat lands of the prairie provinces of U.S.A. and Canada is only from ten to twenty per square mile, but these empty lands are complementary to the teeming cities that consume their wheat, where densities are measured in many thousands. London has nearly 40,000 per square mile, while some wards in overcrowded Bombay have more than 300,000 per square mile.

Urban and rural densities cannot therefore be profitably compared. England and Wales contain forty-four million people on about 60,000 square miles (more than thirty-seven million acres); this is less than one acre per head of population. The average is made up of uninhabited moorlands, rural parishes with 200 per square mile, urban districts with over 1,000 per square mile, and cities with, in places, 100,000 per square mile.

Urban growth is a characteristic of the commercial and industrial age. There were cities in ancient Mesopotamia; quite large cities existed in classical times: Athens, Syracuse, Alexandria and Carthage were probably of the order of half a million, Rome was larger still. They grew in number in the Middle Ages with the rise of commerce, but at the present day the tendency to urbanization is accelerating rapidly. More than four-fifths of the population of Britain lives in urban surroundings; in Germany and Australia the proportion is two-thirds; in France, U.S.A. and Canada more than half.

In spite of the migration into the empty spaces of Canada and western U.S.A., into Manchuria and Siberia, it is in the towns and cities that population is increasing most rapidly, while rural areas are generally static or declining.

But when all is said and done the population of the world is fed from the produce of the land in crops and animal products and, on an average about $2\frac{1}{2}$, acres are needed to support one man.

The total land surface of the globe is 33,000,000,000 acres, but if we subtract the areas of mountains, deserts, swamp and ice we are left with about 13,000,000,000 acres of cultivable land, of which about 5,000,000,000 are in cultivation. This supports, directly or indirectly, a population of about 2,900,000,000 people.

It would seem that the world's surface, if fully utilized, could support about 5,000,000,000 people, nearly twice the present figure. World population is estimated to be increasing at the present time by approximately 2,000,000 a year.

## Test Yourself

1. (a) What are the two principal factors which determine the climates of the world?

   (b) Name the two broad types into which vegetation is classified. Into what sub-types does each type degenerate?

2. Name five important cities throughout the world which are located in the climatic regions known as Cool Temperate.

3. Although animals have tended to migrate from one region of the world to another it is still possible to trace the general frontiers between the regions inhabited by distinctive animal groups. What features of physical geography would you expect to mark such frontiers? Give reasons and examples.

*Answers will be found at the end of the book.*

FIG. 78. *The Black Forest. This dissected plateau of ancient rocks in south-western Germany is largely forested, but there are some limited patches of cultivated land. This aerial photograph shows the characteristics of the region, including the level skyline of the plateau.*

# III LANDS AND PEOPLES OF THE WORLD

CHAPTER V

# WESTERN EUROPE

EUROPE, smallest of the continents with the exception of Australia, falls into three major geographical divisions. Eastern Europe, beyond a line roughly from the Swedish-Finnish border to Istanbul, is a vast plain truly continental in its propor- tions, its climate, and its remoteness from the open ocean. Southern Europe, south of a line from the Pyrenees to the Balkan Mountains, comprises the mountain-girt shores of the Mediterranean Sea and forms a region distinct in structure, climate, vege- tation and human life. The rest of the continent, west of Russia and north of the Mediterranean, is Western Europe as we shall try to interpret it in this chapter. It thus includes, in addition to Western Europe proper, those parts of the continent which are commonly called Central and east Central Europe.

### Cradle of Modern Industry

If we describe a circle on the map, with a radius of some 800 miles from a centre in Jutland, nearly all Western Europe as thus defined falls within it (pages 98-99). Looking northwards from this central vantage-point, the land slopes up to the high plateau and fjord coast of Norway, which, though interrupted by the shallow North Sea to the south-west, is recognizably continuous with the highlands of Scotland and northern Ireland. To the south-east and south-west of Denmark stretches the unbroken European Plain (the Great Low- land Plain), giving way southwards to the upland belt of mid-Europe and beyond that to the high ramparts of the Alps.

It is this broad trough between the Alps and the broken Atlantic rim of Europe

that has been the cradle of modern indus- trial civilization. The sea has played such a vital part in its history that we may think of it as a cradle rocked by the waters of the narrow seas and their many estu- aries.

On a population map the areas of densest settlement in Western Europe have their centre in the region round Cologne. The effective outer limit of the zone of large industrial towns lies on a semicircle with a radius of 600 miles drawn from a centre in Denmark. This line passes through or near Belfast, Cardiff, Rouen, Paris, Dijon, Zürich, Vienna, Cracow, Warsaw, Vilna, Riga and Helsinki. A wider semicircle (750 miles) would bring in Nantes, Lyons, Turin, Milan, Venice, Trieste, Budapest, Lwow and Leningrad; and outside there are only two political and industrial capitals in the extreme south- east—Belgrade and Bucharest (Fig. 79).

Western Europe is differentiated from other major world regions by the length and intricacy of its coastline, a fact which means much more than the torture of the map-drawing schoolboy. It facilitates transport and has tempted men to maritime adventure since the dawn of civilization.

### Stimulating Climate

Over the wide trough of sea and low- land the warm eastward-moving air masses of the Atlantic penetrate inland, keeping the winters mild and the summers wet, and permitting settlement and cultivation to be carried to higher latitudes than in any other part of the world. A temperate and changeable climate, without extremes, stimulates human activity through the seasons. The peoples of Western Europe,

WESTERN EUROPE
SHOWING PHYSICAL FEATURES
AND PRINCIPAL CITIES

ALPINE FOLD MOUNTAINS — OLD PLATEAUX — SCARPS — MORAINES

SEAS DEEPER THAN 100 FATHOMS — MARSHES — APPROXIMATE LIMITS OF WESTERN EUROPE

ARCTIC CIRCLE

ATLANTIC

OCEAN

GRAMPIANS

CENTRAL PLAIN

PENNINES

NORT...
SEA

CENTRAL PLAIN
London

ENGLISH CHANNEL

GREAT

Seine

Paris

Loire

Garonne

PYRENEES

Rhone

ALPS

Douro

SPANISH PLATEAU
Madrid

Ebro

Tagus

MEDITERRANEAN

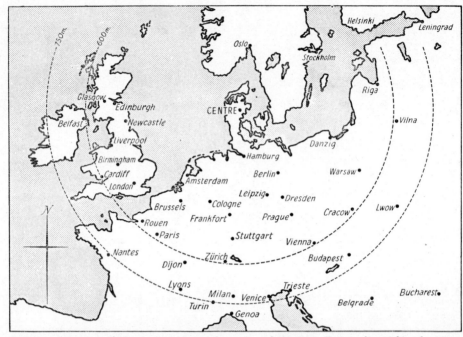

FIG. 79.  *Nearly all the great industrial centres of Western Europe lie within the inner circle, particularly to the south and south-west of the centre.  At the last census England had forty-eight towns with a population exceeding 100,000; Germany had fifty-eight.*

whatever varied racial strains they inherit, have come to be characterized by an alertness of mind and body to which the climate has undoubtedly contributed.

Europe was subjected to many changes of climate in prehistoric times (e.g. the Great Ice Age), and far back in the earth's history this region was repeatedly changing its shape and receiving additions to its land area.  It thus came to be enriched with a great variety of rocks: sandstones, mudstones and shales, limestones, ironstones and coal measures.  Successive periods of folding of the earth's crust, by rearing these rocks high in upfolds and particularly by burying them deep in downfolds, helped to save them from complete denudation; and so it comes about that extensive mineral deposits are preserved, especially along the margins of the old fold mountains (Fig. 81).  Variety of rock, coastform, outline, relief, soil, and economic resources constitutes the keynote of the physical geography of Western Europe.

Variety and painful separation of its parts is also characteristic of its human geography, so that at first sight Western Europe would seem to lack the unifying features proper to a major geographical region.  But restless energy and initiative, even though they are so often displayed in economic and military warfare, are themselves characteristic facts.  And however subdivided the continent has become, her peoples are none the less conscious of the differences between Europeans on the one hand and the peoples of Asia or Africa on the other.  They have shared a common history in a greater measure than the inhabitants of any other continent.

Historically, Western Europe stands apart from the southern peninsulas in its tardy reception of full civilization.  No city worthy of the name made its appearance in our region until Roman times, when many Mediterranean cities had a thousand years or more behind them.  Village life, however, had penetrated to the most favoured parts of Western Europe by 2000 B.C., and the agricultural village has remained in many parts the fundamental unit of settlement.

It was out of this rural background that there emerged, through widening spheres of organization around certain well-placed cities, the idea of the nation-state which has been such a powerful force in the modern world. Historians trace its growth in medieval France and England, and its extension along the Atlantic seaboard from Portugal to Norway, a distribution which reminds us that the sea has

helped to promote freedom and political initiative. It is these maritime countries of Western Europe, with their long experience of nationhood, that have most successfully resisted totalitarian attempts to restrict personal freedom and stifle criticism.

European energy, inventiveness, and love of adventure found their great opportunity following the revival of learning in the sixteenth century, when physical and mental horizons were rapidly expanding. Voyages of Atlantic discovery, initiated by the Vikings in the Dark Ages, were now eagerly undertaken by all the sea-

FIG. 80. *The hemisphere shown here, which has its centre near Paris, contains nearly all the world's land-masses and the vast majority of its population. A future world airport may be located near one of the great cities of Western Europe.*

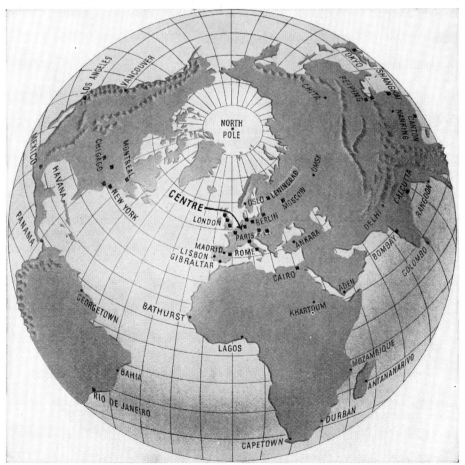

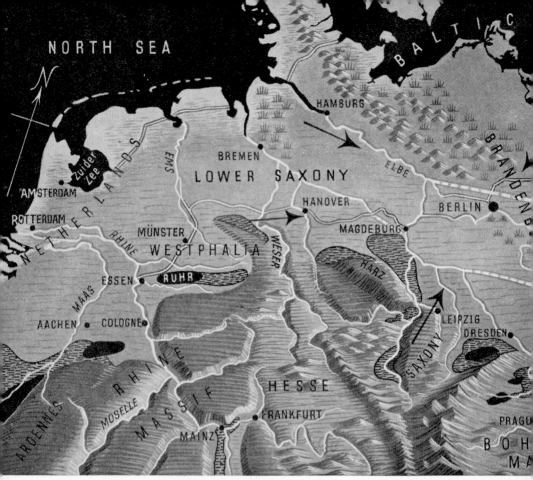

FIG. 81. *Some of the geographical factors in the life of Germany and her neighbours which are to a great degree responsible for the disunity of Europe. The southern hillcountry did not favour political unity. Berlin rose to power as the centre of the Great*

board countries of Western Europe whose peoples were gaining national consciousness. The expansion of Europe overseas, with all that it has meant for the world at large, was the outcome of forces that had been at work since the dawn of civilization. And it was the reaction of new lands and their products that helped Europe—and in the first place Britain— to become the home of modern industry and to increase its population. We may think, for example, of the part played by imported cotton in stimulating the factory system, and of the importance of the potato in the life of Ireland and of Prussia.

If we list some of the distinguishing features of Western European life in the nineteenth and twentieth centuries we shall include the following: mechanical power,

invention, abundant means of speedy communication, the rapid growth of population and its concentration on coalfields and in metropolitan cities, economic and political aggression, and intense nationalism. But we should not forget peasant Europe lying on the fringes of the industrial core and preserving something of an older Europe with its crafts and immemorial customs.

One of the important questions facing the new Europe is the part to be played by aviation in internal, and especially in inter-continental, communications. We need to approach this subject by ridding our minds of the distortions of Mercator's world map which, because of its great utility in sea navigation, has dominated our view of the world and very largely governed our reactions to world relations,

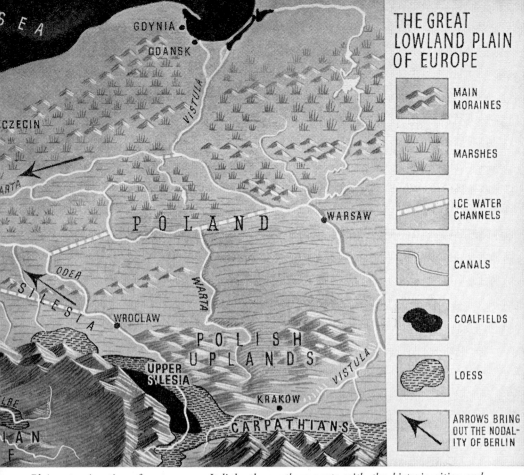

## THE GREAT LOWLAND PLAIN OF EUROPE

- MAIN MORAINES
- MARSHES
- ICE WATER CHANNELS
- CANALS
- COALFIELDS
- LOESS
- ARROWS BRING OUT THE NODALITY OF BERLIN

SEA
GDYNIA
GDANSK
CZECIN
VISTULA
ARTA
POLAND
WARSAW
ODER
SILESIA
WROCLAW
WARTA
POLISH UPLANDS
UPPER SILESIA
VISTULA
KRAKÓW
CARPATHIANS
LBE
KAN

*Plain, at a junction of waterways. It links the northern ports with the historic cities and industrial districts along the edge of the hills. Note the physical basis for the desire of the Czechs for mountain frontiers and Poland's wish to secure a river frontier on the west.*

The continents of the Northern Hemisphere in particular, because of their contiguity and their dense populations, are being affected by "a revolution in accessibility." The greater part of the land surface of the globe falls within the hemisphere contained by a circle with a radius of some 6,000 miles drawn from a centre in Western Europe (Fig. 80). Ninety per cent of the world's cities with a population exceeding one million lie within this hemisphere. A world airport, therefore, would be most suitably located somewhere within the line of the 600-mile semicircle shown on our map (Fig. 79).

Western Europe may be said to consist of two complex peninsulas branching westwards from the Russian Plain, and separated by shallow seas which stretch from the English Channel to the Gulf of Finland.

The northern peninsula has, in the Scandinavian plateau, by far the largest highland unit in our region. Projecting from it are the low-lying peninsulas of Kola (Murmansk), south Finland and south Sweden, which are composed of immensely old fold mountains worn down to low levels, and form what geologists call the Fenno-Scandian Shield. Part of the Shield lies under the Gulf of Bothnia.

Along the north-western margins of the Shield very old sendimentary rocks were intensely folded into what is called the Caledonian system, a name which reminds us that the highlands of Scotland are part of the same series. Folds and faults run from north-east to south-west, a trend which is conspicuous in the great escarpment of Norway and in the alternating ridges and glens of Scotland. The whole system has been repeatedly worn down to a dead level, and uplifted as plateau blocks.

In the Scandinavian peninsula, and more especially in Norway, the famous fjords have been carved out by rivers and glaciers to give a very steep and broken coast, but the difficulties of land movement are offset by the presence of sheltered sea lanes protected by islands and providing a ready means of communication. Sweden is the long, gently sloping back of the Scandinavian plateau, tilted towards the south-east and crossed by many parallel rivers, with long, narrow lakes in their upper courses, which drain into the shallow Gulf of Bothnia. The boundary between it and Norway, running down the high watershed, is one of the few open and unguarded frontiers in Europe.

Both Finland and south Sweden are remarkable for their lakes (Fig. 41), which play a notable part in economic life as means of communication and sources of water-power. Countless small lakes, in addition, occupy rock basins carved out by ice, and others are dammed up behind moraines. Everywhere in Fenno-Scandia the effects of glaciation are apparent: in the scatter of lakes, the bare, ice-smoothed rocks, the deeply-cut fjords, the boulder-strewn clays, and the well-drained lines of sandy moraines. Human settlement and economic opportunity are closely related to the facts of physical geography.

### Central Plain

The Great Lowland Plain, or Polish-German Plain (Fig. 81), separated from Scandinavia by the Baltic Sea, runs east and west, falling gradually from 500–800 feet at the Russian border, towards the west where it narrows and shelves down into the North Sea. It reaches its greatest height along the Baltic coast, touching 1,000 feet in the morainic hills known as the Baltic Heights, near Gdansk.

To the south of, and parallel to, the Baltic Heights is a belt of shallow valleys with flat marshy floors and many small lakes. These valleys, formed by glacial melt-water, are followed by the middle courses of the German rivers before they break through to the coast. Alternating sandy heaths and marshy valleys kept this part of the plain backward and thinly peopled, but the construction of a network of canals, utilizing the long valleys, later played an important part in the supremacy of Prussia and the rise of modern Germany.

### Land Reclaimed

The Vistula basin is more elevated and has fewer marshes and lakes, but on the borders of Russia the waters of the Plain become almost stagnant before they find an outlet by the Pripet to the Dnieper and the Black Sea (page 126). The Pripet Marshes are but the largest of a series which fringes Russia on the west and has helped to isolate it from the rest of Europe.

To the west of the lower Elbe the Plain gradually sinks into the North Sea through a broken line of sand dunes (e.g. the Frisian Islands), behind which land-reclamation on tidal lagoons and deltaic flats has been going on at intervals since the early Middle Ages, when the process began in the Polders of Flanders. The greatest achievement has been the reclamation of most of the Zuider Zee, which was invaded by the sea so late as the thirteenth century (Fig. 82).

The southern edge of the Plain is marked by a series of "bays" running into the Central Uplands—the bays of Cologne, Münster, Leipzig and Silesia—floored with deep yellowish or dark soil of great fertility, known as loess. This fine-grained deposit, carried by winds from dried glacial muds, extends westwards into Belgium and expands eastwards through South Poland as the Black Earth of the Ukraine. It gives rise to a smooth landscape of arable fields, hedgeless and now almost treeless, which has been, since prehistoric days, a zone of settlement, cultivation, and easy movement, clearly differentiated from the marshy lowlands to the north and the difficult hills to the south.

In this foothill zone, and in places actually underneath the loess, lies the belt of coalfields stretched along the hill margins from north-eastern France to Silesia (Fig. 81). This combination of resources,

FIG. 82. *The Dutch village of Zoutelande amid the sand dunes which in this district are the only protection against flooding by the North Sea. Picturesque red bricks and tiles, supplemented by timber, are the building materials used in this stoneless lowland.*

agricultural and industrial, has had important consequences in recent times, for many of the historic cities of Germany were able to take the lead in the industrial expansion of that country after 1870.

Across the southern part of the North Sea and the Straits of Dover the Great Plain re-establishes itself as the English Lowlands, running west and north to the edge of the coalfields. Save for small patches in the Thames basin and in East Anglia, the English Plain lacks the fertile loess but it has neither the extensive infertile moraines nor the continuous marshy belts of the main European Plain. Protected on two sides by the sea, this is the historic heart of England, with London as its focal point (Figs. 83 and 88).

On the mainland, the Great Plain runs south-westwards into France, where the scarps of limestone and clay vales are disposed symmetrically in concentric rings, concentrating most of the drainage into a single river, the Seine, and giving its central city, Paris, a unique dominance (Figs. 84 and 89). Here, too, is abundant loess-like material and hence greater fertility. It has its maritime fringe (Normandy) where

more than one invader has landed, but the most disastrous assaults on this fertile basin have come from the north-east along the Plain.

The uplands which fringe the Plain on the south are the remnants of a once formidable mountain system which extended from south Ireland and Spain eastwards to south Poland, and was folded after the coal measures were laid down. Their shattered remains rise as block mountains out of the younger deposits of the intervening hollows. The four converging peninsulas that front the Atlantic— south Ireland, S.W. England, Brittany and N.W. Spain—are all parts of this system, and they have much in common; their ancient rocks and precious metals, their barren, misty moorlands, their drowned river estuaries which breed fine sailors. They have been the refuge areas of the continent—the Celtic Fringe—and, at times, the pioneering front of the Atlantic.

Two facts dominate the physical geography of mid-Europe: its remarkably broken topography and tangled drainage, and its wealth of minerals including, around the edges, coal and iron. These facts help

FIG. 83. *The south-east of England is a richly cultivated lowland crossed by three chalk escarpments, through gaps in which all traffic routes converge on the metropolis. London has become the centre of nearly every aspect of British life and thought and, as a great port, owes much to foreign influence entering "the continental angle" of Britain.*

to explain its tardy progress towards political unity and its many cities with proud traditions of industry, old and new.

In the north are two plateau-blocks, the Rhine and Bohemian Massifs, drained respectively by the Rhine and the Elbe with their tributaries. The Rhine Massif (Ardennes, Eifel, etc.) is characteristically flat-topped and forested, except where young volcanic rocks bring topographic variety and patches of fertility. Into it the Rhine and its feeders, e.g. the Moselle, have cut deep gorges that provide sheltered strips for vineyards and famous highways of traffic. Along the northern foot from Belgium to the Ruhr, crossing the lowland "bay" of Cologne between Aachen and Essen, is Europe's greatest concentration of industrial towns. These are based on the coal measures and utilize for transport the River Rhine, as well as a dense network of railways and canals.

The Bohemian Massif is a diamond-shaped block flanked by steep, forested hills

reaching 5,000 feet and embracing many sunken lowlands, floored with loess and drained by tributaries of the Elbe. The largest and lowest of these lie to the north of the centrally-placed city of Prague. Throughout history the persistent spirit of Czech nationalism has been cradled in this mountain-ringed basin. Rich in coal and precious metals, Czechoslovakia has become highly industrialized, especially during her independence from 1919-1939.

Between the Rhine uplands and the Bohemian bastion is a zone of weaker relief framed by the Harz and the Thuringian Forest, and rich in historic cities. To the south-west, the low-lying fault valley of the middle Rhine cuts a deep trough between the Vosges hills and the Black Forest (Fig. 78). Here the boundary between French and German speech not only dvides the rift valley itself but runs between the coal of the Saar and the immense iron-ore beds of Lorraine.

Lastly, to the south, fronting the Alps

between Geneva and Vienna, is the Alpine Foreland, a high plain, averaging 2,000 feet, levelled with the debris of mountain denudation and varied with more recent glacial deposits which litter its surface. Its wide central portion, drained by the tributaries of the Danube, is Bavaria; its narrowing ends, despite the penetration of German speech, are the historically well-defined regions of Upper Austria and Switzerland. The latter's lake-strewn plateau is sharply demarcated by the parallel folds of the Jura to the north.

The fold mountains typically consist of a high crystalline central zone—carved into fantastic peaks and bearing the signs of heavy glaciation—flanked by limestone through which the escaping rivers have cut deep passages. For all their height and terror they could therefore be crossed by man, in some places without much difficulty, even before the days of tunnels. Moreover they are breached or outflanked by river-corridors such as the Danube at

Vienna and the Rhône at Lyons, and even the long straight line of the Pyrenees can be turned at the ends. At these gates is concentrated a wealth of European history.

### Climate of Europe

No part of Western Europe is rainless at any season, thanks to the penetration of Atlantic depressions with their rain-bearing winds along the great trough between latitudes 50 degrees and 60 degrees. They buffet the coast of Norway at all times of the year—Bergen notoriously gets the fullest effect—and are hardly less severe in western Scotland and Ireland. They are most intense and frequent in autumn and winter, but it is in summer that most depressions reach the heart of Europe, for the high pressures from the Asiatic interior keep them out in winter, so that they concentrate their fury in the Bay of Biscay and the British and Norway seas.

The Alpine chains, notably the Pyrenees and the Dinaric Alps, are important

Fig. 84. *Since the Middle Ages, Paris has been the focus of its fertile basin. A vast network of road and rail routes supplements the riverways. The city has always been the undisputed centre of France, and the country expanded from this nucleus.*

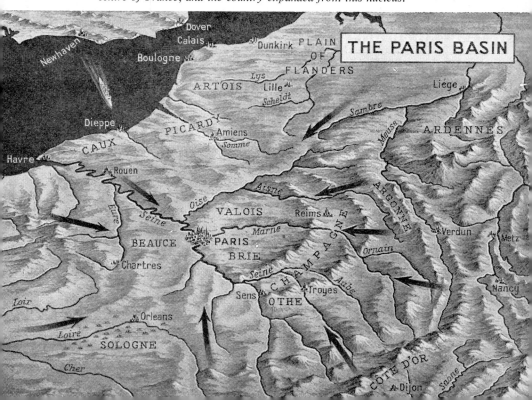

climatic frontiers. The summer cyclones rarely cross them: the Mediterranean gets drought and dry northerly winds just when Central Europe is receiving the bulk of its rains. These cyclonic rains, heaviest in the hills, are augmented by summer thunderstorms. They fall early (May and June) in the basin of Hungary, later (June and July) in central Germany, and later still (July to September) in Sweden.

January and February, the time of maximum cold, are everywhere the driest months in Central Europe, including the Swiss Plateau, but the High Alps, though they, too, receive most precipitation in the summer, have heavy falls (of snow) in winter. Along the Atlantic seaboard spring is the driest season and the heaviest rains come in the late autumn, when the sea winds are much warmer than the land.

### Winter Problems

East of an isothermal line running in a sweeping curve from N. Norway along the Rhine to the mouth of the Danube, there is at least one month with an average temperature below freezing point, and the frost period increases eastwards to four and five months in central Russia. The best winter wheat grows to the west of this line: the bulk of the rye crop—wheat's poor relation—to the east. "White bread versus black bread" is thus not unconnected with "black Christmas versus white Christmas." Further, the bulk of Europe's wines are grown on the warm side of the line. The frontiers of the Roman Empire along the Rhine and Danube were determined in part by the incidence of low winter temperatures beyond those rivers.

If Central and Eastern Europe suffer from the winter cold, the westernmost parts are remarkably mild, but their problem is excessive rainfall, inadequate evaporation and consequent waterlogging. The Irish bogs naturally come to mind here, but peaty accumulations and acid soils bring difficulties throughout the mountain belt of the north-west, and men turn more readily to herding and fishing than to cultivation. Under these oceanic conditions it is the low-lying rain-shadow areas, where the 40–100 inches of rainfall

of the outer coasts is reduced to a moderate 20–30 inches, that have favoured good agriculture and the accumulation of power. All the historic capitals of Atlantic Western Europe—London, Edinburgh, Dublin, Paris, Brussels, Amsterdam and The Hague, Copenhagen and Oslo—are in areas with less than 30 inches of rain.

In summer the lands to the north of a line running roughly from N.W. Spain through Central France to near Krakow are cooler than the area to the south of it, and there is a corresponding distinction between cooler and warmer crops. For example, the producing areas of two crops which Europe has borrowed from the New World, potatoes and maize, are found to the north and south respectively of this line. The native root crops, such as sugar beet, are also concentrated on the cool side, as are oats and flax.

But we need to know also how the natural vegetation of Western Europe was adapted to the climatic and topographic conditions; for, although it has been largely replaced by cultivated crops, it was against a background of natural vegetation that the sub-regions of European culture took shape. This background was one of dark forests and dangerous animals, memories of which enrich our folklore and inspire a thousand folk tales. "Oak, ash and thorn" were among its chief trees, "the big, bad, wolf" its most dreaded inhabitant.

Pine, birch, willow and poplar were the first trees to advance northwards when the Atlantic rains returned to a Europe recovering from the ice-sheets, but a period of warmer climate after 6000 B.C. allowed the hazel, elder, oak and elm to follow them. In the end the dominant tree of the great European Plain became the sturdy oak (Fig. 85), important for its many economic uses (charcoal, tanning, house-frames, ships' timbers, furniture, acorns for fattening pigs) and for its adaptation to deep, firm soils which were worth clearing for agriculture, once populations had outgrown the limited patches of more lightly forested land. For long ages, however, man avoided the damp, oak forest, and archaeologists have shown how belts of thick forest put definite limits to the spread

FIG. 85. *The more fertile regions of the Great Lowland Plain have been carved out of the oak forests. Early economic uses of these forests are illustrated above.*

of early human settlement and progress.

Thus it might be said that the forest provided the framework within which the social and political groupings of the continent took shape. In prehistoric days it was the rivers, sea coasts, lake shores, and above all, the bare moorlands and limestone or loess tracts, that attracted human settlement. In such areas we find ancient racial stocks clinging tenaciously even to the barren moorland, despite all the difficulties it presents to civilized life.

The broad-leaved forests are well adapted to the wet summers and leaf-picking winters of Central Europe. The oak is king of the forest, but the beech tree gives us a more sensitive index of the most-favoured regions. Its delicate leaves that beautify the spring in Denmark and southern England cannot withstand summer desiccation or cold, stormy springs. The beech is absent, as a native tree, in Ireland and Scotland and all Fenno-Scandia save south Sweden and the tip of Norway. Most significantly, its eastern limit runs from East Prussia to the curve of the Carpathians and the Balkan range, almost outlining a frontier that has on one side the historic nations of Western

Europe, on the other the vast spaces of Russia.

The characteristic soils of the areas where the beech grows well are the humid brown earths, intermediate between the reddish iron-stained soils of Southern Europe and the grey leached soils of the north and north-west. The brown earths are well adapted to mixed farming, being neither too dry for grass nor too wet for grain, and wherever they occur they have supported a well-balanced life and encouraged increase.

Forests of pine, spruce and fir, "evergreen" and therefore ready to respond quickly and grow under difficult conditions, still cling to the colder mountain sides and to the poor morainic soils of the Great Plain. Near the transition from oak to pine, along the sixtieth parallel, lie the historic capitals of Northern Europe—Oslo, Uppsala and Leningrad, with Helsinki a little farther north in the oak forest of the south Finnish end-moraines.

In two areas—the tundra and the steppe—open treeless country penetrates into Western Europe from Russia and Siberia, and in both we find Asiatic languages which were carried into Europe by pastoralists, the Lapps of the tundra and the Magyars of Hungary. An arm of the tundra—the fjeld—extends down the high watershed of the Scandinavian peninsula, where its drier patches are utilized as summer pastures, but this zone, frozen for three parts of the year, has contributed little to European life save as a twilight background for tales and songs of dwarfs and gnomes, possibly inspired by the diminutive Lapps.

In contrast to this, the grasslands of Hungary (Fig. 86) and trans-Carpathia have played a very important part in the life of Europe as an avenue both for expanding peasant populations and for periodic incursions of horse-riding swordsmen—Huns, Avars, Magyars, Turks, and their nameless forerunners who brought the Indo-European languages from the Russian steppes. Westward-moving peoples could either enter the Danube basin through the passes in the eastern Carpathians or fan out on patches of loess-steppe into Poland or the Balkans.

East Central Europe as a whole has thus suffered from setbacks which have delayed the emergence of civic and national organizations. Although Hungary boasts of its "thousand-year-old frontiers" and has at times achieved great political power, the economic life of the Magyars was in the main that of the steppes. Like the Ukraine, the Hungarian Alföld (lowland) was devoted almost exclusively to horses, sheep and cattle before the coming of the railway in the last hundred years. And until 1945 Hungary remained mainly aristocratic and feudal, with the leading families still owning one-third of the land. Westernmost Europe was recovering from the barbarian invasions a thousand years ago: the Danubian lands and the Balkans cannot forget Tatar and Turk. But the influence of hostile pressure from the east was also felt, and provoked reaction, farther west.

Europe has been inhabited by men of modern type, i.e. the ancestors of living races, since the intervals between the advances of the ice in glacial times, tens of thousands of years ago. Already various branches of the human family, some of them doomed to extinction, had peopled Europe both from the south and from the

FIG. 86. *Cattle-herding on the Hungarian "puszta" (waste land). The richer parts of the "puszta" are now agricultural. Note the dip-well—reminiscent of the "shaduf" of Egypt.*

east. So early in human history was Western Europe the region of overlap between southern (Mediterranean and African) and eastern (Russian and Asiatic) cultures.

No part of non-Mediterranean Europe was able to enjoy the benefits of city life before Roman times, and in many parts outside the Roman Empire there were no towns until the Middle Ages. Crops and field systems, domestic animals, methods of cultivation, building styles and the organization and social character of the village, as well as the racial elements of the populations—all varied from one region to another, but throughout Western Europe a fundamental pattern of civilization had been evolved before the dawn of history.

This pattern was based on village settlements—small stone-built family clusters among the uplands of the north-west, larger and better-organized timber-built villages in Central Europe—and on the cultivation of scattered plots in open fields (Fig. 207), with schemes adapted to conserve land fertility under different conditions of soil and climate. Most farm work was done with simple hand implements, such as the reaping sickle of iron, still today not entirely displaced, which had evolved from earlier sickles of flint and bronze.

### Large Families

The peasants needed many hands and could usefully employ even young children in many ways. From economic as well as religious motives they wanted sons and daughters, and they used fertility rites to encourage increase in animals and crops as well. The effect of this long tradition is still apparent in the high reproduction rates of peasant Europe. Moreover, it was the fervour of their earth-worship that quickened the cult of the Virgin Mother in medieval times, and helped Christianity to weld Western Europe into a large measure of unity.

Peasant life was adapted to the seasons of the year: seed time and harvest and the periods of movement of cattle or sheep were festivals assuring the completion of allotted tasks and guaranteeing their recurrence. The ideal was to hand on the precious land from one generation to another. In this way the peasantries of Europe, however much they have suffered from overlords and compulsory services, and later on from governments and taxation, have built up and preserved a static form of society, a heritage which for good or ill must still be reckoned with in modern Europe.

It was around the peasantries, for instance, that fixation of languages took place, languages whose forms and boundaries have changed very little in historic times, and to which nationalism has given an ever-increasing significance in recent centuries. One of the forces accelerating fixity and standardization of language was the organization of towns and cities as regional market centres for the peasantries.

### Growth of Towns

It is important to notice that France was the first part of Western Europe to receive cities—in Roman times—from the Mediterranean, and thanks to the power of the Church and the wealth of her resources, many of them survived the Dark Ages to revive in the eleventh and twelfth centuries.

Southern Britain also had its first towns in Roman times, but they were abandoned and the language was lost when Anglo-Saxon invaders came in as settlers during the Dark Ages. In the areas of Celtic speech in the north and west, monastic churches provided the first nuclei of small cities, but there were few towns until the Middle Ages, and very few of any size until modern times. Family and clan ties have remained strong in these regions, with many social and political consequences.

Beyond the Rhine and the Danube—the Roman frontier—the idea of the city did not penetrate before the early Middle Ages, and towns were founded not only by the Church, but by princes and adventurers who offered inducements to merchants and to Jews excluded from the guilds of the Church cities. A great effort of town building, accompanied by a large-scale attack on the forests and by village-founding, marked the eastward expansion of Germanic peoples after A.D. 1000. The oldest towns immediately east of the Rhine date from the tenth to the twelfth centuries;

it was not until the thirteenth and fourteenth that towns were founded in the Slav
lands and throughout the eastern border-
lands of Western Europe from the Baltic to
the Balkans. These towns were often
peopled by German settlers—traders and
craftsmen, miners or crusading barons—
forming alien communities among peasantries that spoke Slavonic or some other
tongue.

### Racial Difficulties

Jewish elements, driven from farther
west, added to the complexities, and the
religious difficulties thus introduced were
increased by the rivalries between Greek
and Roman Christianity and by the penetration of Islam into the Danube basin.
Throughout this zone of minorities, where
conflicting loyalties and traditions exist
side by side, the establishment of stable
regional organizations has been a permanent problem, and the attempt to apply
the principles of linguistic nationalism in
1919 was doomed to failure. Peasant life
has here remained more self-contained than
in regions to the west. Their ancient
customs and crafts have survived, they
depend less on the towns and have not
much need of a money economy, but they
are exposed to the exploitation of political
adventurers and industrial market seekers.

In the difficult margins of our region—in
Norway, western Britain and Ireland on
the one hand, in the Pyrenees, Alps, south
Carpathians and Dinaric Alps on the other
—the peasantry had to face problems of a
different kind: steep slopes, restricted
areas of good soil, and heavy precipitation
in the form of mists, rain or snow. The
peasants in these areas have supplemented
their scanty cultivation—especially in the
days before new crops such as the potato
came to their rescue—by the resources of
sea or lake (Fig. 87), by trade, and by
stock-raising, utilizing the upland pastures
in summer under systems of seasonal
nomadism to which the word "trans-
humance" is applied (Fig. 77).

These activities are well illustrated in the
life of Switzerland. The Pyrenees shelter a
number of smaller self-conscious groups,
notably the Basques in the west, who show

their pastoral heritage and independence.
The people of Andorra farther east have
alone escaped complete absorption in larger
nations. In the Balkans the Vlachs have
retained their nomadic habits into the
modern period, while the transhumant
Rumanians were able to preserve their
identity in the remoteness of the southern
Carpathian mountains and to emerge from
time to time as a nation state.

The economic and social character of
these seasonal migrants can be related to
the circumstances of their homelands, the
distances to be traversed, and the animals
they depend on, whether the emphasis is on
sheep or on cattle. The long journeys and
rough life of the shepherds of Spain and
Rumania, for example, contrast with the
more intimate and civilized family cow-
herding of Switzerland.

A similar background helps us to understand much of the social geography of the
rain-soaked north-western margins of
Europe. Oats and stock farming have long
been their main resources, while fishing and
trading have won them freedom and even
tempted them to expansion. Western
England, Scotland and Ireland are part of
this Atlantic sub-region of Europe, preserving in places to this day ancient Celtic
languages and a tradition of independence.

These marginal and mountain lands
have been forced in the past to export their
surplus population and the process is still
going on, but hydro-electric development
and a greatly expanded tourist industry
give promise for the future.

### Conquest of the Forest

By the end of the Middle Ages towns
had grown up even in these remote fringes
of Western Europe, and everywhere peasant
cultivators had expanded at the expense of
the forest into all the more fertile areas of
the continent. In the richer wheat-growing
plains a strong feudal system had fastened
itself on the bent backs of the peasantry.
Feudalism was weaker in the mountainous
country, where people lived in scattered
hamlets among pathless wilds that horsemen could not penetrate, and where they
found avenues of escape in pastoralism or
seafaring. France and England were

FIG. 87. *Hallstatt, in the Austrian Salzkammergut, illustrates the continuity of lake-side settlement and economy in the Alps. Salt has been worked here since prehistoric times. Hallstatt gives its name to the first Iron Age of Central Europe (1000-500 B.C.).*

developing as nation-states around their metropolitan nuclei, pioneers of a form of organization which was to spread with more or less success to other parts of Western Europe.

It was this north-western area that contributed those further "revolutions" which were to mould the life of modern Europe—the revolt against feudalism, the break-up of the open-field system, the rise of modern industry and the consequent rapid growth of population. The ideas thrown up were adapted in due course to the various environments and social traditions of the continent, and we may now consider some of these sub-regions, without adhering too closely to the shifting frontiers of the political powers which claim to express their aspirations.

It will be useful, first of all, to glance once more at Western Europe from the central vantage-point of Jutland, for here three of the major geographical sub-divisions of the continent meet: (1) Atlantic Europe, stretching from Norway to north Portugal, with the British Isles balanced midway off Cape Gris Nez. (2) Baltic Europe, extending around the shores of that sea. (3) Central Europe, lying to the south and including an outlier in the Lombardy Plain. If to these we add (4) Danubian Europe we shall, within a simple A B C D framework, embrace nearly the whole of Western Europe. Any such division, in view of the complexities of European geography, must be used as a matter of convenience rather than as a rigid classification, for none of these regions is sharply demarcated, nor can any region escape the actions and reactions of its neighbours.

(A). *Atlantic Europe.* The British Isles

may claim our attention first. Insulated but not isolated, they have been able to combine, and make a compromise between, influences from the south and from the east (cf. the English language). Nearly two hundred years ago the introduction of root crops and rotation grasses, known for some centuries in the thickly-peopled lands of Holland and Lombardy, helped to break down the open-field system (Fig. 207) and brought the enclosure movement, by which the peasantry of Lowland England lost their hold on the land and became wage-earning labourers.

The eighteenth century also saw the supremacy of British maritime expansion, and the beginnings of the Industrial Revolution, both of which provided occupations for a landless people and offered a permanent escape from the insecurity of grain harvests in the climatic conditions of Britain. The process of industrialization was to spread, during the nineteenth century, to nearly every part of the continent, but it is of the greatest consequence to her island life that Britain led the way, reaping the benefits and paying the penalties of the pioneer. Her relative security from invasion, her well-established national unity, her wealth of coal and iron, her position in the Atlantic gateway of Europe—these factors gave Britain the lead, but another geographical fact helps to explain the special colouring of the British experiment, and the initiative, competition and often reckless freedom shown in its development.

That fact is the location of her coalfields at the edge of the uplands in the wilder parts of the country, where civic traditions were weak and the established church had little hold. Industry, attracted to the coalfields, brought a vast increase of population in new towns that sprang up with little thought of planning or amenities, and under strong-minded leaders, in many

FIG. 88. *London Bridge* (Centre) *has been for 500 years the head of ocean navigation in the Thames. The Pool of London, between London Bridge and Tower Bridge* (Above), *is served by thousands of lighters or barges and is equipped for all general cargoes.*

cases of Nonconformist faith, it was given freedom to express itself in diverse ways.

The export of goods and capital came to be regarded as the royal highway to peace and prosperity, but the dangers of dependence on exports and the neglect of agriculture have been sharply emphasized in the twentieth century. Moreover the reactions provoked by the British system have taken many forms, most characteristically the alternative extreme of economic nationalism. We see this development, for example, in Ireland, where the Industrial Revolution affected only the north-east, and where an ancient peasantry retains its fierce hold on the land.

### People of France

The life of France, Britain's oldest sister nation, has been moulded to a different pattern. Her peasant population, cultivating fields where harvests that include the vine and many fruits ripen in a warmer sun, has struggled to maintain its grip on the precious soil and has not been drawn away either overseas or to the coalfields to the same extent as in Britain. The French population is still 50 per cent rural, as against the British figure of 15 per cent. If we except Paris and one or two other large cities, her towns, with their strong medieval flavour, share the character of the countryside to which they remain closely attached and which they supply with goods produced in small factories. The stability of her social and economic life contrasts sharply with the British spirit of enterprise and expansion.

The population of France, now 45 millions, has remained fairly stationary, despite a dangerous influx of other nationals between the two World Wars; and the fear of her overgrown neighbours has strengthened that centralized form of government which centuries of slow growth had established in the favoured Paris basin. It is symbolic of French life that her largest coal and iron fields are located on her frontiers, in Nord and Lorraine. Their full economic utilization depends on a large measure of co-operation with her Belgian and German neighbours—to ensure which is among the major tasks of European statesmanship.

Where the Great Plain of Europe narrows in the dread corridor of Ypres, between the Ardennes and Dunkirk, we pass into the Low Countries. Here the convergence of land and sea routes and the debouchment of the mighty Rhine brought a concentration of busy towns and ports in the Middle Ages; and in more recent times Belgium and Holland, however much they differ, have been characterized by their dense populations, skilled in industry (especially textiles), and by their intensive systems of land utilization. Belgium, which had been included in the Roman Empire, was more precocious. Holland, outside the Empire, became Protestant in the sixteenth century and in the seventeenth enjoyed her greatest prosperity, built up her overseas empire and made notable contributions to European life in navigation, international law, art, agriculture, land reclamation, canal construction, town planning, and so on. In no part of Europe, save perhaps Norway, has the spirit of the sea counted for so much.

### "Little Denmark"

Both the Low Countries have a share of the hill-foot coal measures—Holland much less than Belgium—but both are economically dependent on international trade, and serve, through Rotterdam and Antwerp, wide hinterlands beyond their political frontiers. Their small size, their varied resources, and their position in the neck of the Great Plain have repeatedly laid them open to aggression, but in the life of the continent they stand for much that must not be allowed to be submerged.

If Holland in some respects (e.g. its language) may be considered to belong to Central Europe, the position of Denmark is more doubtful, for here three major divisions of the continent meet—Atlantic, Baltic, and Central. Its seafaring peoples established dominion over Norway in the early fourteenth century and it retained, until 1944, a political link with Iceland going back to 1381.

The Baltic islands, a morainic belt half drowned by shallow seas, are the core of the country, and Copenhagen, guarding the main entrance to the Baltic as well as the short crossing to Sweden, drew medieval power from its tolls and functioned as the capital of a territory that included south Sweden. The city has retained its supremacy—it has over one-fifth of the total population of 4½ millions—but it now serves as the manufacturing, commercial and cultural centre of a small country that was transformed after the German aggression, about the middle of the nineteenth century.

### Modern Development

Liberal leaders bought out the large estates, modernized the peasantry and were able, by educational methods, to develop co-operative production and marketing of butter, eggs, and bacon to meet the demands of the industrial population of Great Britain. This specialization of export, together with the large imports of manufactured goods, feeding-stuffs and fertilizers, has left Denmark precariously dependent on other countries, but her people have more than once shown their ability to take advantage of changing conditions. Her small size and strong consciousness of unity have encouraged social and economic experiments which larger countries have not dared to make.

Norway, faced with a high proportion of waste land—nearly three-quarters of its surface—has held its own in the modern world by developing the resources of pastures, forests, seas, and falling waters. The population, about 3½ millions, is almost entirely coastal. Water-power is the basis of the electro-chemical (nitrates) and the electro-metallurgical (aluminium) industries. About half the world's whaling fleet is owned by the Norwegians, and her mercantile marine recently ranked fourth in size. The strong individualism of the people, manifest in Viking days, was displayed repeatedly under the German occupation, though political and economic moderation and intellectual leadership have been outstanding features of her national life in the last half-century.

Finally, mention must be made of the other extremity of Atlantic Europe, the wet coastlands of Iberia from the western Pyrenees round to Portugal. Sharply divided from the dry heart of Spain by physical and cultural barriers, this difficult coast has been the refuge of old elements (cf. the Basques), and has known political unity only under force. Portugal has kept its interest in the sea, its colonial trade and its old economic links with England (thanks partly to its port wine), while the Asturian coast has been drawn into commerce and industry owing to its coal and iron.

(B). *Baltic Europe*. The coastlands of the Baltic, possessing a more obvious unity than those of the Atlantic, have been drawn together by cultural and economic ties more than once in the past. The south-western part of the region—the Nordic cradle of Nazi theory—was the home of successive prehistoric cultures and the heart of the medieval Hanseatic League whose wealthy merchant cities of the Baltic and its approaches won the freedom of the seas and were able to resist feudal aggression. In the course of time most of these cities were absorbed by the various regional groupings that emerged as the idea of linguistic nationalism gained ground.

In 1919 Estonia, Latvia and Lithuania won tardy political independence that lasted precariously for a bare twenty years. None of them much exceeds two millions in population and they remained dependent economically on their German ports and Russian hinterlands. The mass emigration of the Balts, as the Germans were called, has left the peasants in Russian hands. In 1940, at the wish, it was said, of a majority of the people, the three East Baltic countries were proclaimed Soviet Republics.

### Fenno-Scandia

Finland lay for many centuries under the control of Sweden. Despite the difficulties of her northerly latitudes and coasts ice-bound for more than a quarter of the year, she has been able to build up an economy based almost entirely on forest products (timber, pulp, paper, plywood), and a national spirit inspired, in its better moods, by an epic tradition drawn from the dark interior.

Sweden's rise from a turbulent past to a socially progressive modern nation has been assisted by a diversity of resources and of geographical contacts. Her remarkable

Fig. 89. *Paris from the Eiffel Tower, with Montmartre in the distance. Sandy deposits form the wooded hills on the horizon (Forêt de Montmorency). Eight miles of navigable*

achievements have undoubtedly been aided by her central lake-belt of movement. She has been able, in and around her splendid lake-side capital, Stockholm, to synthesize north and south: forest and farm; miner and burgher; folk art and modern architecture; peasant crafts and hydro-electric manufactures; the sledge of the north and modern aids to transport such as the ball-bearings which war brought to public notice. Politically, Sweden shares with her Scandinavian neighbours the ideal of moderation and the retention of the ceremonial aspect of monarchy and public life. In all this she has the advantage, which the east Baltic lands lack, of a single language. Sweden has her difficulties, needless to say, which war brought into relief, but she stands out as an impressive symbol of what Baltic Europe is capable of achieving.

(C). *Central Europe.* The core of the European mainland is Germany, historically a collection of small states ruled by bishops' cities or merchant princes' trading towns. Modern Germany had its beginnings in the expansion of Prussia from Brandenburg in the northern plain, aided by canals which enhanced the nodality of Berlin (Fig. 81) and by new crops, especially the potato, which brought an increase of population in the eighteenth century and enriched the large estates of the Junkers. (These estates, traditional strongholds of feudalism and political reaction, were broken up in 1945 into small peasant holdings which were later collectivized.)

The effort culminating in national unity (c. 1870) coincided with the coming of the Industrial Revolution to German lands, with the result that manufactures and

*river make Paris a considerable port. The island nucleus of the city (Île de la Cité),*
*providing both protection and an easy river crossing, lies to the east (right).*

banking, agriculture and commerce, as well as education and government, were caught up in a vast state organization. The railway net was virtually complete by this time, so that raw materials could be transported where they were needed, and the coalfields did not monopolize industry to the same extent as in Britain. Moreover, many old cities situated on or near the coalfields were able to control the new forces, to divert wealth to civic enrichment, and to maintain proud traditions and amenities while their populations were growing rapidly.

There was not, as in Britain, a great shift of industry and population but a continuity of settlement and economic development. Agriculture and forestry were not neglected, as in England, but were integrated with industry. All this was in striking contrast to

British *laissez faire*. The results in terms of demography and international relations, however, were much the same—a rapid increase of population and dependence on exports, and both these tendencies threatened the security of her neighbours, especially France on the west and peasant Europe on the east.

The mid-European sub-regions of Switzerland, Austria and north Italy are based respectively on the Swiss lake plateau, the basin of Vienna, and the broad valley of the Po, and their mutual frontiers lie along the Alpine crests. Their historical evolution has taken different forms. Switzerland has her famous cantons and a tradition of freedom and international effort maintained even under the stress of modern war. The economic and political unity of the densely-peopled Lombardy basin was long retarded by the obstacle of the marshes and floods of the River Po, and by the rivalry of city states such as Milan and Venice. Austria is the old frontier Mark of the German peoples, guarding the gateway of the Danube basin.

But all are concerned with the traffic through the Alpine passes and have found in the Alps a source of hydro-electric power for skilled industries such as fine textiles and delicate metallurgy. Austria is far behind the other two regions in this respect: it is handicapped by the disparity between its once imperial capital, Vienna, containing two-thirds of the urban population, and a backward countryside.

### Minorities in Central Europe

Brief references must be made to Czechoslovakia and Poland, areas of Slavonic speech separated from the southern or "Jugo" Slavs by the Danubian wedge of Austria, Hungary and Rumania. Both countries fall into a western area of high industrial development, and straggling eastern provinces, almost purely agricultural, whose populations are hardly politically conscious. Here we meet problems common to all this zone of minorities in east Central Europe, problems which are briefly considered in the following section. There is one special aspect of the Polish situation, however, which must be singled out, namely the high proportion of Jews. Down to a century ago, the Jews of Poland numbered roughly one-half the Jewish population of the world. Lessened by emigration since then, their numbers were drastically reduced by persecution and extermination in the Second World War.

(D). *Danubian Europe*. Without attempting to define the complex south-eastern region of Western Europe, we include under this head the middle and lower basins of the Danube and their fringing mountains, roughly coincident with the political areas of Hungary, Rumania, Yugoslavia and Bulgaria. We have already outlined some of the historic difficulties of these lands, and must now briefly consider their present stage of evolution. They constitute an almost purely agrarian zone, where towns are few and small, with the exception of the political capitals, and account for less than a quarter of the total populations. Corporate life is undeveloped, town and country divided, and public services and amenities backward as compared with regions to the north-west.

Most of the peasantries won their right to the land with the break-up of estates and the destruction of landlordism after the First World War, but they were not ready for the experiments in self-government inspired by the idealism of 1919. Over wide areas the wasteful scattering of plough strips in open fields has outlived the three-field system; and in the same way the mental outlook of their owners, conditioned by centuries of custom, has not caught up with changed circumstances.

The peasant lands have been at the mercy not only of their own urban adventurers, but also of the leaders of other countries, especially Germany, who looked in this direction for economic and political expansion. Cereals (wheat and maize) and raw materials (timber, oil, magnesium, copper, etc.) were exported increasingly towards the north-west, until the foreign trade of south-eastern Europe, including Turkey, was almost entirely dominated by Germany. Today it is dominated by Russia.

### Preservation of Rural Life

The education and modernization of the peasantries is one of the major tasks of European statesmanship, and the economic integration of the Danubian lands is one of the most obvious conclusions to be drawn from geographical study. Yet the reformer must beware of applying a standardized scheme to the various parts of this belt: he must allow for the different traditions of mountain and plain dwellers, of shepherds and grain-growers, and so on. And while introducing a larger proportion of industry and increasing agricultural production, he will do well to preserve something of the craft life and devotional spirit which Britain, for instance, sacrificed when she lost her peasantry in her Industrial Revolution.

We have tried, in this rapid survey of the regions of Western Europe, to bring out some of the ways in which the social experiences of various human groups are related to their environments. If we knew more about the intricate relations between man and nature we should be in a better position to point the way to future harmony, but it is clear that a measure of unity in Europe can be achieved only by recognizing the diversity of its parts.

### Danger of Militarism

Europe's greatest need is to get rid of the dangers of aggression and the reactions which it promotes. One of the means of securing this would be to promote the economic integration of its regions, and at the same time to encourage a wider and more even distribution of industrial activity, whereby the peasant nations would be set free from their dependence on, and fear of, the Great Powers. Both raw materials and power, especially electricity, can now be transported with ease. Britain herself, who led the way in the Industrial Revolution, has in recent years diffused her industrial activities outside the coalfields; and the process has been stimulated by the necessities of war. Only when tendencies towards political and economic aggression are held in check and populations more evenly distributed can a measure of real unity be achieved. In east Central Europe the problem of the tangle of boundaries

that might be drawn may seem insoluble unless populations are to be shifted wholesale, as has happened to the German-speakers of Poland, Czechoslovakia and the east Baltic.

But the west is pointing the way to another solution, namely the dissociation of economic and administrative frontiers. The ores of Lorraine and the coal of the Ruhr, for example, instead of being a danger to peace by their separation, have been brought together by international agreement. The European Coal and Steel Community (1952) was supplemented in 1958 by the European Economic Community, and a gradual freeing of trade is now taking place.

### Hopeful Experiments

Certain experiments hitherto confined to a single nation are capable of being adapted to meet the needs of others. Thus the adult education movement has been spreading from Denmark and promises to free young people from insidious propaganda by teaching them to criticize, instead of merely to absorb ideas without question.

But Western Europe has not only to set its own many-roomed mansion in order. It has responsibilities towards those nations and colonies which it has planted overseas in the course of its expansion—above all towards the native peoples of those lands.

## Test Yourself

1. (a) What epithet would you choose to describe in one word the physical geography of Western Europe? Illustrate your answer with examples.

   (b) Which geographical features would you say have contributed most to the development of civilization there, and which have tended to retard political and economic unity?

2. "The history of Britain until the Industrial Revolution is the history of London." Assuming the truth of this statement, explain it as far as you can in terms of geographical factors.

3. Compare the growth of industry in Britain and Germany during the nineteenth century. What were the principal results in either case, and what advantages, if any, did Britain enjoy in minimizing the problems arising from those results?

*Answers will be found at the end of the book.*

Fig. 90. *The Kremlin, Moscow. A fortified enclosure in the centre of the city, it contains cathedrals, palaces and barracks. Similar citadels occur in several other Slavonic cities.*

## CHAPTER VI

# THE SOVIET LANDS AND INNER ASIA

ALTHOUGH considerably less in area than the Czarist Empire which collapsed in 1917, the Soviet Union, in 1939, was already a very much stronger state than its predecessor. After an unpromising start, when civil war, famine and invasion by hostile armies all threatened its destruction, it attained the rank of Great Power, in the short space of about fifteen years. The Second World War proved the strength of the new Russia, but of its land and varied communities the world in general still knows very little indeed. Moreover, the literature (in English) which deals with modern Russia is mostly of doubtful value to the student.

To the geographer, the most important characteristic of the Soviet Union is its enormous bulk. It is an Asiatic as well as a European Power, and its eastern territories attain greater significance with the passing of each year. In Europe alone, however, there is as much Russian territory as the combined areas of all the other European countries. On the other hand the population of European Russia is much more sparse than that of Western European lands, where industrialization is older and has gone farther.

### Vast Extent

Russia is the great continental platform from which peninsular Europe extends, ever narrowing between bordering seas, towards the Atlantic. First to be noted are its vast, compact extent, the simplicity of its structure, and its approximately uniform relief. Although the Russian platform is raised, the altitude is modest almost everywhere, much the greater part being less than 600 feet from sea level.

On account of the monotony of the land surface, climate varies very little over great distances. Winter severity of temperature is common to all districts, save the well-

sheltered southern coast of the Crimea. The cold of January at Kazan is actually as extreme as it is at Archangel, 500 miles farther to the north. Nevertheless, there are important regional differences of climate to be taken into account; and it is climate which determines the main types of vegetation which distinguish the regions of Russia.

South of the Arctic fringe of cold desert (*tundra*), extends a vast zone of coniferous forest (*taiga*), which is continued eastwards over the greater part of Siberia. In its more southerly parts deciduous trees, notably oak and elm, occur, especially on clay soils. On its southern side the great forest has no well-defined limit, but it thins out in the latitude of Moscow. The grey forest-soils are generally poor, agriculture is correspondingly meagre, and population density does not greatly exceed twenty persons per square mile.

### Black Earth Regions

Southwards from the latitude of Moscow, forest becomes more and more rare, and gradually gives place to the wide grasslands (*steppe*) of southern Russia, which are devoid of tree-growth and are now mainly cultivated. The steppe lands vary greatly in their fertility. In the neighbourhood of Kiev the soils belong to the rich *loess* which, from the Ukraine, extends westwards across the heart of Europe. Nearer to the Black Sea soils are even richer—the famous Black Earth (Fig. 91)—on which the agricultural wealth of the Ukrainian Republic is based.

On the other hand, east of the lower Don, and particularly around the northern shores of the Caspian Sea, the *steppe* is poor, and its saline soils receive very little rainfall. Until very recently this eastern district was the home of nomadic Turki-Tatar pastoralists, but irrigation and newly-established industries, e.g. those of Stalingrad, are changing the local mode of life.

Eastward penetration of Russian influence beyond the Ural Mountains did not occur until the close of the sixteenth century. In the first place it was not organized conquest, and was primarily concerned with trade—in furs, particularly.

The first region incorporated was the vast plain of western Siberia, mainly within the drainage area of the Ob-Irtish river system. Tomsk, in the upper Irtish basin, was founded in 1625, and, from that time onwards, eastward movement of Russian traders was rapid. The territories traversed, though diversified in relief, and of different climates and vegetation, were alike in their scantiness of population, so that there was little opposition to the advancing Russian traders.

The distances involved were enormous. From the Urals to Tomsk is about 1,000 miles, and Yakutsk (founded in 1632) is 1,600 miles farther east. There are 4,500 miles between Moscow and the Soviet Pacific coast at Vladivostok, or about twice the distance separating the western and eastern extremities of Europe.

The native inhabitants of Siberia and Russian Central Asia are clearly differentiated from the Russian Slavs. They belong to one or other of the branches of the great Mongoloid stock, and are descended from the communities which provided the armies of Ghengis Khan and Kubla Khan, in the thirteenth century. Despite wide differences of language, they are alike in their ethnic features. They show a marked breadth of head, together with straight hair; whilst the Mongol characteristics of yellow skin and slant eyes also occur (Fig. 224). The distribution of these widely-scattered communities has not greatly altered since the days of the earliest Russian pioneers in Asia, but in recent times there has been large-scale penetration by Russian Slavs into these Asiatic territories.

The main line of advance of Russian colonists lies immediately to the south of the Siberian *taiga* (Fig. 92) and along the zone of good grassland between the forest and the high, semi-arid plateaux of Central Asia. It is the route along which the Trans-Siberian Railway was laid at the close of the nineteenth century.

At first, the Russian Czars were but little interested in their Asiatic domains. In the middle of the nineteenth century, however, they looked Pacific-wards in an attempt to

FIG. 91. *Harvesting in the Black Earth region. The Ukraine, sparsely populated until last century, owes its fertile soil to decayed grass. It is a great wheat-producing area.*

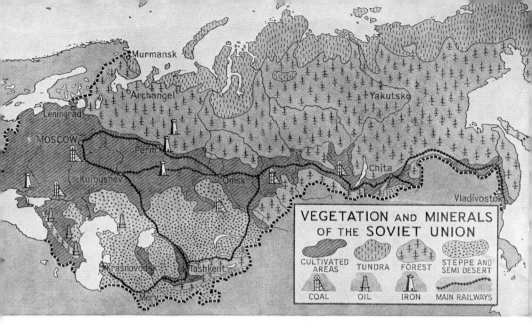

Fig. 92. *The "taiga" (page 123) of the sub-Arctic region merges towards the south into deciduous forest, large tracts of which have been cleared for cultivation. Note, too, how agriculture has spread along the Trans-Siberian and Turkistan-Siberian railways.*

enlarge their empire. The pressure of Russia on China then began, and Russian colonization of northern Manchuria became important.

The Slav family has its headquarters in eastern Europe, but extends westwards, beyond Russia, into Central Europe and the Balkan peninsula. It includes the Poles, Czechs, Slovaks, Slovenes, Croats and Serbs, but, of all, the Russians in their various groups have changed least in ethnic type.

The southern Russians—usually known as Little Russians or Ukrainians—proudly look back to the days when Kiev, "the mother city" of Russia, was, after Byzantium, the most prosperous market of south-eastern Europe. Their total number, if we include those called Ruthenes, is about forty millions.

There is not, and cannot be, a clearly-drawn distinction between Ukrainians and Great Russians, who form the main mass of the Slavonic population within the U.S.S.R. The explanation of the small cultural differences that do exist is that the two groups of Russians have evolved during the past thousand years in environments characterized by wide contrasts in vegetation. Many of the Great Russians are still accustomed to a forest life, or have developed agriculture in clearings of the *taiga*: on the other hand, the Little Russians have always been accustomed to life on the treeless *steppe* (Fig. 92).

Nevertheless, the Great and the Little Russians are now united, and have been for centuries, under one government and, more important, they recognize their common ancestry. Ethnologically the resemblance is strong. Except for stature, which is slightly taller in the case of the Little Russians, they are virtually indistinguishable. The absorption of Tatar strains by the Ukrainians is matched by the Great Russians' incorporation of small, scattered groups of Mongoloid strain, which they encountered in their colonization of the northern forest zone.

Until recently the least articulate of the Russian Slav groups have been the Byelo-Russians (White Russians). They occupy lands, still largely forested, to the north of the Pripet Marshes; and this barrier has, to some extent, segregated them from the Little Russians, who reach the southern confines of the Marshes. As, in the period between the First and Second World Wars, the White Russians were divided politically between the Republics of Poland, White

O C E A N

EAST SIBERIAN
SEA

BERING
SEA

LAPTEV
SEA

*Khatanga*

*Verkhoyansk*

*Indigirka*

*Kolima*

*Okhotsk*

SEA OF
OKHOTSK

Y A K U T S K
AUTONOMOUS REPUBLIC

*Yakutsk*

*Lena*

*Aldan*

STANOVOI MOUNTAINS

R I A

*Lena*

SAKHALIN

*er Tunguska*

R E P U B L I C S

*Stony Tunguska*

*Vitim*

*Amur*

*Upper Tunguska*

Krasnoyarsk

VITIM
PLATEAU

*Khabarovsk*

Lake
Baikal

*YAN MTS.*

Irkutsk

YABLONOI MTS.

KHINGAN MTS.

MANCHURIA

*Harbin*

SEA OF
JAPAN

*Sungari*

*Vladivostok*

JAPAN

PLATEAU OF
KOBDO

*Urga*

*Kerulen*

*Hsinking*

KOREA

MONGOL PEOPLES
REPUBLIC

INNER MONGOLIA

GOBI DESERT

*Hwang Ho*

GREAT WALL

R E P U B L I C

SAIDAM SWAMP

KANSU

TEAU

## SOVIET LANDS AND INNER ASIA
### SHOWING PHYSICAL FEATURES
AND PRINCIPAL CITIES

FOLD
MOUNTAINS

PLATEAUX

SCARPS

DESERTS

MARSHES

SEAS DEEPER THAN
100 FATHOMS

TUNDRA

Russia, Lithuania and Latvia, their aggregate population is difficult to determine, but it is probably between eight and ten millions. Their greatest concentration is around the city of Minsk, which, by tradition and geography, is their national centre.

By 1922 the vast assembly of Asiatic and European territories and peoples inherited by Soviet Russia from Czarist days was welded into a federation of republics (Fig. 93). It is noteworthy that neither history nor geography was favourable to the success of this experiment in federalism. There was the greatest possible diversity of race, tradition and custom, language and environment.

### Phenomenal Progress

The Soviet regime was established first over Great Russia and Siberia. The First Constitution of the Russian Soviet Federal Socialist Republic was adopted in 1918, and served as a model for the other Soviet Republics, which, within a few years, joined the R.S.F.S.R. to form the Union.

Despite the subtraction, from time to time, of communities promoted to the status of Soviet Republics, the R.S.F.S.R., which includes 17 autonomous republics, still occupies about 75 per cent of the total area of the U.S.S.R. Its population, approximately 110 millions, is Great Russian to the extent of four-fifths: the remaining one-fifth is composed of certain widely dispersed Asiatic peoples, who are backward politically. It should be noted, however, that the progress of the politically primitive peoples of Soviet Asia has been quite phenomenal during the last two decades. Within the federal system, the Kazak Soviet Socialist Republic and the Kirghiz S.S.R. have not only been granted cultural autonomy: they have graduated, within the last few years, to full political equality with the more mature communities of the Soviet Union.

In the angle bounded by the Caspian and the northern edge of the Iran Plateau there are three republics, all senior in age to Kazakstan and Kirghizia. The Turkmen S.S.R. is passing quickly from a nomadic stage of civilization, though the sparseness of its population continues to indicate the aridity of its grasslands. As in the case of its neighbour, the Uzbek S.S.R., however, the irrigation engineer has made possible the production of cotton on a scale sufficient to satisfy the needs of the entire U.S.S.R. Uzbekistan is the most densely populated of all Soviet lands to the east of the Caspian Sea, and may be termed the centre of gravity of Russian Central Asia. Its capital, Tashkent, is becoming industrialized at a particularly fast rate, even for a town of the U.S.S.R. The future of Tashkent, as one of the great cities of the world, seems assured.

The chain of republics distributed along the southern edge of Soviet Asia is continued across the Caspian into the Caucasus region. Georgia, Armenia and Azerbaijan trace the recognition of their nationhood, in each case, to the early days of Soviet Russia. Whereas the League of Nations concentrated attention on the difficulties, real or supposed, in the way of the demarcation of their frontiers, Soviet Russia was able to reach a satisfactory settlement without delay. It granted autonomy, without sovereign independence, and eliminated the vexed minority questions, which were troubling the Georgians, Armenians and Azerbaijan Tatars, by gaining the loyalty of each to a supernational state, itself a league of nations of unique design.

### Miniature Republics

Each of the Trans-Caucasian Soviet Republics is on a rather miniature scale—Azerbaijan, the largest, is less than 33,000 square miles—but their densities of population are very much higher than those of any other Asiatic region of the U.S.S.R. In the organization of the vast output of oil around Baku, on the Caspian coast, this Azerbaijan city has become the greatest in Asiatic Russia. The remarkable rise in Russian petroleum production during the last quarter of a century has been due more to the intensive utilization of the resources around Baku than to the opening up of new reserves in other parts of the Soviet Union, important as the latter are, or will, no doubt, become in the future.

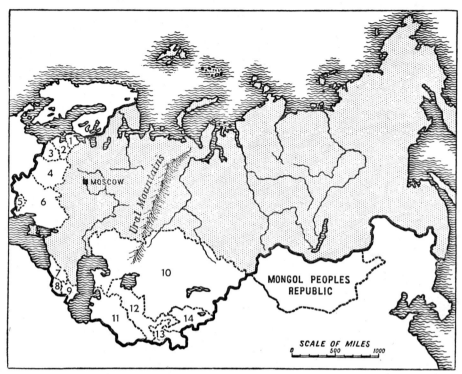

FIG. 93. *The Union of Soviet Socialist Republics. The dotted area represents the Russian Soviet Federal Republic, which includes 18 autonomous republics. Other republics of the U.S.S.R. are: 1, Estonia; 2, Latvia; 3, Lithuania; 4, Byelorussia (White Russia); 5, Moldavia; 6, Ukraine; 7, Georgia; 8, Armenia; 9, Azerbaijan; 10, Kazakstan; 11, Turkmenia; 12, Uzbekistan; 13, Tadzhikistan; 14, Kirghizia.*

To the west of the Urals, the vast area of the R.S.F.S.R. is divided into regions and autonomous republics, as it is in the east. The mass of the population is Great Russian, but here and there are non-Slavonic communities, whose autonomy is recognized. Where full national status is withheld, it is because communities are too small to make self-government efficient, or national consciousness is not yet fully developed.

Decentralization of administration is the established policy of the Government of the Soviet Union, but is not allowed to impair the solidarity of the federation. Such solidarity depends on unity in matters of defence, foreign affairs and the comprehensive planning of economic life. No considerations of local interest are permitted to obstruct the grand design. Nevertheless, in general the political conception on which the U.S.S.R. is founded seems acceptable to the individual nations which make up the Union.

Within the western half of European Russia there are two of the original Soviet Republics—of the White Russians and Little Russians (Ukrainians), respectively. Each community extends widely over territory formerly claimed and held by Poland, and during the Second World War the Soviet Government insisted that the restitution of White and Little Russian lands was one of the conditions necessary to peace in Eastern Europe.

Prior to the Revolution, no Russian community ranked higher in civilization than the Ukrainian. Ancient and proud traditions, especially associated with the "mother city" of Kiev, have long been expressed in a passionate love of country. Indeed, the intensity of Little Russian national feeling led the Western Powers, immediately after the First World War, to anticipate that the Ukraine would demand separation from Soviet Russia. All attempts, however, to detach it from the Union failed: the Little Russians remained loyal to Russia as a whole.

## Balanced Economy

With about forty million inhabitants the Ukraine is easily the most densely populated of all the Soviet Republics. As a consequence of its geography, there is an even balance between agricultural activities, on the one hand, and mining and manufacturing, on the other. Moreover, in respect of both farming and industrial output, the Ukraine retains a leading position in the Union, and its political influence is thereby strengthened. The trend of development within Soviet Asia will inevitably shift the industrial centre of gravity eastwards from the eastern half of the Ukraine—the Donetz coal-basin, in particular—to the Urals and western Siberia. This may well occur within the next half-century, but, in the period immediately ahead, the economic importance of the Ukraine in the life of Soviet Russia as a whole is likely to be still unrivalled.

We have yet to mention the place, within the political geography of Eastern Europe, of the non-Slavonic communities of Estonia, Latvia and Lithuania. These countries, which first knew political independence at the close of the First World War, were re-occupied by Russia early in the Second World War. Before the eastward advance of the German armies forced the Russians to retreat on Leningrad, elections were held which purported to make clear the wish of Esths, Letts, and Lithuanians to rejoin Russia, a result which many disbelieved. However, in 1940 each community was raised to the full status of a Soviet Republic.

We see, therefore, that within the European, as within the Asiatic, area of the Soviet Union there is a considerable variety of nations, some of which are not even Slavonic, much less Russian. If we assume, as we may, that all are willing members of the Soviet Federation, the sympathy which binds them together has obviously nothing to do with race or tradition. The cementing influence must be sought in the willingness of all—Slavonic and non-Slavonic alike—to accept a way of life which offers political and economic opportunity to all communities, and, at the same time, ensures that land is the inheritance of the people.

In the Soviet Union the more backward communities are not relegated to an inferior position because of their comparatively primitive standards, or their skin-colour, or some other consideration equally irrelevant from the Soviet standpoint. Backwardness is considered to be a consequence of unfortunate historical accident, soon to be removed through the process of education. The virtual disappearance of illiteracy within the space of two decades is probably Russia's greatest achievement. Moreover, the equality of all persons, irrespective of skin-colour, is not a mere clause in the Constitution. It is observed everywhere in the Union: indeed, social discrimination against a person because of his race would be just as absurd to Russian minds as to deprive him of adequate food for the same reason.

## Right of Secession

Doubt is sometimes expressed regarding the right of the constituent Republics of the Union to demand their independence, to the point of secession, if they should so desire. The Declaration of the Rights of the Peoples of 1917 did, in fact, admit the right of self-determination, even if it should result in the setting up of independent states. It is doubtful, however, if any of the Republics would be permitted to secede from the Union. The men who founded the new Russia were realists, and recognized, as did President Lincoln of the United States of America, that the strength of the Federation would depend on solidarity. No instance has yet been recorded, however, of a constituent republic wishing to leave the Union or to abandon the tenets of Soviet doctrine. The terrible ordeal of the most cruel of wars has demonstrated—if demonstration were needed—that the loyalty of both Slav and non-Slav is not one of compulsion.

Where centralization is required for certain functions of government, Moscow, at present, is much the most convenient of all possible capital cities. Until the collapse of the Czarist regime, St. Petersburg—the modern Leningrad—was the imperial metropolis. Its outlying position in relation to the Russian Empire as a whole had been, however, always a disadvantage to efficient administration, and the Soviet Government's decision to establish its headquarters at Moscow was unhesitating, in the light of the planned reconstruction of the country. Clearly, Moscow is the natural centre of European Russia, but when the development of Asiatic Russia is well advanced, the city will be no longer central; and it is possible, if not probable, that the functions of the federal capital will then be transferred to some Asiatic centre of population.

The lands taken from western Russia as a result of the First World War stretched nearly all the way from the Arctic to the Black Sea, and included the timber and flax-growing lands of the Baltic Provinces, the Warsaw-Lodz industrial zone, the rich granary of Bessarabia and all the Russian Baltic ports, save Leningrad. Industrial development in days before the Revolution had been concentrated in the western provinces. This was not because the economic resources of the western fringe were more abundant than those of other regions. The wealth of the Asiatic lands was still largely unknown, although by the end of the nineteenth century it was thought likely to prove immense when opportunities for development became possible. Even

FIG. 94. *Oil towers at Baku, chief city of Azerbaijan S.S.R., on the Caspian Sea. Oil is transported to the Black Sea ports of Batum and Poti by rail and pipe-lines. Large quantities are also shipped to Astrakhan, at the northern end of the Caspian Sea.*

so, the completely primitive condition of all lands to the east of the Urals seemed likely to remain until a very distant future. Thus, until the second decade of the twentieth century, the economic strength of the Russian Empire was measured solely by the resources of the small fraction which was European.

There was, for example, a general dearth of coal and of other mineral wealth, and the only considerable supplies of iron-ore lay at Krivoi Rog, to the west of the lower Dnieper. The Donetz valley of the Don basin, rich in coal, was inadequately developed, largely because it lay on the outer edge of foreign enterprise in Russia. On the basis of its scanty resources, western European Russia could never have attained first-class industrial importance. Nevertheless, technical standards and the general level of life were higher in the westernmost provinces than elsewhere in the empire at the time of the First World War. Moreover, the density of population distribution within the Baltic fringe, Russian Poland, and Bessarabia was considerably higher than the average for European Russia as a whole.

### Antagonism Foreseen

The loss by Russia of all her outer European provinces was, therefore, of very serious consequence to her. Taken into account along with the dislocation and losses caused by foreign and civil war, by the presence of several hostile armies on her best soil, and by the widespread ravages of famine and pestilence, this loss made the possibility of Russia's survival as a Great Power seem at that time small indeed.

From the outset the Soviet leaders were fully aware that the principles—social, economic and political—on which the Soviet State was founded would antagonize, for a very long time, the majority, if not all, of the other powers of the world. It was therefore necessary—so ran the argument —for Russia to depend on her own military and economic strength, without hope of allies.

A plan to attain economic self-sufficiency followed, and the impulse was strong to investigate and develop the untapped resources of the vast Asiatic territories. It is these lands, well-nigh boundless and of infinite possibilities, which suggest to the geographer that the Soviet Union could, if its political isolation made it necessary, endure and prosper without commercial contacts with the rest of the world.

### Labour and Transport

Much of the wealth of Siberia and Central Asia is situated in very sparsely inhabited areas. In consequence, new systems of transport had to be devised and built, whilst human labour was introduced from the nearest well-settled areas. Within the Soviet Union inter-regional migration has always been an important factor in the planned economy. It has been mainly from European Russia to western and central Siberia, where new towns have grown up on populations of very diverse geographical and racial origins.

The State Planning Commission began its immense task with little regard for the interests of particular nationalities— Russian or non-Slav—within the Union. At that time Russian statesmen were very critical of the political and economic order in Europe produced by the peace settlement which followed the First World War. They were resolved that planned development should not be frustrated, as it was in Central Europe, by the jealousy and antagonism of rival national sovereignties.

### Planning on Economic Geography

They went so far as to underestimate the strength of national sentiment in several of the more mature communities, including the Ukrainian. Concerned, as it was mainly, with problems of land-utilization, the State Planning Commission preferred to employ economic regions rather than national communities as units of administration. Each of these regions (*oblasti*) was to be defined in terms of economic geography, and was to preserve its distinctive character in respect of its individual contribution to the economic wealth of the Soviet Union. In other words, geography was to be allowed to determine the kind of economic specialization which each region of the Union should undertake.

Thus, the Ukraine was divided into the south-western region (capital, Kiev), whose emphasis was to be on wheat farming, and the south mining region (capital, Kharkov), which was to specialize in mining and metallurgical industries. Two separate administrations would have been adopted for the Ukraine, if the Little Russians had not expressed in the most emphatic way their hostility to the division of their nation. The strength of national sentiment was sufficient to cause the abandonment of the scheme, in so far as it affected the Ukraine.

Disregard for White Russian national sentiment met with a similar response. It was proposed to establish a western region, including those parts of White Russia which had not been annexed by Poland, together with a neighbouring area occupied by Great Russians. The entire region was to be controlled from the administrative centre of Smolensk. White Russian opposition arose, largely because Smolensk, as regional capital, would have had precedence over Minsk, which is the national capital of the White Russians. Because of the popular attitude, the frontiers of the White Russian Republic were left unchanged, and the community retained its distinctive place in political geography.

### Healthy Diversity

The error of disregarding local sentiment was not repeated, and the Soviet Government actually changed its policy to one of encouraging the fullest expression of pride in local tradition. The diversity of national genius and culture came to be regarded as contributing much to the health and vitality of the state.

Amongst the Great Russians, national sentiment was generally favourable to the projected division of their territory according to principles of economic geography.

The greater part is so divided, and each region, such as that of the Moscow district, fulfils an economic plan which is based on the existing geographical possibilities. Regional frontiers have been altered, from time to time, for reasons of administrative convenience.

Once the preliminary survey of the available resources and the administrative framework of the plan were complete, both agricultural and industrial production were undertaken in an atmosphere of pressing emergency. Russia moved in a hostile world, and the possibility of a combination of powers in war against her existed for at least a decade and a half.

The westerly districts, already comparatively advanced in economic development, were intended to carry for a period—as brief as possible—the main burden of output. At the same time, the undeveloped regions of Central and Northern Asia were to be brought into immediate production, no matter how great the difficulties of transportation and labour supply might prove. Wherever resources of fuel, metallic ores, etc. existed, production was to be organized on a scale dependent, not on the demands of a world market or the activity of some prospecting company or other, but solely on the extent of the local possibilities.

### Self-sufficing Regions

Moreover, the Asiatic industries were not to be merely extractive—coal-mining and the like. The economic life of the newly-opened regions was to be as self-sufficing and autonomous as possible. True, it was to concentrate primarily on the types of production for which, severally, they were most fitted and best endowed, but attention was to be given also to a wide range of commodities—including foodstuffs—for local consumption. Thereby it was possible to relieve the inadequate railway system, inherited by the Soviets from Czarist days, from what would have proved a crushing burden of traffic.

The probability of war with Germany, and with Japan also, entered into the calculations of those who planned the immediate future of Soviet Asia. In the event of these two avowedly hostile powers combining against Russia, the only regions relatively secure from land and air attack would be those lying to the east of the Urals and the the west of Lake Baikal. On them might fall the responsibility and burden of the ultimate defence of the Soviet Union, and, therefore, a complete range of primary and secondary industries was essential. In the event of war, Russia had

FIG. 95. *Among the peoples of Soviet Asia are the Tungus reindeer-herders of the region around Lake Baikal. This photograph shows a typical Tungus encampment in the forest*

to be prepared to abandon the western provinces, or the majority of them, and was fully prepared to fall back from White Russia and the western Ukraine. There was, however, one important exception.

On the northern side of western Russia, Leningrad stood some fifty miles only from the Estonian frontier. Yet, on account of its outstanding capacity for metallurgical and other industrial output, evacuation of the great city was not contemplated. It had to be secured against German assault, not only because of its potential war production, but also because of its intimate association with Kronstadt, the near-by Baltic naval base. The latter could not hold out if Leningrad were reduced, and the loss of the naval base would mean the annihilation of the Russian Baltic fleet.

On the other hand, the Soviet Government was prepared to abandon a number of highly valuable western districts to the enemy rather than suffer the destruction of its armies in an over-exposed position. The temporary loss of the richest wheat lands of all Russia, in addition to industrial

centres like Kiev and Odessa, had to be contemplated. And only the most active exploitation of the Asiatic territories could compensate for such grievous losses in the west. The vast programme of development was concealed from the outer world, and its full scope has yet to become known.

Moreover, the Soviet leaders took the logical step—in view of the anticipated military emergency—of slowing down normal industrial development in all districts close to the western frontier, save only Leningrad. We can form a fairly clear impression of the extent to which industrial development progressed or was retarded purposely—for reasons already mentioned —in the vulnerable western districts by investigating the growth of population in towns, both those old-established and those founded subsequently to the Revolution. An immense increase of population occurred in more than seventy per cent of the towns of the U.S.S.R., and in the Asiatic parts of the Union the rise in urban population was particularly impressive.

On the other hand, the towns of slow

*lands south-west of the lake. Although some Tunguses have settled on the land, the majority lead nomadic lives hunting in the forests. They use reindeer as mounts and as beasts of burden.*

growth were all within a comparatively short distance of the western frontier. Yet these same towns, in view of their history and foreign associations, might have been expected to increase rather more rapidly than the average for urban Russia. Odessa is the only considerable Soviet town whose population has diminished during the last thirty years. Undoubtedly, recognition of the military consequences of its proximity to the Rumanian frontier, only forty miles distant, was one factor in the retardation of its industrial expansion. Similarly, the situation of Kiev was regarded by the Soviet Government as dangerously vulnerable, in view of an almost certain German invasion.

Leningrad, prior to 1939, experienced a proportionate increase considerably higher than that of most western cities, and here again the trend was planned in view of military and economic considerations. Because of its leading position amongst industrial centres at the time of the Revolution, it served both as a technical school for the industrial army of the new Russia and as a factory for a large part of the machinery and machine tools so urgently required for the rehabilitation of the country. It may well be that Leningrad will diminish in importance and size of population, both absolutely and relatively to other cities of Russia. As the small Baltic Republics to the south of the Gulf of Finland have been incorporated within the Soviet Union, a series of valuable ports, including Tallinn, Baltiski, Ventspils and—particularly— Riga and Klaipeda, now provide, with Kaliningrad, annexed in 1945, Russia's maritime frontage on the Baltic. Certain of these ports possess natural advantages at least equal to those of Leningrad, and the two last-named have a shorter duration of the freeze in winter.

The remarkable growth of the Russian Asiatic towns was not accompanied by rural increase of comparable proportions. Most of the emigrants from European Russia to Soviet Asia have gone to the towns, leaving the densities of the countryside very little more than they were a quarter of a century ago. There is real need, as Russia is fully aware, for large-scale movement of agricultural workers into the farming belts of eastern Siberia and Central Asia. It seems, however, that having suffered devastation and loss of life in war on a scale which no other nation has experienced, Russia's own population is numerically inadequate for the completion of her economic plan in some of the highly fertile parts of Soviet Asia. Unless the empty spaces can be filled, their very vastness may one day prove an embarrassment.

### Planned Migration

Density of population within European Russia reaches an average of only fifty persons per square mile, whilst for Asiatic Russia it drops to ten per square mile. It is anticipated that the density of settlement of the Urals and other industrially attractive districts of western Siberia will approximate to that of the Ukraine—175 per square mile—in little more than a century, if planned migration continues at its present rate. On the other hand, there is no hope that the vast areas towards the east of the U.S.S.R. will reach a considerable density—say fifty persons per square mile—within measurable time, unless workers migrate from regions outside the frontiers of the Soviet Union.

In Asia, Russia's formerly unfriendly neighbour, Japan, has been temporarily eliminated as a great power. Yet, although Japan has met disaster, its population seems likely to continue to increase and to provide the world with the most serious problem of congestion which has yet emerged. Sooner or later, the dispersal of large numbers of Japanese over the neighbouring Asiatic mainland, to the north of Korea, would seem to be inevitable. Eastern China and Korea are ruled out of such calculations by reason of their own high densities, but in the Yakutsk Autonomous Republic—itself nearly as large as European Russia—and the extreme east of Siberia, the densities of population descend to insignificant figures.

FIG. 96. *Digging the Great Ferghana Canal, Uzbekistan, U.S.S.R. This waterway, more than one hundred miles long, was cut through arid desert in six weeks by nearly 160,000 collective farmers. The feat was accomplished in shade temperatures rising to 115 degrees F. Normally such an undertaking would take six or seven years to complete.*

Fig. 97. *The Great Ferghana Canal, completed. This stupendous achievement was part of the Soviet Government's third Five-Year Plan, its object being to utilize the waters of the Syr-Darya River. Where once was desert is now a fertile region of one and a quarter million acres producing cotton and other crops, such as rice, fruit, vegetables and beet.*

The prospect, at a time not far distant, of many millions of Japanese becoming Soviet citizens may not be extravagant. If, within a few years, Soviet Russia has been able to achieve a political and economic system suited not only to White, Little and Great Russians, but also to Tatars, Uzbeks, Tadzhiks, Georgians, Turkmens and all the other Asiatic communities within her frontiers, it is quite capable of admitting and absorbing any land-hungry Japanese who choose to settle on the Asiatic mainland.

To the geographer there seems to be no other source of large-scale immigration on which it is possible for Soviet Russia to draw, in her endeavour to make her Far Eastern regions much more productive than they are at present. The new China will need all her millions, for, as a whole, that country is not over-populated, and Russia cannot count on Chinese labour.

The impact of Russian ideas, not to speak of more material contacts, on the civilization of China is of the greatest importance to the future of Asia. So far, it has remained obscure to the western world, though certain tendencies are becoming known. The outer lands of the former Chinese Empire, all of which are now claimed as the rightful inheritance of the Chinese Republic, penetrate widely and deeply into Asia. They include the vast region of the Tarim Basin and its bordering highlands—known to the Chinese as Sinkiang (the New Dominion)—the eastern half of the Tibetan plateau, in addition to Inner Mongolia. In the days of their greatest prestige, Chinese emperors claimed the suzerainty of much of Outer Mongolia —beyond the Gobi Desert (Fig. 158)—and its colonization by Chinese peasants followed. All these lands make up the "dry heart" of Asia. Rainfall is meagre and precarious almost everywhere, so that life tends to be nomadic, in striking contrast to the very intensive tillage of the well-watered flood plains of China proper.

The Russo-Chinese frontier in Inner Asia is the longest between any two states in the world, and stretches considerably more than 3,000 miles, if we include Manchuria, as we should, in the Chinese world. The

FIG. 98. *A village set on a hill in the wild, mountainous republic of Daghestan, within the R.S.F.S.R. Four-fifths of this region consists of inaccessible mountains, and the small area suitable for cultivation needs careful irrigation because of the danger of drought.*

inter-penetration of Russian and Chinese cultural ideas, as well as their exchange of products, is therefore an inevitable consequence of the facts of geography. Although the two civilizations seem to turn their backs on one another, and the difficulties of transport across the "dry heart" of Asia are immense, the Russians and Chinese recognize more and more the importance to each other, and to the world, of their friendly relationships and mutual understanding.

From the closing years of the seventeenth century onwards, the frontier guards of Russia and China were in touch. In general, the relations of the governments of the two countries were amicable; indeed, for a brief period only, beginning towards the end of the nineteenth century, were they seriously estranged. Then Imperial Russia pushed her armies southwards across Manchuria, regardless of Chinese sovereignty. Later, however, antagonism was replaced by a common fear of an aggressive Japan.

Certainly as late as the First World War, Russian imperialism was no more threatening to the integrity of China than that of the maritime powers, which, from 1840 onwards, claimed special interests in either the territory or trade of the Celestial Empire. And from the beginning of the Japanese invasion, south of the Great Wall, until 1939, Russian military assistance was more continuous and effective than that of any other power. General supplies and munitions of war moved from Russia, either by way of Sinkiang and the "corridor" of the Province of Kansu, or through the Jungarian Gate which leads between the Thian Shan Mountains and the Altai Mountains.

Of greater influence on the course of events in the Far East than the provision of material aid to China by Russia was the spread of Soviet concepts of economic and political organization, to north-western China in particular. In Kansu and neighbouring provinces, the Chinese Communist army was autonomous whilst the civil administration was equally independent of the Chungking Government. The effect of this was seen when the Communist armies came down from the north and the Government forces opposing them disintegrated, leaving the Communists in supreme power throughout all China. Outside China, but within the zone of former Chinese cultural influence, the Mongols of Outer Mongolia look to Russia for protection. Soviet ideas prevail throughout the vast plateau to the north of the Gobi Desert, and the Mongol tribesmen have established a Soviet Republic of their own (Fig. 93), affiliated to, though not a part of, the Soviet Union. Whether Russian or Chinese influence will ultimately prevail in Sinkiang depends on the strength of the Chinese Government and its ability to exert its authority far afield. Russia has shown no wish to violate Chinese sovereignty by annexing the "New Dominion," although from the Russian point of view its possession during the Second World War would have been of the utmost strategic importance, in view of the possible penetration into Central Asia of Japanese armies.

The Soviet's foreign policy in Central and Eastern Asia for long seemed to be more passive than active, in awaiting the outcome of Japan's attempt to annex all China and to expel both Britain and America from the Orient. In Europe, on the other hand, Russian policy, before 1939, was known much more definitely, because of precise statements issued from Moscow. It should be remembered, however, that Russia recognizes no hard and fast distinction between European and Asiatic problems. Such contrasts as there were at one time, between the land areas to the east and west, respectively, of the Ural Mountains, are in process of elimination, as we have already discussed. Similarly, Russia finds it impossible—and here geographers will agree with her—to segregate the international problems of Europe regionally; that is to say, to regard the questions of Western, Central and Eastern Europe as separate and different in kind from one another.

In revising her western frontier as a result of the Second World War, Soviet Russia clearly indicated her intentions, and her allies, moreover, agreed in principle to her demands. She incorporated all White and Little Russians lost to her in the period between the World Wars, and re-annexed the territories and peoples of Estonia, Latvia and Lithuania, all formerly included in the Czarist Empire. The economic advantages to be derived from the annexation of the small East Baltic Republics are great, and one of them has been discussed already. How far the Esths, Letts and Lithuanians were in agreement with Russia's intention, only they and Russia know.

There can be no doubt, however, that the Soviet ideal appeals to the imagination of a large proportion of these peoples; but whether it is a majority or not, no Western European is in a position to decide. Even by those who supported the independence of the small East Baltic States there is, however, a realization of their political and economic difficulties in maintaining their individual sovereignties. Neutrality in war saved them no more than it exempted other small powers of Europe from German domination.

As the greatest of all Slav States, Russia is naturally sympathetic to the Slav peoples who resisted German conquest. For long the Poles, largest of the non-Russian Slav communities, were antagonistic to Russia, but there is now a government in Warsaw which regards Russia as the only possible protector against renewed German militarism. Moreover, the Polish peasantry recognizes its affinities with all Slav peoples, and not least with the Russians. Geography and cultural associations together cause Russia to participate actively in the affairs of Slavonic Europe, and the ultimate federation of all Slavs under her protection is a distinct possibility.

## Test Yourself

1. (a) Explain in terms of geographical factors why the eastward expansion of Russia has occurred along the route followed by the Trans-Siberian Railway.
   (b) What may be said to be the limiting factors in the industrial development of Asiatic Russia?
2. What gives the Ukraine its political and economic importance in the life of Soviet Russia?
3. Air transport is said to be bringing about a "revolution in accessibility." Explain this statement with reference to the geography of the U.S.S.R.

*Answers will be found at the end of the book.*

FIG. 99.   *Gibraltar, with a distant view of Apes' Hill on the African coast, across the water. The Strait is eight-and-a-half miles wide at its narrowest crossing.   During the Second World War, tunnelling operations on the Rock disclosed a cave, containing a large fresh-water lake.   It is believed that the cave became naturally sealed 20,000 years ago.*

## CHAPTER VII

# THE MEDITERRANEAN LANDS

AMONG all seas, the Mediterranean is unique in its relation to human history. These waters and their shores are said, with justice, to have cradled the civilization of Western Europe: certainly they have cradled more than one civilization of their own. Peoples who lived in less hospitable lands outside the Mediterranean sphere have moved into it from very early times, attracted by its gifts. Peoples who lived in Mediterranean lands moved long ago over this sea to lands beyond it, discovering, trading, and colonizing; and from these lands have flowed some of the strongest streams of migration in the modern world.

The Strait of Gibraltar, eight and a half miles wide at its narrowest crossing, gives access to the Mediterranean Sea from the Atlantic Ocean. From this strait between south-western Europe and north-western Africa the sea extends 2,400 miles eastward to the Asiatic shores of the Levant. If the parallel of 36 degrees N. be followed on a map, it will be seen that most of the western half of the sea lies north of this line, most of the eastern half south of it. This implies a wide range of climatic conditions from north-west to south-east—conditions which we have seen in an earlier chapter to be characteristic of the "mediterranean" type of climate. These conditions, no less than the surface relief of the Mediterranean lands, have borne constantly upon human history and activities.

## Scarcity of Plains

Except in the south-east, all these lands are high-lying: lowland plains of any great extent are few. Small, more or less isolated, habitable lowlands, however, are many. Passes or natural gateways through the protecting high lands to lands beyond are not numerous: from their fewness they acquire importance as lines of communication. As for the south-eastern border of the sea, there could scarcely be a more complete contrast than it presents in comparison with the rest, for here the north African desert reaches to the coast, as it does in the west to the coast of the Atlantic.

In a fairly recent geological epoch an extensive folding of the earth's crust raised most of the major mountain chains from the Pyrenees through the Alps and Carpathians to the Caucasus, and the corresponding downfolds gave us some at least of the basins into which the Mediterranean is now divided. The Western Mediterranean, and the Adriatic, Aegean and Black Seas are the four largest of these.

## General Structure

The whole Mediterranean area excepting the south-east is one of intense folding. The Aegean is not the only part where the present adjustment between folds and the sea level results in the existence of islands. There is a lovely chain of islands along the eastern Adriatic coast, a half-submerged outer range of the Dinaric mountain folds. There is the broken land-bridge between Italy and North Africa, through the island of Sicily.

The intense folding of the area during the Tertiary period, and at other stages of its geological history as well, can be traced through the chains of islands, and it can be seen how the chains connect with the continental lands, for instance in the Aegean. As for the downfolds between the upfolds, we may note those apparent in the deep gulfs of southern and eastern Greece which have so close a relationship with the human geography of Greece.

Broadly speaking, it is possible to make a fourfold division of the whole area:—

1. The Western Mediterranean basin extends from Gibraltar to Sicily and Malta, and is bounded by the mountains of southern and eastern Spain, those of the south of France, the Apennine system of Italy, and the ranges of north-west Africa, which belong structurally to the European rather than the African land-mass.

THE MEDITERRANEAN LANDS

SHOWING PHYSICAL FEATURES

AND PRINCIPAL CITIES

FOLD MOUNTAINS    PLATEAUX    SCARPS    MORAINES

DESERTS    SEAS DEEPER THAN 100 FATHOMS    OASES

2. The Adriatic, which may be regarded as a submerged valley between the Apennines and the Dinaric mountain system to the east of it.

3. A division embracing the Aegean and Black Sea, defined southward by the broken fragments of the ridges connecting the Dinaric and Taurus mountain systems, including the islands of Crete and Cyprus.

4. The south-eastern division, of which the southern coast lands belong to the so-called Indo-African, not to the European (or Euro-Asian) land-mass.

Mediterranean scenery, especially that of lands bordering the sea on the north—the south of France, Italy, the Dinaric seaboard, Greece and the Aegean Islands, Asia Minor—is admired and beloved by all who know it under good conditions. The qualification is needed, for the beauty of Mediterranean scenery lies in contrast and brilliance of colours: blue sea and sky, a clear air, the vivid outline of hills. The atmosphere counts enormously: the scenery of Mediterranean lands does not fit itself to cloudy skies and dull seas. It is to be appreciated also rather through its

broad effects than through its details. In many typical Mediterranean pictures the prominent feature is often a single well-shaped cypress or, it may be, a single column of an ancient building; but always in such views a contrast is pointed by some distant background of sea and sky or cliff or mountain.

A quick survey of the relief of the lands surrounding the Mediterranean Sea must be attempted. The Iberian peninsula, politically divided between Spain and Portugal, consists as to two-thirds of its surface of the Meseta tableland, 2,500 feet or more in average height above sea level, and crossed, generally from east to west, by hills up to 8,000 feet—in the main a rather unwelcoming land, and in parts so much so as to be little inhabited. The Ebro valley separates the Meseta from the mountain chain of the Pyrenees, which parts Spain from France and reaches heights of 11,000 feet. The Cantabrian mountains, continuing the Pyrenees westward, separate the Meseta from the steep seaboard of the Bay of Biscay.

The north-west coast also is high, but indented with inlets of the type called *rias*.

FIG. 100. *Korčula (Curzola), a peninsular town-site and capital of the island of the same name on the eastern Adriatic coast. The dry "karst" limestone hills of Dalmatia form the background. The island, a strong position in medieval days, has often changed hands. In 1918 it became Yugoslav, and during the Second World War was occupied by Italians.*

The Portuguese (Atlantic) coast becomes lower to the south, fringed often with sand dunes, and backed by lowlands sloping gently to hill-country inland. The borderland of Spain with Portugal is rugged and sparsely peopled, with difficult communications through the valleys of rivers deeply engorged (Fig. 103). The Sierra Nevada, rising above 11,000 feet at its highest, stands parallel with the southern edge (Sierra Morena) of the Meseta, and is separated from it by the trough of the Guadalquivir, which forms the Andalusian lowland. From the stately Rock of Gibraltar guarding the entrance strait from the Atlantic, and bound to the mainland only by a low isthmus, the south-east and east coastlands of Spain show heights alternating with low strips, but with few easy accesses to the interior.

The French Mediterranean land between the foothills of the Pyrenees and the estuary of the River Rhône is low, and includes the plains of the marshy Camargue and the dry, stony Crau. Eastward of the river there is an abrupt change to the beautiful and famous coast of the Riviera, where the Alpine foothills fall steeply to the sea, and bold headlands shelter fine bays.

This type of coast extends into north-western Italy. That country may be broadly divided between (*a*) the Italian Alps in the north; (*b*) the lowland of the River Po, which debouches upon the Adriatic Sea; (*c*) peninsular Italy, traversed by the Apennine mountain system, which nowhere exceeds 9,000 feet in height and consists of a series of short ranges rather than a continuous chain, though the narrow valleys which intrude among them do not usually offer easy lines of passage across the peninsula.

The lie of the hills common to this coast is such as to give low forelands principally in Tuscany, Latium, and Campania in the west, and south-eastward (to the Adriatic) in Apulia. The Apennine mountain system is continued across the narrow Strait of Messina into the northern part of the island of Sicily: the south and south-west are generally lower.

The limestone hills of the Dinaric system fall steeply to the Adriatic shore, guarded by islands (Fig. 100). Access to the interior is not easy. The sea breaks deeply into the land in the remarkable T-shaped Bocche di Cattaro, so closely walled by mountains that only a road engineered with much difficulty climbs laboriously from it to the mountain territory of Montenegro. This harsh mountain system passes south-eastward into Greece, where there are so few cultivable lowlands that the agricultural area is reckoned at only one-fifth of the whole. Rugged heights and rough slopes are common to view. The coasts are always beautiful. The sea deeply indents the land, and the Gulf of Corinth parts the peninsula of the Peloponnese from the mainland, save for the Isthmus of Corinth, barely four miles across and cut by a canal.

The valley of the Vardar River strikes through flanking mountains from the north to enter the Gulf of Salonika at the north-east base of the Balkan peninsula. The northern coast of the Aegean Sea in Macedonia and Thrace, little indented, is backed by a narrow foreland sloping up to the rough mountains of Rhodope; and eastward again, the Maritsa valley provides an outlet from Bulgaria. Beyond the peninsula of Gallipoli the strait of the Dardanelles forms part of the narrow waters here dividing Europe from Asia; they widen into the Sea of Marmara, narrow again through the Bosporus, and give access to the Black Sea (Fig. 104).

### The Near East

Asia Minor is a plateau rimmed to the north and south by mountains not easily crossed and rising nearly or directly from the sea; westward towards the Aegean there are long valleys and easier slopes. Eastward, high mountains continue towards the Caucasus and into Persia. The plateau lies from 3,000 to 4,000 feet high and in part is desolate; the better lands are mostly on the Aegean flank. The Taurus mountain system in the south reaches heights between 11,000 to 12,000 feet.

The Levantine seaboard in Syria and Palestine has lowlands narrow in the north and centre, wider in the south. Hills and mountains rise inland from these, or in places directly from the shore. The central mass of Lebanon reaches the height of 10,000 feet. Beyond this high belt, inland again, a central depression runs north and south; it includes the Ghor, part of the rift valley traceable far southward into central

Africa. The Ghor is watered by the River Jordan, which, draining the Sea of Galilee at 680 feet below sea level, debouches into the Dead Sea over 600 feet lower still. Eastward of the depression, a plateau broken by mountains extends and falls away towards the Euphrates plain.

Beyond the south-eastern corner of the Mediterranean the delta of the Nile breaks the desert coast. Westward, the fierce territory of Libya has witnessed efforts to tame it from early to present times. Westward again, the territories of Tunisia, Algeria and Morocco are grouped together physically as the Atlas region, dominated by the mountain system of that name, whose Mediterranean coastal belt resumes the familiar form of a steep seaward face broken at intervals by lowlands of small extent. A depression stretching inland and westward from the Gulf of Gabes lies, at its lowest, a little below sea level and is covered in part by *shats*, usually saline expanses of dry mud, but sometimes, after rains, shallow lakes. The southern Atlas ranges fall southward to the Sahara Desert; the western to the wide lowland behind the Moroccan Atlantic coast.

In relation to human geography, there is implicit, even in so brief a sketch as this of the physical geography of the Mediterranean region, a scene of wide divergence of conditions of relief as well as of climate; and this connotes a wide range of density of population in different areas, from very close settlement down to none.

### Subterranean Phenomena

It is impossible here to summarize all the physical components of the Mediterranean lands, but two features call for special notice: the predominance of limestone among the rocks, and the volcanic phenomena, each of which has its own bearing upon the human geography of the region.

Limestone weathers into striking forms, for unless mixed with other minerals, it is not hard in texture, and its essential constituent, carbonate of lime, is soluble. This accounts for the cliffs, chasms and underground, waterworn river-courses commonly found in limestone regions (Fig. 35). These features are familiar in

Greece, Dalmatia and other Mediterranean lands, and occur also in England, in the hills of Yorkshire and Derbyshire and in the Mendips.

The subterranean watercourses of the Mediterranean limestone have their place in Greek legend; knowledge of them must have suggested the Styx, the river of the underworld, which in historical times gave its name to a stream with a high fall in Arcadia, of which the water is still held traditionally to be poisonous; Alpheus, the river of the Peloponnese, was supposed to flow beneath the sea and to reappear in the fountain of Arethusa at Syracuse in Sicily; Acheron, Lethe and other names in mythology must all be connected with the rather frightening fascination of the underground river system in the limestone.

Soft and partly soluble as it is, the limestone weathers into a surface apt to be rough and dusty, and more pleasing to look at from a distance than to walk over; it is porous and does not hold much moisture at the surface, nor, unless it contains other ingredients, does it make much in the way of fertile soil. The Karst district north-eastward of the Adriatic, exemplifies these features in such extreme measure that its name is applied as a geographical term to define them wherever they occur. By itself, in short, the limestone makes a rather inhospitable kind of land. But it can confer benefits, too. One of its metamorphic forms is marble; and we need little reminding of what the abundant presence of that marble meant for Greek and Roman art.

The upfolding of high mountain ranges and the downfolding of great depths of the sea in near proximity commonly mark weaknesses in the earth's crust where catastrophes may happen; and there are evidences of this in the Mediterranean region. There are several more or less well-defined lines along which earthquakes have occurred down to our own time. The three great active volcanoes—Vesuvius (Fig. 1), Stromboli, and Etna (Fig. 101)—belong to the volcanic edge of one of the deep-sea basins (the Tyrrhenian Sea), which is reminiscent of the volcanic and earthquake belt surrounding the Pacific Ocean (Fig. 10), and of similar formations occurring in the West Indies and the Malay Archipelago.

FIG. 101. *Taormina, on the east coast of Sicily, a popular winter resort on account of its situation and views, has been a habitation of man since the eighth century B.C. at least. The long, gentle slopes of Mount Etna rise behind the town. Characteristic sub-tropical vegetation with thick, moisture-storing leaves appears in the foreground of the photograph.*

Fig. 102. *A camel working a water-wheel (sakia) in the Nile Valley. Such ancient aids to irrigation as this have been used by man for centuries. The peculiar sound made by these contrivances is said to have influenced the music of the East. Another primitive water-raising device in daily use on the banks of the Nile is shown in Fig. 105.*

The volcanic belt which includes Vesuvius, Stromboli and Etna continues around much of the Tyrrhenian basin; there are several old volcanoes, long extinct, to the north along the edge of the Apennines; the Lipari Islands, of which Stromboli is one, are all volcanic in origin, and there are others, or at least various evidences of former volcanic activity, in Sicily and on the broken bridge between Sicily and Africa, also in Sardinia and, on the opposite rim of the basin, in Spain. There is another similar volcanic edge in the south Aegean. It is traceable from Asia Minor through the islands of Nisyros and Santorin and Melos to Greece in the Gulf of Aegina. Santorin is classed as an active volcano because it has blown up several times in recorded history.

Volcanoes, however destructive they may be, possess certain positive virtues from the standpoint of human geography. Some of the materials which they eject weather down in course of time to exceedingly fertile soils, which sufficiently account for the close settlement and high cultivation on the lower slopes, for example, of Vesuvius and Etna—a natural result in districts where the non-volcanic soils are not, as a rule, distinguished for high fertility, but rather the reverse. It may thus be realized why men took the chance of establishing places like Pompeii and Herculaneum within reach of the volcano which destroyed them.

### Varied Climate

The type of climate distinguished as "mediterranean" wherever it occurs in the world, because it is best marked in the Mediterranean region, has as its basic characteristics dry and hot summers, wet and mild winters. But the Mediterranean lands present such a great range of height within short horizontal distances that the mildness of winter, at any rate, if not the heat of summer, is pretty closely confined to the lower levels bordering the sea; and not everywhere to them, for the Mediterranean region is not protected everywhere from the rigours of the mid-European winter, which may easily overcome the moderating influence of the Mediterranean Sea and the Atlantic Ocean to the westward.

The Mediterranean region is one of abrupt transition between cool temperate and tropical conditions—cool temperate Europe, tropical Africa. So long as the region is, so to say, holding the balance between evil influences at work to the north and south of it, it maintains a singularly beautiful climate, with much sunshine and a wonderful clearness of the air. An important factor in the historical geography of the Mediterranean region is that its climate is more favourable than are the climates of regions surrounding it.

It is probably fair to say that the Mediterranean region as a whole is rather subject to high winds (though they usually do not last long), accompanied by a particular kind of weather. They are mostly due to external influences, European or African, and in view of their distinctive features they often have local names. There is Boreas, the north wind, the *bora* of the Adriatic and the *mistral* of southern France, a disgustingly cold blast from the northern heights in winter and spring. There is the *sirocco*, from Africa, either dry, intensely hot, and sometimes dust-laden in summer,

FIG. 103. *This photograph shows terraced cultivation of the vine at Pinhao in the valley of the Douro, Portugal. Large quantities of many types of wine are produced in Portugal, red, white, still and sparkling, but the most famous variety is the best quality of wine from the valley of the Douro, shipped from Oporto under the name of port.*

or in winter starting dry but becoming moist as it crosses the sea and bringing muggy weather to Sicily and southern Italy. These are familiar names, and there are many others.

Again, in regard to wet winters, the word wet is relative to the dryness of the summer: the rainfall in different parts of the region varies enormously according to the extent to which any given points are exposed to rain-bearing winds or sheltered from them.

Not far from Cattaro on the Dalmatian coast, open to wet winds from across the sea to the westward, there occurs the heaviest rainfall recorded in continental Europe—180 inches or more a year on the average; at Athens, on the other side of the Greek peninsula, those same winds are dry or nearly so, and the mean annual rainfall is little over fifteen inches. The average annual rainfall of the south-east coast of Spain falls as low as ten inches. Along the African coast it decreases, broadly speaking, from west to east—from thirty inches at Algiers to sixteen at Tripoli and to three at Port Said.

Nearly all Mediterranean stations have a climax of rainfall in the autumn, earlier in the north-west, later in the south, with a sharp subsequent decline except in the north-west, which has a second climax in spring.

## Vegetation

The long season of dryness, coupled with soils which do not as a rule hold moisture particularly well, cause many plants in the typical "mediterranean" vegetation to adapt themselves in various ways to keeping what moisture they get. Leaves are usually thick and tough (Fig. 101). Many of the shrubs are familiar in gardens elsewhere— laurel, laurustinus, oleander, myrtle, rosemary, and so on. A dense, scrubby growth, perhaps six to ten feet high, and horrid to walk through, is characteristic: the French call it *maquis*, the Italians *macchia*, the Spaniards *monte bajo* (the vegetation of the lower mountain-slopes, distinguished from *monte alto*, the forests higher up). Thorny plants are common, so are resinous and oil-yielding plants, and so are plants growing from bulbs or tubers—characteristics

usual in climates which have long dry seasons. Trees generally grow rather low, and their evergreen leaves are dull or dark in hue; the evergreen oak, cypress, and olive are obvious examples.

The olive is so generally cultivated and so closely limited by the true "mediterranean" climate that the presence or absence of this tree is an approximate test of whether that climate obtains in a particular part of Mediterranean territory or not. Istanbul and the north shore of the Sea of Marmara, for instance, exposed to the central European climate, are outside the olive zone and the true "mediterranean" regime. Yet on the Asiatic side of the Sea of Marmara the olive is present, for that side is sheltered from the more rigorous winter.

## Forested Slopes

Deciduous trees grow as a rule only on higher slopes, where, above the true "mediterranean" regime, they get a more regular and ample water-supply. It is not uncommon to see hills capped with trees, or having a belt of them high up, but bare of trees below: we may see both a lower and an upper tree-line, instead of an upper line only as we do in the north. The vegetation zones on Mount Etna illustrate this (Fig. 101), except that the lower slopes are so fully cultivated that there is little of the natural *macchia* vegetation. Cultivation, with olive-yards, vineyards, and vegetable gardens, runs up to about 3,000 feet; above this there is forest up to about 6,800 feet: evergreen pines for the lower 3,000 feet of the forest belt, birch above them, with some oak and beech here and there, while chestnuts grow anywhere up to 5,000 feet. There is, towards the top, a stunted vegetation, though no actual Alpine flora.

The Mediterranean region is notorious for the destruction of timber trees by man over a long period of recorded history, and examples are sometimes cited from this region in support of the claim that the destruction of forests can directly affect the climate, especially the rainfall, of a region. There is insufficient scientific evidence for this; but forests do break the force of falling rain, catch some of it, and deliver it gradually to the ground. That makes it

Fig. 104. *Where Europe and Asia meet. This photograph of the Bosporus, the narrow strait uniting the Black Sea and the Sea of Marmara, was taken near the entrance to the Black Sea. The shores are well-wooded, and scenery on both sides of the channel is varied and beautiful.*

clear why the destruction of forests has had an ill effect on large tracts of country in this region; for Mediterranean rainfall is commonly heavy for short periods, not slight for long periods. Thus watercourses which may be dry, or nearly so, for most of the year are sometimes subject to sudden high floods, which carry away soil unprotected by vegetation.

It is apparent, then, that the natural vegetation of the Mediterranean lands ranges very widely. In parts of Portugal, with ample moisture and mild temperature, vegetation is probably the richest in Europe, showing sub-tropical, west European and "mediterranean" characteristics together. At the other end of the scale are the desert conditions of the south-eastern Mediterranean, where at best, apart from the oases, dry shrubs struggle for life in the wadis or valleys where sub-surface water is present.

Making allowance for this range, for local conditions of soil, rich or poor, for water-supply, good or bad, and for exposure to, or shelter from, climate rigours, it is possible to classify Mediterranean vegetation in three main belts.

### Cultivation

The evergreen belt is also sometimes called the *maquis* belt, from its principal natural feature, and sometimes the olive belt, from its most characteristic cultivated plant, and it may be regarded as covering the cultivated lands of the region generally. Above it is the forest belt, in which, however, *garigue* (moorland) replaces destroyed woodland.

Almost throughout the region, cultivation has certain features in common, in regard to location and to the crops grown. The cultivation zones establish the most thickly settled agricultural population at heights from 600 feet (but sometimes lower) up to 1,200. The most general grain crop is

wheat (a winter crop, harvested in early summer, on the irrigated lands of Egypt—Figs. 102 and 105). Maize and barley are also of importance; rice appears on the low wet lands of Egypt, Greece, Italy and Spain.

Vines are very generally grown on suitable slopes from Portugal (Fig. 103) to the Levant and from the northern lands to North Africa; wines are made from the grapes in all the Christian countries, though forbidden in the Mohammedan; raisins are a product of wide range; the small-fruited vine which yields currants, on the other hand, is centred upon the western Peloponnese in Greece. The olive, used for food and pressed for oil, is characteristic, as we have seen, of true "mediterranean" conditions throughout the region, and the required conditions of shelter enable it to appear locally also in the Black Sea coastland.

The cultivation of tobacco is mainly localized in the east (Turkey, Greece, and the Levant), but occurs elsewhere, as in Algeria. The cultivation of cotton on the grand scale in Egypt and the Sudan is the main commercial reason for the great modern irrigation works on the Nile; but

cotton is an indigenous crop elsewhere, as in Greece, Asia Minor, and Cyprus.

The chief economic product of the more temperate forest belt is probably the chestnut, an important food in several Mediterranean lands, and an export from some. The cork-oak is localized chiefly in Portugal and north-eastern Spain.

The dry steppe lands, as in north-west Africa, on the Spanish Meseta, and in the interior of Syria and Asia Minor, offer little of use save seasonal pasture, with the exception, in the first two of these divisions, of esparto grass for paper manufacture.

The date palm ripens its fruit in the south of Palestine and in the hot central depression there, in Egypt, Libya, and the Atlas lands. The banana has been introduced in the Levant and in Cyrenaica.

Livestock calls for no special observation, save that the herdsman's calling is commonly distinct from that of the farmer. A seasonal movement of shepherds and their flocks is characteristic where hill pastures are available in summer when the low grasslands are dry: this movement may be seen in southern Spain, western Italy, Yugoslavia, Thessaly, Asia Minor and elsewhere.

It is general knowledge that there is no common level of commercial development among the Mediterranean lands, and in some of them there may be substantially greater mineral wealth than production hitherto would suggest. Mining on a large scale has been under the impulse and with the help of great manufacturing interests outside the Mediterranean area, as for instance in Spain, where it has been most fully developed. Iron in Cantabria and Murcia, copper in the Sierra Morena, lead, silver and mercury elsewhere, are all important, and there is coal in Cantabria and Andalusia. In Mediterranean France there are considerable workings of coal, iron, and (in Gard) asphalt.

Italy, where in the north manufacturing industries have been established on a scale above those in other Mediterranean lands, is practically without minerals on the mainland; though among the islands Elba yields iron, Sicily sulphur and asphalt, and Sardinia zinc and lead. Greece has some coal; there are silver, lead, and iron in the Lavrion district, and magnesite in Euboea. Turkey has an important production of chrome, exported for use in the alloying of steel, and among her other minerals are borax, copper, emery and zinc, with coal on the Black Sea seaboard.

In Algeria and Tunis, iron, lead, zinc, and phosphate have been worked. In northern Syria there are workings of coal and iron, and both here and in the districts of the Dead Sea and the Sinai peninsula, oil deposits are believed to be present.

The water of the Dead Sea is subjected to intense evaporation and is highly mineralized; and the circumstances of the Second World War increased the importance of its contents of potassium salts, bromine, and (in smaller measure) magnesium salts. Among other mineral products of the Mediterranean region, reference should be made to the emery of Naxos, and to the copper from which the island of Cyprus derived its name in antiquity, when its wealth in that metal was relatively great. This island also yields asbestos.

## Important Passes

It was said earlier that natural gateways between the Mediterranean and lands beyond are few, and therefore all the more important. The chief of them are these:

1. The entrance from the Atlantic through the Strait of Gibraltar, guarded by the Rock and the British fortress.
2. The Strait of Messina between Italy and Sicily carries a heavy traffic: more important still is the passage between Sicily and North Africa, guarded by the brave British island of Malta.
3. The passage, previously mentioned, from the Aegean to the Black Sea, through the Dardanelles, Sea of Marmara, and the Bosporus (Fig. 104). The city of Istanbul (Constantinople) stands at the junction of Marmara and Bosporus, on a natural site of strength, where also a natural land-way between Europe and Asia Minor is broken by the strait.
4. Within modern times, the short sea-route through the Mediterranean and Red Seas, between Europe and the East, was interrupted by the Isthmus of Suez, which joins Africa to Asia. Through communication by water was achieved by the cutting of the Suez Canal, with Port Said and Port Fuad at its Mediterranean end, the port of Suez at the other.
5. The Pyrenees Mountains are not crossed by any important route: the lines of communication between France and Spain skirt both ends of the range.
6. The Rhône valley in France carries a trunk route from the north to the port of Marseilles which, like other ports in the region, e.g. Salonika and Alexandria (Fig. 106), stands aside from the shallow waters of the river's delta. A land route follows the Riviera coast into Italy.
7. The routes through the Alps used by railways and descending upon the northern plain of Italy are the Mont Cenis line from France, the Simplon and St. Gotthard

FIG. 105. *Raising water from the Nile near Cairo by means of a "shaduf." Note the gutter connecting with irrigation channel.*

FIG. 106. *Alexandria, chief seaport of Egypt, as seen from the air. The photograph illustrates the low and fragmentary coast of the Nile Delta, with lagoons behind it. The city's population includes Europeans and Orientals of many nationalities. More than eighty per cent of Egypt's exports and imports pass through the port.*

from Switzerland, the Brenner from Austria, and the Semmering from Austria. In the plain are cities receiving the traffic along these routes—Turin from Mont Cenis, Milan from Simplon and St. Gotthard, Verona from the Brenner, the port of Trieste from the Semmering.

8. The line which crosses the Danube at Belgrade traverses the valleys of the Rivers Morava and Vardar to Salonika, on the gulf at the north-eastern angle of the Greek peninsula. From Nish a line branches through Bulgaria and follows the Maritza valley till that turns south to the Aegean with no good port at its mouth: the main land route continues to Istanbul, as already stated.

There are, of course, other routes through the Mediterranean mountain-barriers, from railways and highways down to mere tracks, but those mentioned above are the lines of the first international importance.

As for air routes, apart from the local importance of Malta and other points especially in Italy and Greece, the region contains one of the great world junctions of airways—Cairo, a natural centre of routes between Europe, Asia and Africa.

The historical geography of the Mediterranean region, viewed broadly, is a story of discontinuity and movement, largely dictated by natural conditions. It is impossible even to summarize it here, but a few examples may be taken.

Navigation was an early art. Thus the very old civilizations centred in Mesopotamia and Egypt were followed by the Minoan civilization in the island of Crete, which maintained sea traffic with Egypt and westward with Sicily and perhaps beyond. The central power in Crete threw off colonies and traded in the eastern sea at least, but was broken about 1500-1200 B.C. by attacks from Greece and the north. The Phoenicians moved outward from their settlements on the Syrian shore, through the length of the Mediterranean, through the Strait of Gibraltar, and into the Atlantic both north and south. Classical Greek civilization, from the eastern part of the peninsula, spread through the Aegean islands and to the coast of Asia Minor beyond: their colonies appeared later in Sicily and southern Italy, and as far northwest as Marseilles.

The hill-girt valleys of Greece and the coastward basins opening to the sea were ideal for the development of centres of culture and political power, each for itself. Their climate and their physical setting were inspiring, more so than in the old lands of Mesopotamia and Egypt, more so than in the Russian plains and central Europe, from which hard-living barbarians came sometimes into conflict with the Aegean centres of civilization. Sea communications were easy, even for primitive mariners who did not willingly lose sight of land. Land communications were not so easy: it might well be simpler to travel by sea, for purposes of commerce or war, than to cross the mountains to trade or argue with one's next-door neighbour. This self-centredness of peoples in Aegean and eastern Mediterranean history is a commonplace of historical geography. Thus the city-states of the Aegean area never combined effectively into a Greek nation from the ninth century to the subjugation of Greece by Rome in the second century B.C.

Italy, in early history, was divided, like Greece, between a number of states of small area, but Rome was mistress of the peninsula by the third century B.C. Trade and conquest extended her power, at first across the narrow seas to Sicily, western Greece, and Northern Africa; later, far beyond these limits, and overland. In the early years of the Christian era, the empire began to disintegrate. It fell apart into eastern and western empires, the final separation taking place in the year 800; but cultural influences transcended geographical limitations, and Rome remained a centre of European culture into and beyond the Middle Ages.

### Period of Invasions

While the broken relief of the Mediterranean lands helped political disunity, the great mountain barriers which in large part demarcate them did not completely bar invasion from without. As Roman power became divided and weakened, the Goths came in from the north; the kingdom of the West Goths covered most of the Iberian peninsula; the Vandals established themselves in the Atlas region; and the East Goths controlled the Italian peninsula and Sicily. The Mediterranean phenomenon of the city-state repeated itself in the case of some Italian towns, notably Venice, which in the Middle Ages pushed out little territorial trading centres along the coasts and long maintained its independent power.

The phenomenon of disunity repeats itself in the case of the Arabs, who, from the seventh century A.D. onward, pushed northward into Syria, westward through Egypt, right through northern Africa, into Spain, and even, for a while, beyond the Pyrenees. They survived in part of Spain until the fifteenth century, but had already become divided into separate caliphates.

Lastly, in studying the historical geography of the Mediterranean it is pertinent to notice what have been called the bridgelands—territories which, within certain confines, afford passages of communication between others. Syria very early carried lines of traffic between Mesopotamia and Egypt and into Asia Minor, which itself afforded passage for the Persians in their operations against the Greeks in and after the sixth century B.C., for Alexander of Macedon for his movements in the contrary direction in the fourth century, and, among later instances, for the Turks, whose descendants are there now. The Turks came from Central Asia six centuries ago; their expulsion from the Balkan lands, Greece, Egypt, and as far west as Tripoli, is a matter of history.

Mediterranean history has left its monuments in the architectural treasures to be found everywhere from city to wilderness, from Egyptian and Minoan, Greek and Roman remains to the choicest specimens of early and medieval Christian and Mohammedan building and craftsmanship. The present age has been one both of preservation and of destruction; but at least it may be said that none of the destructive influences, past or present, has wholly overthrown the splendours which it has asaulted.

### The Mediterranean Peoples

The northern Mediterranean peninsulas —Spain and Portugal, Italy and Greece— have each their own fairly homogeneous people: the same applies to Egypt, where the narrow populous belt along the Nile is hemmed in by desert as a peninsula is by the sea. Geographical conditions have helped to dictate the separation of the Spanish from the Portuguese; there are strong differences of language in different parts of the peninsula, and the Basques, a people of ancient but unknown origin, have survived through their own vitality aided by the isolation of their country, extending into the mountains behind the south-east corner of the Bay of Biscay.

Italy, again, shows marked distinction of speech between the north and the rest: in character, too, there is discerned a greater energy among northern Italians, in contrast with those of the south, due, in

FIG. 107. *A busy street scene in Cairo, the Egyptian capital, city of sun and shadow, where people of many races and nationalities mingle with the native population.*

some measure at any rate, to the less enervating northern climate and the occurrence of malaria in the south. Mediterranean France is merely one edge of the territory of a great nation, where no strongly marked admixture of population is to be expected, although the Provençal speech is related to the Catalan of Spain.

Elsewhere in the Mediterranean lands, mixed populations are rather the rule than exception. The Balkan lands are neither physically nor politically united. Ethnical units have been preserved by conditions of geographical isolation, as in the mountains of Albania and Montenegro, and the shepherd Vlachs of western and northern Greece and Macedonia are related to the Rumanians beyond the Danube, though history does not account for their separation. Along the eastern coast lands of the Adriatic, however, there is a mingling of Italians with Slavs. In eastern Yugoslavia and Albania the most westerly contact of Christian and Muhammedan occurs.

FIG. 108. *Carpineto, a typical hill-town south-east of Rome. As the restricted area of the site prohibits lateral expansion, the closely packed buildings are several storeys high.*

The port of Salonika (Thessalonike) is a meeting-place of all Mediterranean peoples and others, and Jewish traders have formed in recent times a strong element. The foreland of Macedonia and Thrace, bordering the Aegean Sea and having the difficult mountainous country of Rhodópe to the north of it, is an old highway between east and west. Both passage along it and settlement within it have gone on through the ages, and thus it contains Greeks, Turks, Bulgars, Serbs, and a few Albanians and Vlachs, and its political domination has been repeatedly contested. The inhabitants of the Aegean islands and of Cyprus are predominantly, though not wholly, Greek. In Asia Minor the Turks are the rulers, having subjugated earlier inhabitants whose descendants survive, though rated now as Turks, as in the narrow isolated Pamphylian plain bordering the south coast. Greeks on the coasts, Armenians mainly in the east, also remain despite periods of oppression, and, mainly on the plateau, there are found nomad Kurds, Turkomans, Yuruks, and gipsies.

The Cilician plain, crossed by traffic between Asia Minor and Syria, is a point of junction between the Turkish and Arabic languages, and Egyptian, Ethiopian, and Tatar incomers are among other peoples who appear there. In Syria we find a settled native peasantry, with nomad (and to some extent also, settled) Bedouin Arabs,

and again an admixture of Turks, Kurds, Turkomans, and Armenians. In Israel there are the Jews, of recent settlement; the problems of reconciling their interests with those of the Arabs have been acute.

In North Africa there is a broad distinction, though not a defined line, between nomad Arabs and the settled Berbers from whom was derived the old regional name of Barbary. The term Moor applied to a native of Morocco has no exact ethnic connotation, for the population is mixed. In the North African lands generally, there are many Italians, French, and Spaniards, according approximately, but not exactly, to political divisions. Jews form strong communities, and Maltese have spread to Tunisia from their own overcrowded island. Indeed, one might find settled in any land in the region natives of almost any other Mediterranean land.

Modern political divisions are dictated by geographical considerations up to a point. The Iberian peninsula, marked off as it is from the rest of Europe by the Pyrenees, is not a natural unit to the extent of forming a political unit as well; its division between the states of Spain and Portugal has, as we have seen, a measure of reason in physical geography, and the internal divisions of Spain itself are sharply demarcated by nature. Italy, Yugoslavia, Greece, Turkey, and Egypt are political units on a physical basis, again up to a point. Each has had its frontier problems, constantly recurrent in history.

Effects of geographical environment are well exemplified in the Mediterranean region. Preceding paragraphs have suggested examples. Disunity due to environment has been mentioned. Along with isolation of communities, great or small, whether by rough mountain barriers or, in the islands, by the sea, there is found in different localities every standard of living, from the highest to the primitive. There are outstanding instances of the fierce spirit of independence which goes with natural isolation—Albania, Montenegro, Yugoslavia, Greece come to mind in this connexion. That spirit has shown itself often in Mediterranean history when strong invaders have found less strong opponents far from easy to overcome, as—to go no further back—the Axis Powers found the Greeks and the Yugoslavs.

### Political Dissension

The same spirit is found in smaller units also, from the sharp political dissensions of Greece down to the vendetta or family feud, of which the rugged island of Corsica provides the typical example: it is not unreasonable to associate these with the geographical environment of the communities in which they occur.

The frequent occasion for defensive precautions, whether against neighbours on a small scale or external enemies on a larger, is an obvious reason for the form of human settlement in hillside villages or small towns (Fig. 108) to be seen so often in this region. The Mediterranean region is not a countryside peopled with detached homesteads, and there are natural reasons for this apart from defence.

### Problem of Water Supply

Lowlands are often unhealthy, and seldom of sufficient area or fertility for extensive cultivation. Mediterranean agriculture, as suggested in an earlier paragraph, consists usually of the intensive working of small bits of land laboriously cleared of stones, tilled and often terraced and irrigated, close-grown with vegetable crops maturing quickly during the moist winter, or dependent upon subsurface water during the dry summer season of ripening, as in the case of the vine and the olive.

Of the forms of human achievement necessitated by local geographical conditions, perhaps the use of water provides the most obvious example. In earlier times Greeks, Romans and Arabs all developed great skill in building aqueducts for supplying their homes and cultivated lands, and fine examples of their work remain. And yet (as illustrating the primitive end of the scale of progress suggested above) there can still be found, as among the Berbers of the Atlas country, hill settlements whose water supply must be carried by women and children from streams in the valleys below. Indeed, one of the enduring characteristics of the region is persistent rural poverty in contrast with the periodic rise and fall of great cities.

## Test Yourself

1. What are the two predominant types of soil in the Mediterranean lands? Explain how these have affected vegetation and the lives and culture of the Mediterranean peoples.

2. (a) The type of climate distinguished wherever it occurs as "mediterranean" has certain basic characteristics. What are these?

   (b) This climatic type is identified on the climatic map on page 74 by the letter $E_1$. What other places in the world enjoy this type? What do you notice about their position in each case?

3. What are the main natural gateways giving communication between the Mediterranean and the outside world?

*Answers will be found at the end of the book.*

FIG. 109.  *New York from the air.  The majestic, mile-wide waters of the Hudson River sweep down to the harbour of New York, past Manhattan Island with its busy wharves and the impressive group of skyscrapers at its lower extremity.  In the middle of the island is Central Park, and farther south, where the hard, ancient rock foundation outcrops to the surface through the sand and gravel deposits, another fine group of skyscrapers has arisen.  They can be seen in a white cluster in the centre of the picture.*

# CHAPTER VIII

# ENGLISH-SPEAKING AMERICA

ALONG the Rio Grande, from the Gulf of Mexico to El Paso and thence fairly directly across to the Pacific Coast, wanders the international boundary between Mexico and the United States. It marks the political division of the Americas into the English-speaking north and the Latin Americas of the centre and south. Except for parts of French-speaking Quebec (and this is quite a big exception) the whole continent north of the Rio Grande has been settled by people who speak English, even if it is not their native language.

### A Vast Continent

This great area is divided into two national states: the United States of America and the Dominion of Canada. The island of Newfoundland with its vast mainland dependency, the almost uninhabited Labrador, used to be a third national state. But in 1949 Newfoundland and Labrador became a province in the Dominion of Canada. Though an immense area forming the most easterly part of North America, Labrador is a bleak and rocky wilderness playing little part in the life of the continent.

A European who lands at New York or Montreal from his transatlantic liner rarely has any idea of the size of the continent ahead of him. Suppose, for instance, that he lands in Montreal and wants to entrain for Vancouver. He will leave Montreal on the Canadian Pacific *Dominion* or the Canadian National *Continental Limited*, shall we say on Sunday, at 8.00 in the morning. Next morning he wakes up in the forested wilderness of North Ontario, north of Lake Huron. He does not reach the prairies at Winnipeg until breakfast time on Tuesday. At the same time on Wednesday he is still gazing out across the seemingly endless prairie.

Shortly before lunch, however, his train begins to climb into the Rockies, and by nightfall he is through Kicking Horse Pass or Yellowhead Pass and is heading down into the deep valleys of British Columbia. Eventually he arrives in Vancouver in time for breakfast on Thursday, about ninety-six hours after leaving Montreal.

But long as the east-west journey is, the north-south journey across North America would be even longer if anyone chose to make it. Northern Canada is within the Arctic Circle; there are permanent snow-fields, and there is a midnight sun in summer. Eskimos and missionaries are the only inhabitants, except for an occasional miners' camp and the Royal Canadian Mounted Police. At the other end of the continent there are the hot, mosquito-ridden sand-bars and marine marshes of the coast of the Gulf of Mexico, in latitude 30 degrees N. Between these extremes there lie some of the richest as well as the most barren of terrains. The keynote of North America is variety: endless variety of resources, of environment, of scenery, of people. But across all this variety is imposed the unifying link of the English language.

### Physical Structure

Look for the moment at the physical setting in which nearly 200,000,000 English-speaking people live. Most of us have vague recollections from our experiences in the cinema, or through reading American fiction, that America is not just a simple physical unit. Every schoolboy can distinguish between the plains and prairies of the west and the early forest conditions of the east; he remembers the buffalo-hunting Comanche Indians of the wide, open plains who could be spotted by waggon trains miles away, but he also remembers the silent attacks of the forest Indians like the

Mohawks, and the Choctaws who could drop from the branches of a tree on to the heads of their enemies as they pushed along some forest trail. We have recollections of luxuriant vegetation and of labouring Negroes in the legendary South, and we distinguish this from the spectacular deserts and steppes of the Far West. In this way we realize that America is a varied continent, and that human responses to it differ from place to place. Our ideas are, however, vague and ill-formed. To understand the modern geography we have to be more explicit about the physical make-up.

The map of North America opposite illustrates the main physiographic units of the continent, and will serve as the outline upon which the rest of the chapter will be drawn. The units we distinguish are these:

(1) In the north is the Canadian Shield, the old nucleus about which geological history has built the modern continent. This huge shield-like mass of ancient rocks is now a low-lying plain over much of its surface, though the ground is everywhere very rough and infertile. Bare rock outcrops over great areas, and a deep soil is rare. A dense forest covers the southern half, but in the north the trees give way first to a poor sub-Arctic scrub and then to the mossy tundras of the Arctic zone itself. Enormous numbers of lakes and streams break up the surface, about one-sixth of which is covered by water (Fig. 111).

(2) In the west is the complex series of ranges, valleys and plateaux we sometimes carelessly call the Rockies (a name which strictly applies only to the easternmost chain). This Western Cordillera stretches unbroken from Alaska through Canada and the U.S.A. into Mexico, effectively cutting off the plains of the heart of the continent from the Pacific shore. If we look more closely at this complex highland we find that the main mountain ranges occur chiefly close to the Pacific (the Alaskan, Cascade and Sierra Nevada ranges), and along the eastern flank of the Cordillera (Rockies and Selkirks). In between there are high plateaux, but few real mountains. Between the Pacific ranges there are also some broad, deep valleys like that of California and the Puget Sound, as well as

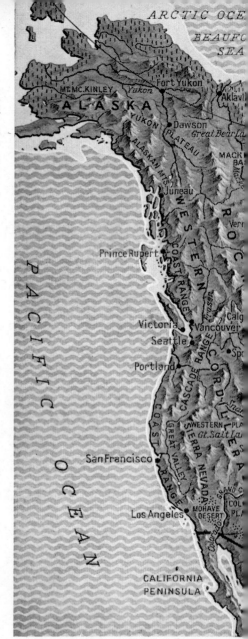

the lowland of Washington and Oregon.

The Pacific ranges get a very heavy rainfall from Pacific storms, and they are densely forested; the world's tallest and finest trees grow on these cloudy, wet mountain-sides. We have all heard of Alaska's Sitka spruce (used in making Mosquito aircraft), British Columbia's Douglas fir and the redwoods and big

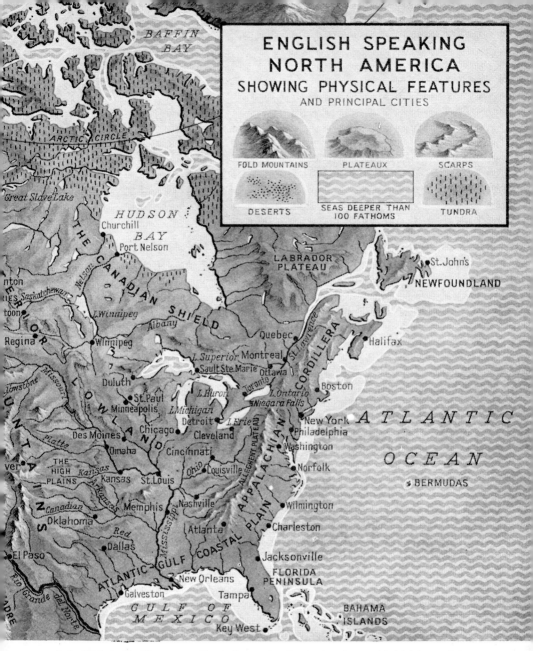

ENGLISH SPEAKING
NORTH AMERICA
SHOWING PHYSICAL FEATURES
AND PRINCIPAL CITIES

FOLD MOUNTAINS · PLATEAUX · SCARPS

DESERTS · SEAS DEEPER THAN 100 FATHOMS · TUNDRA

trees of the U.S.A. Pacific coast. East of the Pacific ranges, however, there is little rain or snow, and much of the land is semi-arid or desert. Even the Rockies attract little rain. This is the land of the "Western story," with its sage-brush, its cactus, its mesas (Fig. 110), its gallops across the salt-flats of old lake beds. Only in the north is there any appreciable rain or snow.

(3) Corresponding to this highland of the west is the Appalachian Cordillera in the east. Though much lower and narrower than its western equivalent, this cordillera has been throughout history a formidable barrier in the way of westward movement from the Atlantic coast. At one time dense-ly forested (for the rainfall is heavy) and the home of some of the cruellest and

fiercest Indians, the Appalachians are now thoroughly knit into the American national legend. Today they contain the world's greatest coalfields and steel foundries, and along their valleys wind the roads and railways that carry the varied commerce of a great industrial nation; yet the hills are still forested, and a view from a hilltop shows little sign of settlement by man.

(4) Between these two cordilleran belts lies the great Interior Lowland, by far the largest and most productive of the world's farmlands. The heart of the lowland is the Mississippi valley and those of its tributaries, the Ohio (which is the real masterstream) and the Missouri. There are long extensions of the lowland north-westwards into the Canadian prairies and north-eastwards to the St. Lawrence valley of eastern Canada.

### Extremes of Weather

Although most of this lowland is well watered, the west and north-west have a perennial drought problem. In the U.S.A., the dry country lies west of about longitude 100 degrees W., and in Canada includes south-western Saskatchewan and Alberta. But along the Mississippi valley and to the east of it there is ample rain and no particularly dry season.

A feature of the climate of the Interior Lowland, the Appalachians and the plain behind the Atlantic and Gulf of Mexico

coasts is its extreme changeability. Because of the lie of the hills, there is little hindrance in the way of invasions of tropical air from the Gulf of Mexico, which bring the sticky heat waves in the summer. A New York summer is an ordeal from which only September can bring relief. In winter, however, the Arctic cools to many degrees below zero (−30 degrees to −40 degrees F. is common), and from this dark reservoir there comes wave after wave of clear, dry, but bitterly cold air, taking sub-zero weather to most parts of the Interior Lowland. Between these cold waves the warmer air from the Gulf of Mexico or the Atlantic makes its way northwards, at times even reaching the St. Lawrence valley, but after a short stay it is swept away again by a renewed advance of the Arctic air, often with remarkable suddenness. In this manner all parts of the centre and east of North America are subject to rapid and severe changes in temperature in all but the summer months.

There is no doubt, however, that these extraordinary changes are stimulating. A beautiful sunny afternoon in Ottawa, for example, with the temperature at 46 degrees F. and with a soft, gentle breeze from the south-west, may be followed the next morning by a steel-grey sky, with a northerly wind bringing the temperature down to 20 degrees F. below zero. Fur caps and ear muffs reappear, and no one can fail

FIG. 110. *A "mesa" (table-land) 400 feet high in New Mexico, U.S.A., with the pueblo (town or village) of Acoma on its summit. Discovered by Spaniards in the sixteenth century, this is one of the oldest settlements in the United States. The primitive Indian inhabitants are agricultural, peaceable and conservative.*

to feel the stimulus of the sudden change.

(5) The Atlantic and Gulf of Mexico coasts south of New York City have behind them a broad, flat, coastal plain, with much ill-drained or waterlogged ground. Other areas have a better drained, richer soil through being raised a little above the general level. This lowland area is called the Atlantic-Gulf Coastal Plain. It has for the most part a warmer, damper climate than the Interior Lowland, thanks to its proximity to the sea and to its relatively low latitude. Florida is a peninsular extension of the plain out into the warm southern seas.

These, then, are the primary physical units of the continent. They correspond broadly to similar differences in the vegetation of the country as it was when the Europeans first colonized it. Most of the Canadian Shield, the eastern Interior Lowland, the Appalachian Cordillera and the Atlantic-Gulf Coastal Plain was originally densely forested. In the cold north the forest trees were mainly of the hardy coniferous type such as pines, hemlocks and cedars, but to the south of the Canadian Shield there were also many fine deciduous trees like the maple, the oak and the chestnut. Conifers predominated again along the sea-coast. But if the east was forest, the west was grass or scrub almost to the Pacific. West of the Mississippi the forests gave way to the rich, rolling grasslands of the Middle Western prairies, and they in turn to the short grass of the endless High Plains, the westernmost parts of the Interior Lowland. Beyond the Rockies the grass was replaced by a poor scrub, consisting of drought-resisting shrubs and (in the south) even of cactus. On the west-facing slopes of the Pacific ranges, however, the forests reappeared, this time with the giant trees we have already described.

Today this natural vegetation has been widely changed. The forests of the east have been cleared where they grew on good cultivable land, and they now survive only in patches, chiefly on the infertile soils. The long grasses of the prairies have vanished under the plough, giving way to the rolling cornfields of the world's greatest granary. But the grassy High Plains and the scrub of the arid west remain largely as they were when Indians and buffaloes were their only inhabitants. The Pacific forests are being felled far more quickly than they can be replanted, but there are still many untouched areas.

### Rapid Changes

Nowhere is it so difficult to separate history from geography as in North America. The land has nearly all been settled since 1600, and to a very large extent since 1800. The American people and the land in which they live are in every way a modern phenomenon; processes of change are so rapid that a geography book is out of date in ten years. Hence, to understand the present American scene one must look at the recent past, and see how it was affected by the physical structure of the continent.

Why is North America English-speaking? Partly the answer lies in European history, involving the changing status of the colonizing powers; the early settlers of the continent came from France, Spain,

Holland and Britain, and their fortunes in America often depended on the fortunes of their parent nation in Europe. But geography also played an important part in determining the final victory of the English-speaking settlers. Though the prevailing wind systems of the Atlantic were probably in part responsible for guiding the Spanish to Central and South America and the British and French to the North Atlantic coast, how this came about is best explained by looking in turn at the three main streams of settlement.

### Settlement of North America

The French were really first in the field. In the seventeenth century they began to settle in the St. Lawrence valley below Montreal. The great river highway led their explorers westwards to the Great Lakes, from which region they could carry their canoes a few miles to the tributaries of the Mississippi. By 1682 the explorer La Salle had reached the Gulf of Mexico. But despite the lure of this western gateway, New France (as it was called) grew slowly, and remained confined to the lower St. Lawrence and Acadia (what is now Nova Scotia and New Brunswick). By the mid-eighteenth century the French numbered only some 55,000, and had settled only the St. Lawrence valley as far west as the Ottawa confluence. They had trading-posts and forts along the Mississippi and Ohio Rivers, but there were no settlers in these western domains.

The Spanish, the first to settle in the Americas, played little part in the settlement of the north. Their Jesuit and Franciscan missionaries planted missions in places along the Gulf of Mexico coast, notably in Florida and near the Mississippi, but the main movement was northward from the old Spanish colony of Mexico into what is now California, Texas and the arid land in between.

The English established their earliest settlements along the Atlantic coast. These colonies multiplied in number and population quite rapidly, mainly because of immigration. By the mid-eighteenth century the settlers numbered over 1,000,000, all concentrated along the coast and the eastern slope of the Appalachians. The latter were a formidable barrier in the way of westward movement, especially as the Indians were often hostile. The French, too, had their forts on the Ohio, discouraging the use of the most obvious westward route. With the fall of French power on the continent in 1761, however, the way was cleared. Cautiously at first, and then in an ever-growing flood, the English-speaking pioneers moved west through the gaps in the Appalachians. They were joined by emigrants from every European country.

In the nineteenth century the great prairies and plain of the central lowlands were occupied, and the west was being opened up. Driven on by the search for silver and gold, or for new lands to settle, the pioneers crossed the Cordillera and began to occupy California and Oregon. After a brief clash with the Mexicans in 1848, the claim of the English-speaking peoples to the continent north of the Rio Grande was undisputed. With the American Revolution in 1776 came the division of the continent between Canada and the newly-created United States of America. Although neither country then extended far west, these two units today span the continent, the international boundary running from the Great Lakes to the Strait of Juan de Fuca along the 49th parallel of latitude. Immigration into both countries continued until just before the First World War, by which time the settlement patterns and population densities had taken up their modern shape.

We shall now look at the modern geography of these two great countries.

### Canada

Canada is the senior self-governing Dominion of the British Commonwealth. In area she is very nearly twice the size of Europe, and makes up more than a quarter of the lands of the Commonwealth. Yet her population is only 18,000,000. Vast stretches of the Dominion are entirely unpopulated, and considerable areas have been explored only from the air.

Canada includes nearly all the old French settlements of the St. Lawrence valley region. Under the British flag the population of these French lands has increased enormously, until it now numbers some 4,500,000 people, most of whom live in Quebec province. Against this there are some 7,000,000 inhabitants of British origin, including some 4,000,000 from England itself. It is, therefore, a fallacy to regard Canada as a British country pure and simple. French and English are both official languages, although politically and economically most of the power and wealth of the Dominion lies with the English-speaking peoples. In Montreal, for example, there are over 1½ million inhabitants, of whom about two-thirds are French, and there are three great Catholic cathedrals to testify to the religion of the Jesuit missionaries who played so notable a part in the country's settlement. Street signs, public notices, the voices of the announcers at the railway stations, are all bilingual.

The Canadian environment presents extreme regional contrasts, and these are reflected in a clear-cut regional habit of life among her people. We must look at each region separately to understand the life of the Dominion.

### The Canadian Shield

The Canadian Shield (pages 160, 161) is a vast area of ancient, hard rocks, which form a hummocky, irregular lowland with a hilly rim in the east and south. In recent geological times great ice sheets covered the Shield as they now cover Greenland. The ice stripped off most of the soil, leaving the surface rocky, irregular and bare. The Shield is today covered with a confused network of streams and lakes; it is possible to go in any direction by canoe along these streams, although at times one has to carry the canoe a short way across some low and swampy watershed. The edge of the Shield is lined with large lakes such as the Great

FIG. 111. *An air view of Port Radium, on Great Bear Lake, showing the bleak landscape, dotted with lakes, which is characteristic of the Canadian Shield. Radium and uranium are extracted from the pitchblende mined at Port Radium.*

Bear and Great Slave Lakes and the Great Lakes of the St. Lawrence system—Superior, Huron and others farther south.

The winters are long and extremely cold. Frosts occur in all months but July and August in most parts of the Shield. Frequent blizzards occur in autumn, winter and spring, and the brief summer has fairly frequent thundery rains. The southern border of the Shield is densely forested, mainly with evergreen conifers such as the spruce, hemlock and white pine. Farther north (beyond 50 degrees N.), the forest thins out, the trees growing smaller and poorer in species. Mink, bear, arctic fox and caribou roam the forests. The extreme north is a tundra land, with permanently frozen subsoil and a cover of moss, lichen and small shrubs and herbs.

Apart from some scattered farms along the edge of the St. Lawrence valley and its tributary the Saguenay, farming settlement is largely confined to the clay belt of north Ontario, where a thin layer of clay covers the rocky surface. Despite the long winter, farmers here have raised crops of oats and potatoes, and an active dairy-farming region is developing. But most of the Shield's inhabitants are workers in the mining and lumber industries. Much of the world's supply of non-ferrous metals is raised in mining centres in Ontario and Quebec. There is a good yield of gold (6–7 per cent of the world's production), cobalt, nickel (85 per cent of the world figure), copper and silver. Far away in the north-west on the shores of Great Bear Lake are some of the world's richest and most abundant uranium ores. The mining towns that have grown up round these ore deposits are oases in the stony or forested wilderness. Their population has not grown beyond what is needed for labour, essential supply services and amenities.

The lumber industry is largely concen-trated in the south-eastern border of the Shield, where its uptilted rim overlooks the St. Lawrence valley. Here enormous numbers of coniferous trees are felled, floated down on the tributaries to some point with good water-power, and there pulped and converted into paper, especially newsprint.

The Shield, though hostile to settlement, has therefore played an important part in the development of the Canadian national life. It provides much of the raw material for the Dominion's flourishing manufactures, as well as a large fraction of her exports. It must continue to serve this purpose; its harsh climate and soilless surface will never encourage dense settlement.

Under the rim of the Canadian Shield from the Great Lakes to the Atlantic flows the St. Lawrence, the world's greatest inland waterway. Something will be said later about it as a routeway. Here we are concerned with the settlement of the narrow, fertile valley through which the river flows and with the great cities along it.

FIG. 112. *Lumbering in Canada. A gigantic raft of logs at the sawmills at Kenogami, Quebec. With over 770,000 square miles of productive forest land, Canada has developed huge timber, pulp and paper industries, the products of which are among the Dominion's leading exports.*

Unlike that of the Shield, the solid rock of the valley is mainly unfolded, lying in gently tilted slabs upon the hard Shield beneath. Over all there is a rich cover of clays, silts and gravels, the deposits of the lakes, seas and rivers of the Ice Age. The main areas of extensive lowland are the peninsula of south-west Ontario and the Montreal basin. In the rest of the valley only very narrow strips of fertile lowland line the river. The valley has severe snowy winters. The St. Lawrence freezes in December and does not thaw until April. The summers are hot, with a good deal of thundery rain and intervening sunshine.

The lowlands are densely settled (by Canadian standards), in Ontario mainly by English-speaking farmers and city-dwellers, and in Quebec mainly by the French. In both areas the basic unit of land industry is the small, mixed farm, which gets most of its profits from dairy and market-garden produce for use in the great cities. In the French zone a succession of these neat, white farms lines the river, each a long, narrow strip running back a long way inland. The devoted Catholic farmers have tenaciously preserved their identity as a cultural unit quite alien to their English-speaking countrymen, and in so doing they have created a picturesque and beautiful landscape. The Ontario farmers, however, have a wider, less rigid agriculture, made possible by the less severe winters. The landscape in places looks very English (Fig. 113); orchards, vineyards and even peacheries appear in some places, while the maple is grown for its sugar (Fig. 114).

Many towns and cities have grown up along the valley. They have developed extensive manufactures based on the enormous water-power available. Although some of this power is used directly to drive mills, most of it is converted to hydro-electric power in great turbine plants. The needs of a hydro-electric plant are an

FIG. 113. *Southern Ontario. Rich farming country near Toronto, reminiscent of rural England. This photograph should be contrasted with Figs. 111 and 121.*

abundant flow of water, a sudden fall in level (such as occurs at Niagara), and an even flow throughout the year. The streams coming down from the Laurentian hills (the rim of the Shield), are good for power developments, having many falls or rapids, though their regularity of flow is impeded by the winter freeze. Particularly large plants are sited at Shawinigan Falls near Trois Rivières and on the Saguenay River near Lake St. John. The St. Lawrence itself has the famous Niagara in Ontario, where the output exceeds 1,000,000 horse-power (Fig. 122). This supply of power has helped the development of large-scale manufacturing in modern factories which utilize raw materials from other Canadian regions. Such, for example, are the paper and woodpulp plants of Trois Rivières and Shawinigan Falls, using lumber from the Shield. Again, the Canadian prairies provide the grain milled in Montreal.

Overshadowing all others among the cities are Toronto and Montreal. Both have enormous manufacturing interests, largely connected with the clothing, railway and engineering industries. Both are rail-way centres of the first order. Toronto (1,798,000 in 1961) is the largest English-speaking city in the Dominion, and is to an increasing extent the social and cultural capital. It owes much to its lakeside site, which gives it access to the great stream of Lakes shipping. Montreal (2,059,000 in 1961) is largely French-speaking. It is the commercial and financial capital of the Dominion, the hub of its railways, and its greatest port. Although 1,000 miles from the Atlantic and closed by ice from December until April, it remains one of the great bulk ports of the world. Here much of the enormous grain export of the prairies is shipped to Europe. The site on an island near the junction between the Ottawa River and the St. Lawrence was chosen by the French in the seventeenth century. It also commands the Lake Champlain-Hudson route to New York, the corridor in which many of the continent's decisive battles have been fought. Few cities have more advantages of site (Fig. 115).

Quebec and Ottawa are smaller cities, centres of government, the one of French Canada (Quebec Province) and the other, the Federal capital of the Dominion.

South of the St. Lawrence, near its mouth, is a prolongation north-eastwards of the Appalachian highlands. This area is divided between the one-time colonies, now provinces, of New Brunswick, Nova Scotia and Prince Edward Island. These provinces are cut off from the rest of Canada by distance and by forested mountains. They have several links with New England, of which they are structurally the continuation. The Maritimes are thinly populated, though less so than the prairies, and have in recent years undergone some depopulation because of the depressed state of their agriculture and industry. The population is mostly English-speaking, but the old French colony of Acadia was sited here, and many French settlers remain. They constitute about a third of the population of New Brunswick, and, as elsewhere, are increasing in numbers in proportion to the English-speaking people.

Much of the ground is rather high, consisting of low, flat-topped, forested hills. The lower ground is mainly floored by gently folded rocks faulted below the level of the surrounding hills. The sea has drowned some of these lowlands, forming deep bays (such as the Bay of Fundy, noted for its

high tides) or straits like that cutting off Prince Edward Island. There are long, severe winters with heavy snowfall, and a rather warm summer with frequent rains. Wheat, oats, potatoes and the temperate fruit trees all do well.

The hills have largely remained forested, though cutting is in progress. The lowland areas are under arable and pastoral farms, with many dairy herds. The soils are rather stony, and farming has not been prosperous in recent years. Some poorer land has been abandoned, as in New England; Prince Edward Island, with its fertile red soils like those of Herefordshire, is the richest area. The whole region is handicapped by distance from the large consuming centres. Round many of the deep coves and inlets

FIG. 114. *Collecting the sap of the maple tree in Ontario in early spring. The sap, which flows from incisions made in the bark of the tree, is thickened by boiling until it is converted into maple syrup or maple sugar. This method of making sugar is one of the oldest rural industries of Canada, where about 25 million pounds of maple sugar are produced annually. Apart from its yield of sugar, the sugar maple is highly valued for its hard timber, especially for furniture.*

are small fishing villages or ports which send trawlers out to the Grand Banks of Newfoundland, one of the great fishing grounds of the world. Many of the small coastal towns and villages have become summer tourist centres.

In Cape Breton Island, near Sydney, is

thaw. The summer is short and sunny, and has a moderate rainfall. The natural vegetation is grassland, though a line of thin bush separates the grasslands from the true forests on the Shield.

These prairies form the southern part of the provinces of Alberta, Saskatchewan

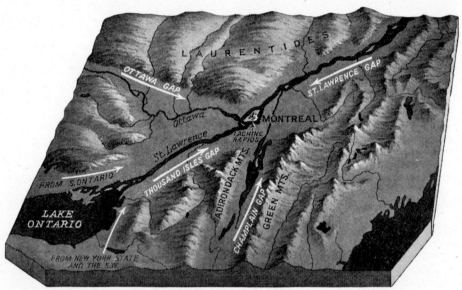

FIG. 115. *Montreal marks the conjunction of four great routes with the St. Lawrence gap.*

Canada's main bituminous coalfield. About a third of the coal is dispatched up the St. Lawrence to Quebec and Montreal or down the coast of Maine. The rest is used locally, chiefly in the large steelworks at Sydney, which are among the largest in the Dominion.

### The Prairie Provinces

Between the Canadian Shield and the Rockies is a wide area of young, little-folded sands, clays and limestones. They form a low plateau slightly dissected by the rivers that drain eastwards from the Rockies. This area has an extreme climate. In winter there are periods of intense cold, when temperatures drop to 40 degrees F., or even 50 degrees F., below zero. At intervals a warm, dry wind called the "Chinook" springs up from the west across the Rockies, and the snow and ice begin to

and Manitoba. The northern part of each is in the Canadian Shield, but they are called the Prairie Provinces since nearly all their people live in the south. The Prairie Provinces and the neighbouring U.S.A. States of the Dakotas and Minnesota form one of the biggest wheat granaries in the world (Fig. 121). The short, hot summer is admirable for spring wheat farming, particularly in years with enough spring rain.

Settlement of the prairies began around Winnipeg in the early nineteenth century, but spread only slowly. Communication with the outside world was by Hudson's Bay Company posts or across the U.S. frontier. Rail connexions with the U.S. were opened up in 1879. The prairies were saved for Canada only by the Canadian Pacific Railway, which in 1883 opened its line through the 1,000 miles of wilderness separating the prairies from the

St. Lawrence valley. As the rails pushed westwards, settlers moved in, and today nearly all the best land has been occupied, and for many years the areas of heavier rainfall have yielded enormous crops of wheat from large, mechanically efficient farms. The prairie farmer lives in the middle of an endless wheatfield in summer, and on a frozen and often snow-covered plain in the winter. Large modern cities such as Winnipeg and Saskatoon collect his wheat and supply his needs of manufactured goods. Much of the wheat goes by rail to the Lake Ports of Fort William and Port Arthur (Fig. 116) whence ships take it to Buffalo or Montreal. It is eventually exported from New York or Montreal to Europe, chiefly to Britain. An increasing weight also goes west to Vancouver, which sends it to Europe via the Panama Canal.

The dependence of the prairie farmer on the one main crop makes him an easy prey for economic depression. The slump of 1931, followed by several years of drought, led many farmers to abandon their holdings and thousands of acres went out of cultivation. Soil erosion set in, and many of the areas became almost desert. The area of low rainfall round Medicine Hat in Alberta has largely gone back to ranching, for which it is best suited.

The soft shales and sandstones on which the prairies are developed contain enormous reserves of low-grade coal. Output is about the same as that of the Sydney field, and nearly all of it is used locally, much of it by the railways. Mining is seasonal, employing more than twice as many people in winter, when farm labour becomes available. Oil has recently been found in Alberta and is being developed.

### The Far West

Going west from the Alberta prairies the transcontinental railways soon begin to climb towards the line of the Rockies, which rise to 10,000 ft. or more, overlooking the prairies by precipitous escarpments. From the Rockies to the Pacific coast the country consists of mountains, high plateaux and deep valleys. There are no extensive lowlands. The highest ranges are the Coast Range and the Selkirks, on the west and east respectively. Between them is con-

FIG. 116. *Grain ships loading at the elevators at Port Arthur, Lake Superior, whence much of the wheat from the Canadian prairies is shipped east to Europe, chiefly to Britain.*

fused land of high plateaux, small enclosed basins, some with lakes, and deep, narrow valleys. The Selkirks are separated from the Rockies by a deep, elongated trench.

British Columbia receives its weather from the Pacific: the Rockies protect it from the extreme cold of the interior in winter, but the milder westerlies from the Pacific often penetrate the province. The winters are mild and very wet along the west-facing Coast Ranges and Vancouver Island, but in the deep valleys of the interior there is less rain and greater cold. The summers are cool and drier on the coast, almost rainless in the south and warm and dry in the interior. The total annual rainfall is low in the interior, but the coast is very wet.

The province is thinly populated: there is not enough flat land to allow a dense farming population. The deep interior valleys support many large orchards, where fine apples, cherries, peaches and apricots are harvested in summer. The hot summer sun ripens the fruit quickly, but the rainfall is usually low enough to make irri-gation necessary. Some of the higher ground in the middle Fraser valley is used for cattle ranching. But although these specialist farmers often get a good living out of the soil, the province will never rival the Prairie Provinces as a farming land. Its primary wealth is in its forests, its fisheries and its minerals. The damp coast ranges are densely forested by Douglas fir and other conifers (Fig. 118). All along the coast are huge cutting areas, sawmills and pulp factories.

The streams which flow into the Pacific, notably the Skeena and the Fraser, are great salmon grounds, and salmon fishing and canning are great local industries, especially at Prince Rupert. There is a large production of copper, lead, zinc and silver from scattered mines all over the province: at Trail on the Columbia River there is an enormous refining and processing plant that ranks among the world's largest. There are great coal reserves, which are scarcely developed as yet, for lack of a market. Pacific Canada is thus a land of large resources and a small popula-

FIG. 117. *A cattle round-up in western Canada, on the steep banks of the Milk River, Alberta. The periodical round-up is necessary for branding as well as for marketing.*

tion; its drawback has been its remoteness from the densely settled parts of North America and its lack of flat land. Vancouver, its main port and capital, is a large and growing city on a splendid site near (but not on) the Fraser delta. It has become a main exporting centre for the western prairies, as the expensive rail-haul for grain is shorter than the haul to the Lake Ports. Victoria, on Vancouver Island, has a climate very like that of England, and with its large colony of retired people the town, more than any other in the New World, resembles a British resort.

As the map shows, there is a strip of lowland running northwards from the prairies to the Arctic coast, separating the Rockies from the Canadian Shield. This lowland has the same general form and surface-character as the Interior Lowland, of which it is the structural continuation. It is drained by one of the world's great river systems, the Mackenzie and its tributaries. To the west is the Yukon Territory, the northernmost part of the western Cordillera.

This North-West has remained largely undeveloped, and there has been little settlement of an extensive, permanent character. The winters are long and intensely cold, temperature averaging some 20 degrees F. below zero in January over large areas. The summers, however, are surprisingly warm. The high latitudes—60 degrees to 70 degrees N.—give a very long midsummer day, and there is much sun. Even on the Arctic Circle the average July temperature is nearly 60 degrees F., which equals that of much of Britain. The frost-free period is, however, short, and the subsoil actually remains permanently frozen in the northern part of the valley. The long hours of daylight allow wheat of special breeds to ripen in 20-30 days less than the prairie wheat, but little is at present grown.

There is today a considerable traffic on the river in summer and some movement by air or dog-train or tractor in winter, chiefly to supply the mining areas of the Shield lying on the northern tributaries, like Yellowknife. There is also a small population of trappers. But agricultural settlement has so far been attempted only in the southern half of the valley, in the Peace River territory. There is much land in this southern section which has a good, well-drained soil and a summer long enough and rainy enough to allow first-class wheat to be grown. The big handicap is the difficulty of communication with the outside world.

The Yukon Territory is even less hospitable to settlement. Fig. 119 shows a great glacier on the boundary of Yukon and Alaska (U.S.A.). Yukon was the scene of the great Klondike gold rush of 1897-8 but today it is almost uninhabited by white settlers. Dawson City, the capital, is only a shade of the bustling, rowdy saloon city that it became during the rush. As in the Mackenzie valley, the long, cold, harsh winter and even greater remoteness have discouraged agricultural settlement.

### United States of America

By far the greater number of the inhabitants of North America live in the United States, which, like Canada, is a land of clearly marked geographical regions. The area of continuous settlement is, however, much greater than in Canada, and the natural regions are not separated by great stretches of wilderness. One region passes into another without any sudden change. The great exception is the Pacific coast, which is cut off from the east by the wide spaces of the western plateaux. But though they are less sharply delimited than the Canadian regions, each has its characteristic influence upon American life. From each particular mode of living spring cultural developments, political viewpoints and social problems. Above all, each region has a characteristic landscape, which partly rises from the structure and climate and partly from the uses the inhabitants make of the soil.

Over 181,000,000 people live in the U.S.A. Most of them live in the cities and farms of the Middle West and northeast. The west is thinly populated except for a narrow belt along the Pacific coast. English and Scots-Irish settlers were the most numerous pioneer groups in nearly all areas, but there were large immigrations of central and south European settlers in the nineteenth and early twentieth centuries. English has remained the spoken

language, but in most places a majority of non-English surnames reveals the composite origin of the American people. In addition to the white population there are some 15,000,000 coloured people, chiefly in the south and in the cities of the north-east.

The United States is now the world's first industrial power. She is largely self-supporting in food and other necessities and has a very high standard of living. As well as feeding her own people, she has a large exportable surplus of foodstuffs, chiefly grain. Both her agriculture and her industry increased their output during the Second World War, and her economic problems are chiefly those of disposing of her plenty with profit, which is not easy in a world of unrest.

The American farming countryside is often dull, and sometimes unsightly; but it is none the less productive, and the U.S.A. is one of the great food-producing countries of the world. There is a simple and natural division into three great clim-

Fig. 118. *The Alcan Highway, linking Alaska with Canada (whence the name Alcan), extends from Fort St. John, British Columbia, to the Yukon boundary and thence to Fairbanks, Alaska. Skirting the eastern flank of the Canadian Rockies, it runs past mighty glaciers, vast lakes and dense coniferous forests. Much of this magnificent country is preserved as a national park, abounding in wild life of great variety.*

coast and the humid east are devoted to arable farming or to food production for the greater cities. The arid west, on the other hand, is mostly poor grazing land. Because of the considerable latitudinal range of the country, however, these major divisions can be subdivided further by lines running roughly east-west, and depending on temperature. In the south of each division conditions are sub-tropical, but temperature falls off northward, with consequent changes in the farm economy. These main divisions will now be examined.

Most heavy rain in America falls from moist warm air coming from the Gulf of Mexico or the Atlantic, either when the heat of the sun causes thunderstorms to develop or when the warm air is forced to rise over wedges of colder air from Canada. The former is usual in summer, the latter in the remaining seasons. The rainfall is greatest in the region most often reached by the rain-bearing winds, i.e. the south-east. Rainfall falls off north-westward. In general, it is adequate for arable farming to about longitude 100 degrees W. all the way from the Gulf to the Canadian border. In the extreme south-east it is actually too heavy for the ordinary temperate crops.

The whole of this great area gets hot summers and cold winters; the heat of summer does not vary much, but the length and severity of winter increase rapidly from south to north. Along the Gulf coast the winters are milder than those of Cornwall, but along the Canadian border they are long and fierce; the rivers freeze and a deep snow-cover accumulates. The use to which it is possible to put the land depends mainly on this variation in the length and severity of the winter. The east is therefore divided into a series of belts, each with its

atic belts: the Pacific belt, with humid, mild, west-coast climates like those of western Europe; the arid west, with a semi-desert climate marked by too little rain and too much sun; and the humid belt east, roughly, of 100 degrees W., with enough rain but great extremes of temperature, the winters being very cold and the summers hot.

A glance at the map shows that these major climatic divisions show up quite clearly as agricultural regions. The Pacific

FIG. 119. *The Great Barnard Glacier, near the Alaska-Canada border. The thickness of the ice is estimated at one thousand feet, and the glacier is a mile in width. This great stream of ice, which flows for twenty-five miles, carries numerous medial moraines collected from tributary glaciers which join forces with it at different points along its course.*

The range of mountains seen in the background of this magnificent air photograph by W. Washburn, of the New England Natural History Museum, Boston, Mass., marks the boundary of Canada with the Alaskan Territory of the U.S.A. Glaciers are found in the Polar regions and in high valleys of mountainous tracts where the snow falls faster than it melts.

typical methods and rural landscape. We cannot deal with all the regions in detail, and must concentrate on those most significant to the national economy.

In the warm and rainy south the dominant crop is cotton. Cultivated and picked by Negro labour, this sub-tropical plant is grown in the regions where more than two hundred frost-free days can be expected in a year, for frost kills or damages the crop. Although the plant has been attacked by pests for many years, about half the world's cotton is grown in the southern states. Texas, traditionally the ranching state, is the biggest producing area, the cotton being grown in the wetter eastern half of the state. Soil erosion, discussed later in the chapter, has been active for a long time in the "Cotton Belt," and many areas have been crippled or rendered permanently unsuitable for cultivation.

### The Middle West

Perhaps the most "American" land of all is the Corn Belt, occupying the broad plains between the Missouri and Ohio Rivers, but not crossing the Appalachians. Here much of the land is under maize, which is mainly fed to beef cattle and pigs, the main market products. This now prosperous farming land, the Middle West, is covered by the deposits of the continental ice sheets which spread out from Canada in recent geological times. These fertile, easily ploughed soils are now closely cultivated. The farmers live in isolated farms scattered far and wide over the landscape. Most of the animals slaughtered at Chicago are fattened in this region. The farming community of the Middle West is one of the strongest and most conservative elements of American society, having a political influence far beyond its numbers. It is the traditional home of isolationism.

Farther north than the Corn Belt is a wide area stretching from Wisconsin into New England where the primary objective in farming is to provide milk, eggs, and vegetables for the big cities. The St. Lawrence valley of Canada is very similar, so that no further description need be given here.

The great wheatlands of the U.S.A. lie, as in Canada, on the western edges of the humid east. Here, on the once grassy prairies, there has developed the same extensive culture of wheat that characterizes the Canadian prairies. Even more than the Canadian prairies, these lands (with their erratic rainfall) have suffered from frequent crop failures and disastrous erosion of soil. There are still, however, enormous wheat acreages, spring-sown in the Dakotas and Minnesota, winter-sown in the warmer lands of Kansas, Missouri and Oklahoma farther south.

Wheat, livestock, cotton, maize—what are their ultimate destinations? The wheat and cotton are partly used at home. The rest of the cotton mainly went to Europe or Japan before 1940, but the depressed state of Lancashire's cotton industry had affected this trade. The wheat surplus is shipped to Europe, with that of Canada, from the ports in the east. The dairy produce, eggs and meat are mainly used in America, but some comes to Britain.

### The Ranch Country

The life of the people of the droughty plains, plateaux and ranges of the west is familiar to the world through the "westerns" of the cinema and the circulating library. The gun-packing cowhand and the Texas longhorns have vanished from the range, but the range itself is there still, if a little the worse for wear. The longhorn has given way to the better beef breeds, and the cowhand now rides the ranges in an automobile or a high-powered truck. The ranches of the cattle and sheep farmers are still scattered at remote distances, for one needs a lot of land of this poor quality to feed a steer. The cattle are bred and reared on the dry, healthy, western ranges, but they are railed east to the Middle West for fattening. The west has suffered badly from over-stocking and soil erosion (page 187).

Some of the higher ranges of the Rockies and other mountain systems have a heavier rainfall and snowfall than the lower plateaux. Perennial streams come down from the ranges, often to be lost in the sands of the arid plateau surface. Some, however, make their way to the sea in spectacular canyons, like those of the Colorado (Grand Canyon) and the Snake, or the

FIG. 120. *Cotton-pickers in southern U.S.A. emptying raw cotton from their collecting sacks into baskets. The work is done by coloured labourers, mostly of mixed descent.*

gorges of the Columbia. Many of these streams have been dammed, and now feed rich irrigated lands. These artificial oases are found in many places in the arid west. Typical is the old Mormon colony of Utah, centred round Salt Lake City. The Great Salt Lake is the salty relic of a once greater lake, whose fertile silts and loams surround the modern shores. Irrigation water from the Wasatch Mountains has converted the once arid landscape into an area of great fertility, where sugar-beet, wheat (with enormous yields), fruit and vegetables are grown.

Parts of this western region are so rainless that they are true deserts, like the Mojave and Colorado deserts of California. The arid west, strictly speaking, includes even the Pacific coast of California south of latitude 35 degrees N. The Los Angeles basin is perhaps the greatest of the rich, irrigated areas.

### Pacific Farmlands

Most recently developed among America's farmlands, those of the Pacific states are among the richest and most colourful. Here there is abundant water, for the Pacific storms give heavy rain or snow, chiefly in winter. The summers are in most areas brilliant, sunny and hot, with few rainy periods. The rains or snows fall mainly in the hills, especially on the west-

ern face of the Cascade Mountains and the Sierra Nevada. The lower ground between these hills and the Coast Ranges is much drier, and in the Great Valley of California rain is definitely inadequate. But the streams coming down from the mountain maintain a good supply of water for irrigation, and the Great Valley is hence one of the world's main fruit-growing areas. The corresponding valley in Oregon and Washington has enough rain for general farming without this assistance.

The main Pacific crops are fruits, vegetables and cereals; citrus fruits like oranges and lemons in southern California; peaches, prunes, raisins and the like in the Great Valley and in southern Oregon; apples in the north. Wheat is extensively grown on the plateau behind the Cascades in Washington, where the plateau is trenched by the gorge of the Columbia River. The early vegetables of many American homes come from the areas of lowland in coastal California. These rich but scattered farmlands have contributed much to the wealth of the American larder.

The Great Valley of California is potentially an even richer farmland than it is to-day. There are large areas of good soil whose development has so far been hindered by the erratic nature of the water supply. The valley has three main streams,

FIG. 121. *A fleet of giant reaping machines at work on the wheatlands of Alberta, Canada. The wheat belt of North America extends on both sides of the Canada-U.S.A. border and*

all of which are fed by snow melt-waters, and are consequently subject to very irregular flow. In past years the uncontrolled use of their water for irrigation led to a fall of the water-table in the valley, with a consequent diminution in soil fertility and in the surface-flow of water. It is now proposed to dam the headwaters of these streams so as to regularize the flow, and to distribute the water more evenly through the valley, the whole programme being organized by a collective authority resembling the famous Tennessee Valley Authority. As in the case of the T.V.A., the scheme provides for the generation of enormous quantities of hydro-electric power, but the sale of this power at low prices has so far been successfully opposed by privately-owned power companies. Similar opposition was raised to the sale of T.V.A. power, but in that case it was eventually overcome. In any event, the Great Valley scheme will bring many more acres under cultivation in one of the finest climates in the world for fruits and cereals.

### Industrial America

But when all is said and done, it is as an industrial nation that the U.S.A. has risen to pre-eminence in world power. She is not only the greatest industrial power; her industry is also, collectively speaking, the most efficient and the most forward-looking. It is not only true that she is the world's greatest steel-producer, but no other nation can rival the way in which she turned that steel into the colossus of American industry. Her position springs from her great natural wealth in the raw materials on which all industries depend. What these materials are and where they are found are primary facts of geography. We cannot trace the whole history of big business in America, but we can at least show why the main industries occur in certain definite places. We shall look at some of these industries in this section.

The high Allegheny plateau, which is the westernmost part of the Appalachian Cordillera, contains bed after bed of high quality bituminous coal. The coal is little disturbed, and, unlike coal in Britain, occurs in thick seams. It actually crops out along the valley-sides, so that the mines can be driven in horizontally instead of vertically. Nine hundred miles away, around the western point of Lake Superior, are the world's richest iron-ore deposits. These two areas have between them very largely accounted for the growth of the American steel industry.

A geographical accident has very much favoured the growth of steel manufacturing in the Alleghenies. The abundant Lake Superior iron ores were a very long way off, and to rail them to Pennsylvania or West Virginia (where the main Allegheny coalfields are found) would be prohibitively expensive. But stretching almost from the iron mines to within a hundred miles of the

*occupies the grassland area known generally as the "prairies." A corresponding region in the southern hemisphere is the "pampas" of the Argentine, illustrated in Fig. 137.*

coalfields was the great inland waterway of the Great Lakes (see map on page 161).

A huge, flat-bottomed ore boat, probably displacing 20,000 tons, can leave Duluth or Superior, steam east across Lake Superior, then through the Soo canals into Lake Huron, along the St. Clair River at Detroit, and land its ore on the south shore of Lake Erie at one of the great ports, such as Cleveland. It is then a short rail haul to the coalfield, or the coal can be railed down for smelting the ore at the port.

The great steelworks are found mainly in the Pittsburgh area. In many ways this smoky city resembles Sheffield, both in site and function. It is at the junction of the two main headstreams of the Ohio River, and, like Sheffield, draws its ores from far afield. Of smaller, but growing, importance are the steel industries of Alabama, centred round Birmingham. Using the cheaper local labour (much of it coloured) and the coal and iron ore from local fields, this producing area is fortunately placed in all but transportation facilities. It is far from the great waterways which have assisted the industries of the north.

The Great Lakes have become the world's most important inland waterway as a result of this traffic. Not only does the iron ore come along this highway, but nearly all the Canadian prairie wheat which moves eastward is shipped from Port Arthur and Fort William to Buffalo or Montreal. The use of the Lakes by large steamers has been made possible by constructing canals to by-pass the few obstacles which exist along the route. The waters of Lake Superior drain into Huron at Sault St. Marie ("Soo") along the rapid-choked course of the St. Mary's River. Today, five canals (the Soo canals) bridge the gap. Similar deep channels link Lake Huron to Lake Erie. But the greatest obstacle was at Niagara, between Lakes Erie and Ontario. This obstacle is now circumvented by the great Welland Canal, which enables large lake steamers to go directly from Fort William or Port Arthur to the ocean port of Montreal. Some idea of the importance of the Lakes is given by the fact that more than five times the tonnage of shipping uses the Soo canals in six months than uses the Suez Canal in a year. With the completion of the whole of the St. Lawrence Seaway, even ocean-going ships are able to sail into the Great Lakes and back again.

Of an entirely different character are the great oilfields. These are scattered over many parts of the country. Two groups of fields, however, outweigh all the others in importance, for between them they raise about one-third of the world's oil. These are the mid-continental group (chiefly in Texas and Oklahoma) and the southern California group (between San Francisco and Los Angeles). Much of the output of the mid-continental field is pumped along very long pipe-lines to Chicago or the north-east. The U.S.A. has great secondary manufactures. The greater part of these industries is, however, concentrated round the cities and plains of the north-east, round New York, Boston, Philadelphia and the like. This was one of the results of the historical accident of early settlement, and is intimately bound up with the growth of cities.

### The Great Cities

New York has a population of over 8,000,000; Chicago over 3,700,000, Los Angeles and Philadelphia over 2,000,000; Detroit nearly 2,000,000; Baltimore, St. Louis, Cleveland and Boston (with suburbs) have about 1,000,000. These cities are all centres of amusement and social amenities, of utilities, of services and communications. Each has its industries, some to meet the miscellaneous needs of its own population, some for export to a wide field. We can do no more here than sketch the development of three great groups of urban communities: (i) the north-eastern group, including New York, Philadelphia, Boston and Baltimore; (ii) Chicago; (iii) the rival Pacific cities of Los Angeles and San Francisco.

Most of the big cities of the north-east are quite old. They are mainly coastal in site, and were first built as ports of supply for the British colonies. Later, as the great westward pioneering treks began, they grew rapidly as ports of entry both for

immigrants and the supply of imports needed by the rapidly growing colonies. Today they are still ports, but now their traffic is in commodities and not in immigrants. Although there are many small ports along the Atlantic coast, those that grew in the manner described owe their growth to these main factors:

(a) a good harbour,
(b) a rich and well-settled hinterland, and
(c) easy access across the Appalachians to the interior.

*New York* is by far the greatest of these cities (Fig. 109); it handles half the overseas trade of America. Its harbour is excellent, it has had for two centuries a

FIG. 122. *Niagara Falls are among the grandest natural spectacles of North America. They are situated on the Niagara River, which flows from Lake Erie to Lake Ontario and forms part of the border between Canada and the United States. As explained in Fig. 26, the falls are gradually receding upstream. The Horseshoe (or Canadian) Fall is seen on the right of this illustration, and the American Fall (U.S.A.) on the left. Between the two falls is Goat Island. At the foot of the Horseshoe Fall, which is over 2,000 feet wide and 158 feet high, is one of the world's greatest hydro-electric power-stations. The America Fall is 162 feet high and 1,000 feet in width.*

short-range hinterland of some richness, but above all it stands at the mouth of the Hudson River, which, with its tributary the Mohawk, provides the only easy crossing of the Appalachians. Once the Indians were cleared from this route, it began to canalize the greater part of westward-moving immigrant streams, firstly along the Erie Canal and later along the water-level tracks of the New York Central Railroad. Today New York is America's greatest port, and as long as America's seaborne trade looks mainly towards Europe it is bound to remain so, because of its unrivalled access to the rich interior. The richness of the Pacific market is, however, turning the eyes of American exporters to the Pacific coast, away from the Atlantic ports.

*Philadelphia* and *Baltimore* were also ports which handled a great deal of the immigrant traffic; they command possible routes across the Appalachians, but the gaps concerned (used by the Chesapeake and Ohio, the Baltimore and Ohio, and Pennsylvania railroads) are quite hilly, and have not been able to compete with the Hudson-Mohawk gap. Both cities are still considerable ports, but they are small by comparison with New York.

*Boston* is in a class of its own. It has never served, as the others have, as a main continental port of entry or of commerce. It has served the rich industrial hinterland of New England, the group of states north-

east of New York City. It has lost a great
deal of its trade to New York, and is now
only the port of a ring of industrial towns
immediately on its doorstep. But Boston
is unique in having been the cultural capital
of the American colonies, and Harvard
University, now world-famous, was founded in 1636 in nearby Cambridge. Even today many of America's great publishing
houses have their offices in Boston, and
there are few intellectual activities in which
the city is deficient. It has a charm and
a dignity lacking in many other cities, and
it even boasts an aristocracy of birth, which
it shares with few other American cities.
The equalitarian philosophy of American
life does not extend to the old families of
this unique cultural centre.

Around these old cities of the north
there has sprung up the largest and most
productive manufacturing region in the
world. It is impossible to deal adequately
with the whole complex industrial network,
but mention must be made of the cities of
the lowlands round Boston, where much of
America's cotton, woollen, leather and shoe

manufacture is localized. These towns
have lost some of their work and people to
New York, which is in itself much the
biggest of the manufacturing centres. All
the big cities, however, are centres of manufactures of miscellaneous description. If
we can distinguish the Middle West as the
rural heart of America, then there can be
no question that the north-east is the
industrial heart, eccentrically situated
though it is.

The great cities of the Middle West are,
however, of quite a different character.
They are mostly very young, having sprung
into existence in a brief but hectic pioneering phase and grown to maturity as the
supply centres of America's agricultural
nucleus. The greatest of these—indeed
one of the world's greatest cities—is
*Chicago* (Fig. 123), the Windy City on the
banks of Lake Michigan. The latter projects south into the heart of the fertile
mid-west; therefore when lake shipping
brought settlers and supplies to its southern
extremity, they were within easy reach
of the newly opened lands. Chicago grew

FIG. 123. *Chicago, on Lake Michigan, hub of the Middle West and second largest U.S. city, is notable for its great meat-packing industry and for its handsome modern buildings.*

Fig. 124. *The Golden Gate, San Francisco. This splendid entry from the Pacific into San Francisco Bay is flanked by San Francisco City on the south and on the north by hills and a wooded National Park. Two beautiful bridges cross the Golden Gate and the Bay.*

up on the site of an old French fort, and in its early days it served as the lake port through which much of the supplies of the growing west had to pass. Railways were built away from it in all directions, so that it became the natural centre of the mid-west not only in supplies, but in all the multifarious commerce of a growing country. Today its function as a lake port is less significant, and it is pre-eminently the hub of America's railways. If in England all trains go to Crewe, then in the U.S.A. they all go to Chicago. Furthermore, it is a railroad terminal town: there are few through routes or trains. It has grown from a small lake-port into a city of 3,700,000 inhabitants. The site has made it the capital of the American mid-west, and one day may make it the economic capital of the entire continent.

Chicago's industries are very varied and important, but the greatest are those concerned with the farm products of the Middle West and West. It is above all a meat-packing centre. Every year millions of hogs and beef-cattle are slaughtered in its abattoirs and canning factories, to appear on the world's dinner table. There are many by-product industries, as well as a great organization for the manufacture and supply of farming implements. By her remoteness from the sea, Chicago has been the heart of isolationist America, and her people have been little concerned with the affairs of the outside world. Their own city was too dazzling a spectacle for them to be concerned with European affairs. The impact of the Second World War has materially changed this attitude, though it cannot be said to have eliminated it.

Perhaps the most remarkable of all America's cities are the great Pacific rivals of *Los Angeles* and *San Francisco.* San Francisco (800,000), with its famous outlet, the Golden Gate (Fig. 124), is the chief American Pacific port. Sited on the gap in the coast ranges of California which brings the sea into direct contact with the Great Californian Valley, it has acted not only as the natural centre of this developing agricultural region, but also as the Pacific outlet for the great local oilfields and of the

FIG. 125. *The Hoover Dam, Nevada-Arizona, is 730 feet in height and measures 1,000 feet along its crest. Its function is to control the lower Colorado River for irrigation purposes and the generation of power. The Dam is administered by the U.S. Reclamation Service.*

nation generally. Los Angeles, however, is a phenomenon that cannot be explained by geography alone. Set in a small enclosed coastal basin in south California, it has a warm, sunny, and very dry climate. There are extensive fruit orchards and plantations in the surrounding hills, but the local environment is singularly sterile; there is not even a good natural harbour. Yet Los Angeles has grown to be America's fourth city, with more than 2,000,000 inhabitants. This growth is to some extent conditioned by her climate, which has attracted the film industry—Hollywood is part of Los Angeles—and wealthy retired people who have settled by the thousand in the city and surrounding hills. But the growth of the modern city in this rather barren though colourful corner of California is some-

thing of a mystery even to the Americans themselves. An American from Los Angeles once said to the writer that he thought that the city might some day explode into fragments, as its inhabitants suddenly woke from dreams into consciousness. However this may be, it is true that Los Angeles is the centre today of many of the lighter manufacturing industries, notably the aircraft industry, for which the climate is eminently suited.

The interest of the American nations in the Pacific and its vast potential markets has grown rapidly under the stimulus of war. The predominance of European trade in the overseas economy of the U.S.A., for example, can no longer be regarded as permanent. The Pacific ports and cities are undergoing a "boom" more dramatic in some ways than the gold rush. There is more law and order about it, but the importance of the westward migration of industry and population far exceeds that of the gold rush. One often reads in the Press of some new westward move on the part of industry, chiefly of light manufactures whose raw materials are inexpensive to transport. Behind these movements there is much more than a psychological factor of the kind to which American society is prone; there is a hard-headed calculation as to the future importance of Pacific trade and the stimulus it will give to the general economic life of the coast.

### Wasted Assets

The use of the natural resources in both Canada and U.S.A. has been careless and wasteful in many cases and both countries are now faced with vital conservation problems. Greatest of these is the preservation of the soil, a wasted and still wasting asset. In many ways America still suffers from the pioneer outlook, with its optimism, carelessness of resources and lack of thrift. As each pioneer group entered the westward-moving frontier, it at once made the utmost use of each new resource encountered, usually with little regard for the future. In the words of W. W. Atwood: "When forests are cleared away to provide farmlands, huge logs of birch, beech, oak, walnut, maple, hickory, pine and hemlock were piled up and burned. . . . Soils were overcropped, pasture lands over-grazed, fish and game ruthlessly destroyed. . . . Later, in the mining of coal, great columns of the black fuel were left and but a fraction of the most saleable . . . was taken from the ground. For many years great torches burned day and night in western Pennsylvania, where natural gas had been released from the ground. . . . The great torches now burning in the mid-continental oil and gas fields demonstrate that some problems of conservation have not yet been solved."

In the pre-pioneer days most of the surface of America was covered either by forest (in the humid east and on the Pacific coast) or grass (the drier west). The heavy and torrential rainstorms characteristic of the climate of almost all areas, even the arid west, could do little damage to soils so protected, nor could the high winds of droughty summers whip them up to form dust storms. The soil, the vegetation and the climate were in a state of hidden and delicate equilibrium. When the pioneers arrived and began to farm the lands, this equilibrium was disturbed. In the east, the lower ground was cleared and ploughed, and planted mainly with crops familiar to the Europeans who settled the country. In the drier west the ground was ploughed where there was even a hope of enough rainfall to raise wheat. Finally the driest lands with their thin grass and scrub cover were heavily grazed by cattle and sheep. Natural equilibrium was gone, and it became apparent that a new equilibrium would be hard to find. Erosion of the soil began, and was soon proceeding rapidly.

### Soil Erosion

The agents of erosion are rain and wind. Rain acts in two principal ways, both of which are at their most effective in heavy storms when the rush of water is very great. "Gullying" is the growth of deep, steep-sided gullies or shallow ravines, chiefly along slight pre-existing shallows. Some gullies have attained depths of over 100 feet in thirty or forty years, and, in the steeply sloping western ranges, have even been known to achieve this depth overnight. They occur chiefly on steeply sloping land.

"Sheet erosion" implies the removal of the whole of the soil from the steeper slopes by rain wastes flowing directly down the gradient. Though less spectacular than gullying, sheet erosion has actually destroyed more topsoil than any other agent. The deep soils of the Piedmont of Georgia and the Carolinas have suffered disastrously both from sheet erosion and gullying. Farther west, in Oklahoma, almost half the state has gone—and Oklahoma is a young, recently settled state. Many of these eastern lands are sown with inter-tilled crops like maize, where the ground between the widely spaced rows is kept free of weeds, thus exposing it to ready erosion.

Today there are few areas whose soil is quite intact. In the east and west alike, destruction has been widespread. About 50 per cent of the soil of the country has been badly damaged by erosion to date. It is being re-deposited in river deltas, on floodplains, or (by the wind) in the oceans.

Wind erosion affects the drier ploughed lands and the over-grazed grasslands of the arid west. It takes the form of the lifting of the finer soil particles by gusty winds. Strong and turbulent winds passing over a dry, bare soil may raise a cloud of dust which can be transported miles from the source before being re-deposited. In drought years the loss of soil may be very severe. The droughts of the middle thirties led to fierce dust storms and to the ruin of huge areas of the ploughed surface of the high plains and the prairies.

Much has been done in recent years to halt this disastrous loss. The U.S. Soil Conservation Service has embarked on an extensive campaign of prevention and cure, or at least of stabilization. It is too early to say that the disaster has been arrested, but much loss has already been averted. Education of the public and particularly of the farmers has been a main method of attack. The gullies are being blocked,

sometimes by dams, sometimes by tree planting. The heavily damaged steeper slopes are being re-forested. The remaining sloping areas still under cultivation are now being ploughed along the contour, so that water tends to percolate instead of running down the slope. The perennial sowing of arable land under one crop is being replaced by intelligently planned crop rotations, which are aimed at maintaining the soil structure and fertility, and which will help to improve the balance of the agricultural economy. The intelligent use of fertilizers to replace lost soil components is also an important item of policy.

The new awareness of the Americas of the conservation problems is one thing, but to translate that awareness into effective action is quite another; it requires political action and enforcement, and these have not always been forthcoming. Most of the major problems, such as flood-control and soil erosion, need action at the federal level. They are not local problems, though they may affect one locality far more than another. Both Canada and the U.S.A. are federal countries in which the powers of the central government are

FIG. 126. *Soil erosion is a national menace in the U.S.A. Until a large-scale policy of reclamation was adopted, vast areas of valuable farm land had been reduced to the barren condition of the valley shown below, and erosion was progressing at an alarming rate.*

Fig. 127. *Land reclamation under the T.V.A. Project. By contour ploughing and the sowing of nitrogen-fixing plants, fertility has been restored to this previously barren countryside. In the early years of the Project, the 2,000 farmers participating had to sacrifice a part of their livelihood, but later they were repaid by vastly increased yields.*

strictly defined and limited. Since these conservation questions were little understood at the time of the confederations, the federal authority is often found not to extend far enough to deal with them.

In the U.S.A. particularly, this difficulty has been overcome partly by the creation of intermediate planning authorities, which lie somewhere between the state and the federal levels of government. The greatest and most significant of these is the Tennessee Valley Authority, created by Congress in 1933, under the Roosevelt administration. Since its inception it has regularized the flow of the Tennessee River, notorious for its floods, provided facilities for cheap hydro-electric power, improved the social conditions of the people of the valley, and embarked on a campaign to eliminate soil erosion and develop this backward area.

The dams, the modern architecture, the progressive social policy of the Authority have made a great impression on the American peoples. But more significant than the new installations has been the rehabilitation of the people. Fig. 127 illustrates some of the good work. Furthermore, the programme is being undertaken by a body whose authority extends into several states. It is probably by means of such organizations that land conservation will ultimately be carried out in North America.

## Test Yourself

1. What are the three main climatic divisions of the United States? What types of agricultural activities are associated with each of these divisions?

2. Trace in detail the course of the border between Canada and the U.S.A. This frontier is a customs and exchange barrier, but is undefended. What do you suppose would be the economic significance of a shift southwards of the border west of the Great Lakes?

3. Explain how the delicate equilibrium between climate, soil and vegetation in North America came to be upset and what disastrous results have followed. Describe the measures taken to remedy the situation.

*Answers will be found at the end of the book.*

Fig. 128. *Buenos Aires, capital of the Argentine and largest city and port in the south-ern hemisphere. In the centre of the photograph is the Palace of Congress, situated at the end of the mile-long Avenida de Mayo, in one of the most beautiful plazas in the world.*

# CHAPTER IX

# LATIN AMERICA

FROM the Rio Grande del Norte, which divides U.S. from Mexican territory, to Cape Horn, almost the whole mainland of the New World bears the distinctive impress of the Spanish and Portuguese colonial empires and has come to be known as Latin America, a collective title that marks it off from the predominantly Anglo-Saxon areas of the United States and Canada. The West Indies were also under the domination of Spain, and were indeed the jumping-off grounds from which its stream of conquest worked northwards into California and southwards into Chile; but being more accessible to aggressive maritime powers—British, Dutch and French—they were lost to Spain one after another and are less Latin than the mainland countries.

## Early Conquerors

Spain and Portugal owed their vast colonial empires in the New World in the first instance to the discoveries of Columbus and the Portuguese navigators who opened the ways to conquerors such as Cortes and Pizarro and their followers. Within fifty years of Columbus's first voyage Spain had carved out an empire which stretched from California to Chile, while within a century Portugal had secured the eastern coastlands. The occupation and settlement of these vast domains by Spain and Portugal were never seriously interrupted till the break-up of the respective empires by internal revolt in the nineteenth century, and even since then the chief external cultural ties have been with Spain and Portugal. Thus Brazil is Portuguese in language and civilization; and the republics into which the Spanish colonial empire has been divided—Argentina, Mexico, Chile, Peru and Colombia among others—are Spanish in language, culture and customs.

The outstanding feature in the geographical environment of the Latin American mainland and of the West Indies is their tropical climate. Of all continents, South America has the greatest proportion of its area within the tropical zone, while all the West Indies and Central America, and most of Mexico that matters are also within the tropics. This feature combined with much high relief gives rise to a generally heavy and often excessive rainfall, many rivers and cataracts, extensive primeval rain-forests and an enervating, unwholesome climate on the tropical lowlands. Such conditions are hostile to men of any race, and large areas remain even now, after the four centuries of European settlement, little developed and thinly populated.

On the tropical plateaux of Mexico at upwards of 7,000 feet, of the Andes, which range in height from over 3,000 feet in Venezuela to 9,000 feet in Colombia and Ecuador and to over 12,000 feet in Peru and Bolivia, and of Brazil which rises to more than 3,000 feet over a wide area, the cooler and commonly rather dry climate and the absence of forests have been favourable to human settlement. Fairly large populations have grown on these plateaux, living mainly by agriculture and pastoral activities. It is significant that the capitals of Mexico, of most of the Central American republics, of Venezuela, Colombia, Ecuador and Bolivia are all at elevations of 3,000 to 12,000 feet above the sea.

## Temperate Regions

The temperate, tapering part of South America from the tropic of Capricorn to about 40 degrees S. has, in contrast with the rest of Latin America, a pleasant and healthy climate, a high average agricultural productivity, and a comparatively dense population. It includes the southern extension of the Brazilian plateau, the River Plate lowlands, and the valley of central Chile, all of which have been settled largely by people of European origin. South of 40 degrees S. in the belt of stormy westerly winds, the mountain barrier of the Andes against the Pacific divides the peninsula

lengthwise into two inhospitable zones—a rugged narrow one to the west which is bleak, rain-drenched and sunless, and the broader Patagonian plateau to the east which is mainly arid, windswept and cold. Poor in resources, neither of these is ever likely to attract numerous settlers.

The features which compose the physical setting in Latin America are on a grand scale. Their forms are striking, and their size is overwhelming. Nowhere else are there such continuous high chains as the Andes, nor such an array of volcanoes, extinct and active, as those of Mexico and the Pacific countries of South America; there is no other river in the world that can compare with the Amazon in size and length of navigable waterway, and no forests so extensive and unbroken as those which cover its lowland basin; nor is there any desert so absolute as that of the Chilean-Peruvian coast; the Pampas plains of the River Plate are unequalled in their extent of temperate grasslands which stretch almost dead level for hundreds of miles around Buenos Aires; while the tropical grasslands of the Brazilian plateau are surpassed in area only by those of Africa.

These and other great works of Nature in Latin America have influenced the character and the lives of the people who have lived with them. The native Indians seem to have regarded them as master spirits, and thus developed, except in the extreme south, a stolid passivity which has condemned them to poverty, and which made them an easy prey to their European conquerors. The latter, coming fresh from driving the Moors out of Spain and Portugal, were stimulated by the grandeur of their new surroundings. The energy they developed in the new world was amazing, and the dramatic and violent qualities in their character were accentuated, as was shown by the speed and ruthlessness with which they took and occupied vast areas.

The numbers of Spanish and Portuguese who settled in Latin America, and even of their descendants by intermarriage with native Indians have always been small compared with the areas occupied. Thus settlement by Europeans has been selective, being concentrated in the more attractive parts, many of which in tropical Latin America are situated high upon the Andes or on the Brazilian plateau, distant and difficult to reach from the sea. Even in temperate South America only the more productive and accessible parts have been properly settled, while between them are wide gaps of thinly peopled or uninhabited country.

The isolation of many regions of settlement throughout Latin America, such as those of the Andean, Brazilian and Mexican plateaux, has forced their inhabitants to be self-sufficing and so to remain backward, especially where most of the people are largely of Indian descent. More-

CARIBBEAN SEA

WEST INDIES

NORTH ATLANTIC OCEAN

Barranquilla
Cartagena
Caracas
TRINIDAD
Maracaibo
Georgetown
Paramaribo
Medellín
Bogotá
LLANOS OF THE ORINOCO
HIGHLANDS OF GUIANA
Gulf of Panamá
Panamá Canal

Quito
Guayaquil
SELVAS

Para
Sao Luiz
EQUATOR
Ceara

OF THE AMAZON
Manaos
Natal

Marañon
Pernambuco

Trujillo
Lima
R. Rimac
Callao
Cerro de Pasco
A N D E S

PLATEAU OF MATTO GROSSO

BRAZILIAN

Cuzco
L. Titicaca
La Paz
PLATEAU OF POTOSI
BOLIVIA
Iquique

MINAS GERAES
PLATEAU
Ouro Preto

SOUTH

Antofagasta

EL GRAN CHACO
Asuncion
Sao Paulo
TROPIC OF CAPRICORN
Rio de Janeiro

PACIFIC

ATACAMA DESERT

Santos

OCEAN

Tucuman

P A M P A S

SOUTH

Valparaiso
Santiago
Cordoba
Rosario
Porto Alegre
Lagoa dos Patos
Rio Grande do Sul

ATLANTIC

AN FERNANDEZ ISLANDS

Buenos Aires
Montevideo
River Plate

OCEAN

Concepcion
Bahia Blanca
Valdivia
Colorado
Negro

FALKLAND ISLANDS

Magellan Str.
Punta Arenas
TIERRA DEL FUEGO
Cape Horn

LATIN AMERICA
SHOWING PHYSICAL FEATURES
AND PRINCIPAL CITIES

FOLD MOUNTAINS    PLATEAUX    SCARPS

DESERTS    SEAS DEEPER THAN 100 FATHOMS    MARSHES

over, isolation has produced separatism. A constant problem in Brazil and the other larger countries has been to weld into a national unit these widely separated and often diverse centres of population.

Three races—native Indians, southern Europeans, and Negroes—have contributed in different proportions in various parts of Latin America to the composition of the peoples who inhabit it today. The native Indians were never numerous except in scattered districts of the Inca empire in Peru, in the heart-region of the Aztec empire in southern Mexico and in some of the West Indies, in all of which their numbers were sadly reduced under Spanish rule. However, Indian blood predominates in the peoples of most of the inland areas of Latin America, and in some less accessible or less inviting places such as Bolivia and the Amazon valley, pure or nearly pure Indians form the majority of the population.

### White Populations

Europeans, on the other hand, predominate in the temperate lands of the River Plate, in the Santiago-Valparaiso district of Chile and in the Rio de Janeiro-São Paulo region of Brazil. They are also the most numerous element in the capital cities of Lima in Peru, Bogotá in Colombia, Caracas in Venezuela, and in Mexico City, whence they control the political life of the whole of their respective countries. Even in these capital cities, however, *mestizos* (as people of mixed Indian and European descent are called) are common, and elsewhere the European element declines with distance from them.

Negroes, descended from the slaves who were imported to work on the plantations in former times, are numerous on the tropical northern coastlands of South America and in most of the West Indies except Cuba. Indeed, in some of the coastal towns, such as San Salvador (Bahia) in Brazil and Barranquilla in Colombia, they make up the bulk of the population, as they also do in Jamaica, Haiti and the smaller West Indian islands.

These various classes of population have each their own special character. The Europeans of Spanish and Portuguese descent are vigorous enough, but in general avoid manual labour if possible; as the principal landowners, they expect others to perform the necessary work; they are rather haughty in their bearing, and devote themselves to administering their estates, to law and to politics, or to the arts. In recent times numerous Italian immigrants have settled in the River Plate country of Argentina and in the coffee lands of Brazil. They are generally industrious, and have either found employment as labourers in the towns, or have taken over land for grain cultivation (on a crop-sharing basis) on the Argentine *estancias*, or have worked on the coffee *fazendas* in Brazil.

The pure-blood Indians, scattered in groups throughout Latin America, naturally belong to different tribes; the more advanced are peasant cultivators, others are simply herdsmen, and the most primitive, such as those of the Amazon forests, are little better than savages, still living by hunting and fishing. In general, these are stolid and backward, having little understanding of scientific method or energetic effort to improve their lot. Many of the *mestizos*, however, are quite different in character, especially the cattle-men of the Argentine plains, of the highlands of eastern Brazil and of northern Mexico. The famous Argentine and Uruguayan *gauchos* (now fast disappearing with the fencing-in of the cattle *haciendas*) were of this class.

### Mixed Blood

In these three regions, the mixture of European and native blood has produced a dashing, fiery type of men, primitive in their passions, active and picturesque in their ways of life. In some of the Andean republics, and also in Mexico and Paraguay where *mestizos* are numerous, those who can claim to be more European than Indian share in administrative and business life, while elsewhere, for example in Chile and in the mining districts of the Andes and of Mexico, the less European *mestizos* are only *peons*, a depressed labouring class.

Wherever Negroes are in the majority

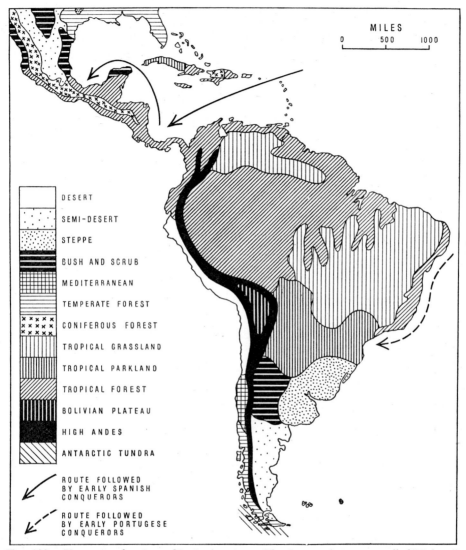

FIG. 129. *Vegetational regions of Latin America. The Amazon forests are called "Selvas," the grassland of the Orinoco, the "Llanos," and the steppes of the Argentine, the "Pampas."*

they remain for the most part backward. They are apt to be childish, inactive, and indifferent to progress. Living in the tropical lands of Latin America, where Nature is generous in providing for their simple needs, they have little stimulus to effort even though slavery has gone. They form an element which is difficult to assimilate into an economy based on European ways of life. It is only fair to add, however, that in the more stimulating climate of the West Indies, where, also, they have had some opportunities of making good, they provide labour for the sugar-cane and fruit plantations, and have become independent cultivators.

Ever since the European conquest the Roman Catholic Church has played an outstanding part in social life. Churches have been built, and the natives nominally converted. The central *plaza* or square, with its church or cathedral, is a feature of most Latin American towns. Many place names—São Salvador, Asunción and Vera Cruz, for example—are taken from the Catholic liturgy, and national holidays, or *fiestas*, are celebrated with religious pomp and ceremonial. Latin America outwardly bears the impress of the Church which has been so powerful in Spain and Portugal.

Though the known natural resources of large areas of Latin America are scanty, others are unusually rich, and it is generally thought that, great as is the output of agricultural products and minerals from the resources already developed, these and others as yet untapped are capable of yielding much more in the future. The lure of precious metals attracted the Spaniards to the high plateaux of Peru and Mexico, in both of which mining has continued to be of great importance down to the present. The mountain or Cordilleran belt in Mexico and in numerous places along the Andes has a great wealth of mineral deposits, not only of gold and silver, but also of copper, tin, and lead. Mining operations have had to contend with difficulties, it is true, in the wild mountain region at high elevations, but the resources are large enough to make it worth

while constructing modern plants and transport facilities.

Of greater importance now than these metal ores are the petroleum fields in the lowlands adjacent to the Cordilleran highlands in eastern Mexico, in northern Peru and southern Ecuador, in Colombia up the Magdalena valley, in Venezuela (the most productive in Latin America) around the southern shore of Lake Maracaibo, and in Trinidad. These fields together contribute about one-sixth of the world output, and the proportion is likely to rise. Moreover, it is probable that petroleum also exists along the inner arc of the Andes in the forested country of eastern Bolivia and Amazonia.

In the state of Minas Geraes, on the higher eastern part of the Brazilian plateau, there are deposits of copper and manganese ores which are worked for export, and the largest known reserves of high-grade iron ore, which are now being exploited. The nitrate deposits in the north Chilean desert, which have supplied the world for a century with nitrate fertilizers and iodine, contain ample reserves, but the output has declined from the peak of three million tons in 1913 owing to the competition of synthetic nitrates.

Almost all these mineral resources have been worked by foreign enterprise, which

FIG. 130. *Petroleum derricks, Venezuela. Extending into the water from the shores of Lake Maracaibo, Latin America's richest oilfield produces daily about 1,500,000 barrels of oil.*

Fig. 131. *Cutting sugar-cane in the island of Barbados. Barbados specializes in sugar production, for which its climate and fairly flat surface are suitable. Its population, like that of most other West Indian islands, is largely composed of the descendants of Negro slaves.*

has supplied the capital for operating the mines, and also for the railways which connect the mining centres with the ports. The products have been exported, generally in a crude state, and any profits have gone to foreign shareholders. Till recently the peoples of Latin America have had little benefit from the working of the mineral resources in their territories, other than the doubtful one of supplying the necessary unskilled labour. Now, however, the governments of some countries, for example Mexico, Venezuela, and Chile, are insisting upon taking substantial shares of the proceeds by the imposition of export taxes and by other means.

The agricultural resources of Latin America are very great, but have been developed slowly, on the whole, for various reasons. These include lack of foreign markets, shortage of labour and insufficient inland transport. Though large areas are unproductive, being mountainous or covered with jungle forest, there is much fertile land. This often occurs in scattered patches but sometimes continues over areas as large as Britain, as in the Argentine Pampas

and the coffee lands of São Paulo in Brazil.

In those parts of the world where productive land is abundant in proportion to the population (which is the general rule throughout Latin America, as in other lands of the Southern Hemisphere), pastoral farming is the most practicable means of utilizing agricultural resources wherever the climate is suitable for livestock. At a later stage, when labour is more plentiful and transport has been developed, the same land is gradually taken into cultivation for grain or for plantation crops. With some notable exceptions, pastoral farming still occupies a foremost place in the agricultural economy of the Latin American countries, even within the tropical zone. The potential output of crops from Latin America is enormously greater than present production, even in those favoured areas such as the River Plate where cultivation is firmly established; and there are large areas of forest country which remain unused, but which are highly suitable for tropical and subtropical plantation crops.

The most notable advances have been made in fairly accessible areas, such as the

West Indies and the Caribbean coastlands, where sugar-cane and tropical fruits, especially bananas, are produced on a larger scale than anywhere else in the world; the southern temperate section of the Brazilian plateau from Rio de Janeiro southwards, in which coffee and maize are cultivated, the former in greater quantities than in all other countries combined; the River Plate lands in Argentina and Uruguay, which have become the world's greatest exporter of linseed, maize and beef and, in some years, of wheat; the valley of central Chile, which, though intensively cultivated, is limited in extent and produces little more than is needed to meet Chilean requirements; the southern part of the Mexican plateau; the north-east coastland of Brazil; and the irrigated valleys of the Peruvian desert.

### Political Divisions

Present-day Latin America comprises numerous political divisions, large and small, which are the succession states to the former Spanish and Portuguese colonial empires. Brazil, which is much the largest with some three million square miles of territory, is the sole heir of the former Portuguese domains, and differs from the rest, not only in speech but also in physical make-up, in traditions and in its course of economic development.

The Spanish empire, apart from what has been incorporated in United States territory, has been split up into a number of separate republics. The former colonial empire was far too extensive and contained too many diverse elements to be organized as a unit, and was sub-divided into viceroyalties soon after the conquest. When independence was gained by successful revolts, early in the nineteenth century, the viceroyalties were further divided, with the result that there are now seven large and two smaller Spanish-speaking republics in South America, and six small Central American republics and Mexico in North America. The Panama Canal Zone, a strip of land ten miles wide, is administered by the U.S. government for the operation and protection of the Canal.

In addition, Latin America comprises the three Guiana colonies between the former Spanish and Portuguese domains. In the sixteenth century the Dutch and the French took possession of strips of land along the Caribbean shore, and in the eighteenth century the larger and more productive part of the Dutch strip was seized by Britain. Later the southern boundary of these three colonies was drawn along the inland watershed.

The West Indies have had a chequered history since they were discovered by Columbus. After all had first been occupied by Spain, a number of the outer and smaller islands fell to the British and the French before the end of the eighteenth century, some of them changing hands time and again. The larger islands, Cuba, Haiti (with its Spanish settlement of Santo Domingo), and Puerto Rico, remained in Spanish control till late in the nineteenth century. In 1898, as a result of the Spanish-American War, Cuba became nominally independent and Puerto Rico became American territory. Haiti had already become divided into the republic of Haiti and the Dominican Republic.

### Spanish Colonists

Spanish government in the new world was of a highly centralized type in which the sovereign through his viceroys exercised close and autocratic control over political, religious and economic affairs. The original Spanish conquerors were brave, but brutal; they were wonderful soldiers of fortune, but knowing little of the arts of peace, were poor administrators. They regarded productive work as beneath their dignity, they despised agriculture and looked upon the Indians as little better than slaves who existed for their convenience. The whole colonial enterprise was managed from Spain by the government, which used it primarily as a source of revenue. Though some serious attempts were made, by regulations, to safeguard the welfare of the native, these availed little against the cruelty of the military caste and the greed of the colonists for quickly-amassed wealth.

In many ways the Spanish empire in America contained the seeds of its own

FIG. 132. *A mud-hut village in northern Peru. Indians form the majority of the highland population; they are mostly poor and their dwellings are still very primitive.*

destruction, and the wonder is that it lasted so long. There was no chance that a Spanish peasant population might migrate across the sea to found a vigorous colonial people. Greed and corruption on the part of the ruling class caused the wholesale destruction of the Indians in the mines and the transport services, and this population was the only source of labour for development in the long run. Moreover, the close regulations of the trade of the whole colonial empire in the supposed interests of Spain led to evasion, excited the envy and attacks of other nations, and in the end caused such resentment among the people from Mexico to the River Plate that when their chance came they made successful bids for independence.

The Portuguese were much slower than the Spanish in building up their New World empire, owing partly to natural obstacles, but mainly to their being a small nation with other colonial enterprises on hand. The government was much less auto-cratic than that of Spain and allowed considerable freedom of action to the military leaders, to whom large territories were allocated. The Portuguese were perhaps fortunate in not finding precious metals in Brazil in the early days; those who crossed to Brazil took to agriculture, and thus became firmly rooted in the land, which has always provided most of the country's wealth. It is interesting to note that when the break came between Brazil and Portugal, the change was made gradually and without serious bloodshed. Brazil became first a separate empire with a member of the Portuguese royal house as emperor, and only in 1889 a republic.

Political boundaries in Latin America are, with one or two notable exceptions, very artificial. This has been due, first to the scattered points along the coasts and on the accessible highlands at which Spanish settlements and political and religious authority were concentrated, second, to the accidents of political history when the

FIG. 133. *A village of pile-dwellings, western Colombia. Here, natives and Negroes have constructed pile-dwellings similar to those of the Maracaibo Lagoon of Venezuela, which owes its name to the fancied resemblance of these villages to a Venice in miniature.*

independent republics emerged; and third, to the gradual expansion inland of the various states into the previously unknown and undesired interior, till the claims of rival expanding states overlapped, and piecemeal settlements of boundaries were made which had little relation to physical geography.

Argentina is the only Latin American republic which has rational boundaries, that with Chile following the crest of the Andes, and that with Uruguay and southern Brazil being formed by the Uruguay River. Mexico, it is true, is separated from the United States along part of the boundary by the deep gorges of the Rio Grande del Norte, but elsewhere, not only are boundaries merely lines on the map, but the Andean republics of Peru, Ecuador, and Colombia contain completely diverse elements, and communication between them across the mountains is extremely difficult. Bolivia would be a similarly incoherent assortment of diverse regions had she not lost the coastal belt to Chile in the Pacific War of 1879-82.

Brazil, on the other hand, though vast in area and comprising such contrasting regions as Amazonia and the southern plateau, has natural advantages for co-

herence in the 3,000 miles of sea-way along her coasts and in the navigable waterways of the Amazon-Madeira rivers, in the north, and of the Paraguay-Paraná rivers flowing south, which link the deep interior with the coastal shipping routes.

After the period of intense and ruthless mining activity during the first centuries of Spanish occupation in the New World, the pace of exploitation slowed down because of its unsound character and for lack of sufficient labour. Though the mining industry had passed its zenith before independence was gained, large-scale tropical agriculture, for which there were highly suitable areas, never became firmly established in the Spanish New World empire. The Spaniards there were not interested in forms of industry that demanded patient husbandry and the application of scientific knowledge. In Portuguese South America, where mining never became a major pursuit of the conquerors, varied forms of agriculture were established according to the conditions; for example, plantations of sugar-cane were developed on the coast-lands and cattle farming was undertaken inland on the plateau.

Thus when Spanish and Portuguese rule was overthrown early in the nineteenth century, Brazil was in a better position to proceed along the path of sound economic development than were the republics formed out of the Spanish territories. In the latter the whole economic system had been inverted to serve the policy of exploitation; the basic industry, agriculture, had atrophied through trade restrictions and the draining of labour into the mines. While the development of Brazil had been on sounder lines it, too, brought evils in its train; the land was parcelled out in large estates, the *fazendas* of present times, and Negro slaves were imported in large numbers from Africa to work on the plantations, and their descendants today form an inert mass that hinders progress.

In Spanish Latin America also, much of the best land is held in large estates—in Argentina and Chile as well as in the northern republics. In general the natives, *mestizos*, and immigrants are landless wherever Europeans were tempted earlier to settle in any numbers, and that was in the more fertile and otherwise desirable places. The unequal division of landed property is an evil heritage of the colonial days, when Indians were dispossessed to become a servile labouring class. It is unfortunate that the majority of the people have no share and little interest in the land, for while this lasts it is difficult to raise the general efficiency and standard of living, and it is virtually impossible to build a stable democratic government on such an undemocratic foundation.

There was but little systematic development of agricultural resources in Latin America until cheap sea transport and the growth of population in Britain and Western Europe provided ready foreign markets for the surplus. Cattle were introduced at an early stage by the Spanish and the Portuguese, and multiplied especially on the *campos* country of the Brazilian plateau and on the natural grasslands of the River Plate. In addition, some introduced crops were cultivated for local needs.

Fig. 134. *An air view of the Selvas along a tributary of the Amazon, taken by Dr. A. Hamilton-Rice. Another picture of the tropical rain forest is shown in Fig. 71.*

During the last hundred years the leading types of production have resembled large-scale plantation agriculture in being operated in large units and mainly for the export trade. There is, it is true, much subsistence farming in the more remote (and even in the settled) parts, in which the occupiers produce mainly for their own requirements or for the local markets. But large-scale capitalistic organization is common, not only in those branches of industry producing tropical commodities like cane-sugar, coffee, cocoa and rubber, but also in temperate farming in Argentina and Chile and the Brazilian *campos* (producing great quantities of meat, hides, wool and cereals) as well as in mining enterprises.

Latin America's staple industries, inasmuch as they have depended upon external markets for the sale of much of their products, have been sensitive to world trade conditions. They suffered severely in the great depression of 1929-32; so severely, in fact, that most of the larger republics became unable to pay the interest on capital borrowed abroad, in spite of severe cuts in imports. The commercial history of South America during the century 1830-1930 was marked by alternations between prosperity and depression, and was punctuated by acute crises which threatened the existence of some industries altogether.

Though the economic career of Latin America during the past century has been chequered, there has been general expansion, and in some directions even rapid development. Mining declined in the first half of the nineteenth century, but tropical agriculture and pastoral farming went ahead, in response to the British, European and North American demand for such products as sugar, cocoa, wool and hides. During the half-century 1875-1925, each of the major industries—mining,

FIG. 135. *A typical hacienda in Mexico with the Sierra Madre in the background. Note the nopal cacti, characteristic vegetation in arid regions, and the steep, rugged mountains.*

Fig. 136. *Ixtaccihuatl, the "Sleeping Woman" volcano, Mexico. This is one of a series of active, dormant and extinct volcanoes on the southern edge of the Mexican plateau.*

tropical agriculture, the collection of forest products, stock rearing, temperate agriculture—had its period of expansion.

The introduction of foreign capital, the construction of railways and improvements in sea transport helped to make the products available at competitive prices in external markets. Thus Latin America's natural resources were stimulated into productivity by contributions of capital, modern inventions, and scientific methods, from the countries which were the chief markets for their produce.

Except during this period of development through loans from abroad, Latin America has suffered from shortage of capital. It has not been able to accumulate much itself, and the difficulties in obtaining sufficient supplies which were experienced in the 1930's are likely to appear again. Foreign capitalists who have invested in railways and public utilities, or who have advanced loans to Latin American governments and municipalities, have had unpleasant experiences, and the knowledge of these has tended to make investment in Latin America unattractive. Yet without large supplies of capital it is impossible to construct the internal means of communication required for the establishment of strong and stable central government, for the development of known resources, and for general economic progress, including in

particular modern industrial development.

Until 1914, in fact, there were few manufactures in Latin American countries. During the First World War some were started to fill the gap caused by the breakdown of supplies from Europe, and since then they have grown considerably, especially in central Brazil, Chile and Argentina, under strong nationalist policies and high protection.

With the exception of Brazil, where there is a large domestic market and a variety of raw materials, Latin American countries have fewer advantages for manufactures than for primary industries. Their attempts to divert resources from the latter to the former are uneconomical though understandable, as they have had bitter experience of fluctuations in the price of their primary products sold on the world market. Where there is lack of fuel, as in Argentina, or a small and backward population which neither warrants much specialization nor permits of the economies of large-scale production, as in most of the other republics, the artificial encouragement of manufactures will not ensure prosperity, though it may make for stability. It may be hoped that the Food and Agricultural Organization of the United Nations will help to stabilize prices of many primary products.

The average density of population in

Fig. 137. *Cattle on the Pampas, Argentina. Large herds of beef cattle are raised and fattened on the natural grasses of the humid eastern Pampas, and also in Uruguay. They were formerly allowed to roam at large, being rounded up occasionally by the part-Indian, part-Spanish gauchos. With the demand for better-quality animals, which followed the development of refrigeration and a growing export trade, the "criollo" (native) stock was improved by the importation of pedigree bulls. Now most Argentine cattle are Shorthorns (Durhams) or Herefords, and the "estancias" (big estates) on the Pampas have been divided into large fields by wire fences, to preserve the strains of livestock. The gaucho is faced with extinction, except in the unenclosed country of the interior.*

Latin America—some fifteen to the square mile—is lower than that of comparable inhabited lands, e.g. Anglo-American North America, where it is about twenty-five per square mile. The greatest concentration is found in the more accessible areas, in southern Mexico and the West Indies, and in the marginal parts for some distance inland in South America. Population is sparse in northern Mexico, and very scanty in the great interior triangle of South America. This markedly uneven distribution of population is partly due to lack of communications, but even where great navigable rivers, such as the Amazon and the Paraná, provide highways far into the interior, the inland regions along them are sparsely settled, because of the hot, wet climate and the resulting forests and swamps.

Some seven areas in all have been settled and developed by people of European descent, namely the southern Mexican plateau, Cuba and the smaller West Indies, and in South America (in order of importance) the River Plate, eastern Brazil, central Chile, the tropical Andean plateaux and the Peruvian and northern coastlands.

*The Southern Mexican Plateau*, situated at an elevation of about 7,000 feet in a tropical latitude, and receiving sufficient and reliable rainfall, has an extremely pleasant climate. It has, moreover, a fertile volcanic soil and its border mountains are rich in minerals, especially copper, silver and iron. It is well suited to the cultivation of maize (which is native in Mexico), and of wheat and cotton introduced from the Old World. Long before the Spanish conquest of 1525, the Aztec Indians had become numerous in this favoured region, which has supported a dense population ever since. In essential requirements other than special manufactures the people are largely self-contained, relying upon the exported minerals to pay for the imported manufactures. Though silver mining has declined, copper is produced in very large quantities.

The lower slopes of the eastern border mountains are both hotter and wetter and are clothed with forests, while along the coastal plain bordering the Gulf of Mexico sugar-cane is grown, and behind Tampico, farther north, a productive oilfield extends parallel with the coast. Up on the plateau, within sight of the snow-capped volcanoes to the south, lies Mexico City, capital and chief commercial and social centre of the whole republic, linked with the outside world by the railway to Vera Cruz on the Gulf.

*Cuba and the smaller West Indies.* These islands, Cuba excepted, are rather mountainous, being the upper and exposed portions of chains which swing northward in a

curve from the Venezuelan Andes. They are very wet on the north-eastern slopes, which are densely forested and mainly unproductive, but contain fertile lowlands and hill slopes on their leeward sides. All these islands have a pleasant tropical climate with marked wet and dry seasons, which makes them suited to the cultivation of sugar-cane and bananas on the lowlands, and of various tropical fruits and coffee on the hill slopes.

Jamaica and other British West Indies, as well as the French islands of Martinique and Guadaloupe, have long specialized in the sugar industry, which, however, has suffered from high costs in relation to selling prices since the abolition of slavery in 1833. In all the smaller West Indies there is a high proportion of Negroes in the population who are rather lacking in industry and efficiency—a heritage of slavery. The fruit trade has fared better than the sugar industry, being less exacting in labour, and especially since the introduction of refrigerated transport.

Cuba is fortunate in being composed of mainly undulating land of moderate elevation covered with deep, fertile soil. This island and Puerto Rico together contain a large area of the best sugar-cane lands in the world, and Cuba is capable of producing double its present peak output of five million tons of cane sugar a year—if

markets could be found for this increased yield.

The two most important towns in the West Indies are Havana, in the western tobacco-growing part of Cuba, and Kingston, in Jamaica, which besides its local trade has become a port of call for vessels on the Panama route.

*The River Plate.* A warm, temperate climate, flat plains covered with deep fertile soils, absence of forest and easy access by the River Plate (Rio de la Plata) to the Atlantic have combined to make the lands around the estuary one of the leading pastoral and grain-growing lands in the world. The chief industry till the opening of this century was cattle ranching and sheep farming, the natural pastures being supplemented by lucerne as a cattle fodder. Though stock-rearing is still of great importance, agriculture now leads.

Very large quantities of maize, wheat and linseed are grown, maize towards the warmer north, wheat rather inland from the coast where the rainfall is lighter, and linseed throughout the plain as a first crop when pasture land is broken up. Refrigeration has done much to save stock-rearing from eclipse by grain cultivation, which has, in its turn, been stimulated by the construction of railways and the provision of elevator facilities.

The extensive import and export trade of

the River Plate region passes largely through four ports, of which the two largest, Buenos Aires and Montevideo, are on the La Plata estuary. Buenos Aires, with a population of some three million, is the largest city and the greatest port in the Southern Hemisphere. The other ports are Rosario, situated above the first bend on the navigable Paraná, and serving the northern section of the plain, and Bahia Blanca on the southern edge of the region; both these are leading grain ports, the former especially for maize and the latter for wheat.

*Eastern Brazil.* An extensive zone of considerable and varied resources lies along the 2,000 miles of the east coast of Brazil and reaches inland for some 300 miles to the line of the São Francisco, Paraná and Uruguay rivers. The eastern edge of the plateau rises often steeply to a height of several thousand feet from a coastal strip which is narrow to vanishing point in the central section, but widens out to some thirty miles to the north and south.

The climate is tropical on the coast north of 30 degrees S. and subtropical to warm temperate according to latitude on the highlands, while the rainfall is heavy, with a marked summer maximum. The soils on the plateau range from indifferent where formed from weathered granites and other crystalline rocks, to very fertile where derived from decayed volcanic sheets as in São Paulo state.

In this belt covering an area five times that of the British Isles there are three more closely settled regions: the northern triangle bounded west by the meridian of 40 degrees W.; the central area within a radius of about 500 miles of São Paulo City; and the state of Rio Grande do Sul in the south.

The most important of these is the central area, which is the most productive in the whole of Brazil in crops, cattle and minerals, and also contains the chief commercial and manufacturing centres. It grows half the world's supplies of coffee, and, in addition, large quantities of maize,

Fig. 138.    *A view from the air, looking north over Rio de Janeiro, the principal port of Brazil. The harbour is considered to be one of the finest in the world. The photograph shows the famous Sugar Loaf at the harbour entrance, one of the many residual granite*

teans, sugar-cane and rice; it has over ten million cattle, and the mining region of Minas Geraes produces a variety of minerals (page 196).

Of the two cities of Rio de Janeiro and São Paulo, each containing over two million people, the former has developed as the leading port of Brazil, and the latter as the centre of the coffee-growing lands, the bulk of the coffee being exported through the port of Santos. These and other towns in central Brazil have large and growing manufactures encouraged by abundant local supplies of water power, and by the large Brazilian market for disposal of the finished goods.

Rio Grande do Sul is primarily a cattle and sheep area, and produces large quantities of dried beef, called *xarque* in Brazil. It also grows maize and wheat on the uplands, and rice on the lowlands round the Lagoa dos Patos, near the mouth of which is the chief port, Rio Grande. Here there are large works for making salted and dried beef, as well as numerous other factories.

North-east Brazil is composed of two distinct regions, the coastal belt, which is fairly hot and wet, and the plateau or Sertão country, which is dry and subject to severe droughts inland. In the northern part of the coastal belt sugar-cane has been cultivated from early colonial days, and southwards beyond Salvador (Bahia) cacao (the cocoa plant) is grown more than anywhere else in South America. In the Sertão country the only important industries are the herding of cattle and goats under ranching methods, and the growing of cotton from a native, perennial, tree-like plant.

The leading towns are all ports—Salvador (Bahia), Recife (Pernambuco) and Natal. As Natal is the nearest place of any importance in the New World to the West African promontory of the Old World, it has become a leading airport for the services connecting Europe and South America.

*Central Chile*, the only fertile part of Chile, consists of the Longitudinal

*masses in eastern Brazil. Coast subsidence has also produced numerous islands, promontories and inlets. In this region inland transport is made difficult by the forest-clad mountain country which rises sharply from the alluvial plain upon which most of the city is built.*

Fig. 139. *Carácas, capital of Venezuela, with the Venezuelan Coast Range in the background. Situated in a narrow valley, 3,000 feet above the Caribbean Sea, the city is six miles in a straight line, but more than twenty miles by rail, from its port, La Guaira.*

Valley, bounded on the west by the coast range and inland by the high Andes. It has a pleasant Mediterranean climate from just north of Valparaiso to about 38 degrees S., and can be readily irrigated from the rivers which cross it. All crops which grow in Southern Europe, including wheat and barley, do well here, and cattle are fed on lucerne pastures. There are also deposits of fair quality coal in the neighbourhood of Concepción, and this, together with some water power, has enabled the larger towns to develop manufactures for the Chilean market. Copper is worked on a large scale in the Andes at an altitude of about 8,000 feet.

Farther south the climate becomes wetter, and beyond Valdivia it is suitable only for pastures, fodder crops and potatoes. The chief towns are Santiago, the capital, situated at the northern end of the valley, and Valparaiso, which is the chief port both for coastwise traffic and for foreign trade.

*The Tropical Andean Plateaux and the Peruvian Coastland.* In the Andes of Bolivia, Peru, Ecuador and Colombia, at heights of from 8,000 to 13,000 feet, are plateaux mostly enclosed by higher chains. Their climates vary but are generally dry, sunny and invigorating, though the largest plateau, that of Peru and Bolivia, once the seat of the Inca empire, is distinctly cold in winter and at night.

Mining, chiefly by foreign companies, is still important in the tropical Andes, but the majority of the people, consisting of rather depressed and poverty-ridden Indians, live by agriculture and stock-rearing. Though railways have been constructed from the coastal ports to each of the more important plateau regions, except that of Bogotá in Colombia, these railways have been costly to build owing to the very steep ascents to the high passes. Freight rates are therefore high, and passengers and valuable goods are carried more and more by aeroplane, for which mountains are no obstacles. The chief towns are either the capitals of their respective republics, for example, La Paz in Bolivia, Quito in Ecuador, and Bogotá in Colombia, or former capitals such as Cuzco in Peru, or alternatively, the centres of mining districts

FIG. 140. *Indian church in the Bolivian Andes. Most of Bolivia's population, estimated at three millions, is of pure, or nearly pure, Indian blood. Some of the natives are cultivators, but many (in the mountain country) are herdsmen rearing llamas, alpacas and sheep on rough pastures. The stone dwellings and the whole existence of these people are primitive.*

such as Potosi in Bolivia and Pasco in Peru.

The coastland of Peru is a desert crossed by streams from the Andes, whose irrigated valleys cultivated for food crops as well as for cotton (to the south) and sugar-cane (to the north), present a sharp contrast with the desolate desert between them. The inhabitants of each valley are confined by the desert on either side like the people of Egypt, and live mainly on the produce of their own irrigated strip of oasis. Communication between the valleys has been very difficult except by sea, though recently a motor highway has been constructed along the coastal desert from the capital, Lima, in the Rimac valley, to Trujillo at the mouth of the most productive of the northern valleys, and also along the coast southwards.

*The Northern Coastlands* include the alluvial plain and delta of the Magdalena, the Sierra de Santa Marta, the Maracaibo lowlands, the Carácas plateau of the Venezuelan Andes, the swampy Orinoco delta and the coastal belt of the Guianas. Except on the mountains the climate is hot and enervating, with distinct wet and dry seasons. The northern coastlands were formerly important as the Spanish Main, but because of the climatic handicap active development has been limited to a few selected areas.

Among these we may mention the coastal strip at the foot of the Sierra de Santa Marta where there are the largest banana plantations in the world; the south-east shore of Lake Maracaibo, which ranks high among the world's most productive petroleum fields; the narrow coastal strip in British Guiana, where sugar-cane has been cultivated since drainage canals were constructed by the Dutch; and the Carácas plateau in Venezuela, over 3,000 feet above the sea, which produces a great variety of crops, including cotton, and contains the city of Carácas, capital of Venezuela.

Other coast towns are the ports Cartagena and Barranquilla in Colombia, the former relatively less important now than when it was the chief port of the Spanish Main for traffic over the Panama isthmus. Maracaibo, the chief port of the Venezuelan oil-fields, and Georgetown, capital and leading port of British Guiana, are also important.

## Test Yourself

1. Latin America possesses great agricultural resources, but these have been slowly developed. Give reasons for this.
2. The average population density of Latin America is lower than that of comparable countries. Why is this so?
3. Explain the importance each to the other of the Argentine and Britain.

*Answers will be found at the end of the book.*

FIG. 141. *The Great Rift Valley in Africa stretches from Ethiopia in the north to Lake Nyasa. The photograph shows part of this remarkable fracture formation in Kenya Colony.*

# CHAPTER X

# AFRICA

THE geographical discoveries of Livingstone, Stanley, and other nineteenth-century explorers made possible the opening of the vast continental interior of Africa to the commerce and industry of Europe and to the whole range of ideas on which European civilization is founded. In consequence, revolutionary changes are now taking place in the life of the African population. Native civilization, with its deeply-rooted traditions and institutions, has met the impact of advanced, technically efficient states, such as Great Britain; and the response is evidence of patience and adaptability under most difficult conditions.

### Economic Exploitation

Until the world conflict of 1914-1918, the European Powers with territories in Africa were, for the greater part, accustomed to regard the continent as a mere economic and political appendage of Europe. It was not regarded as possessing a civilization worth preserving. In the economic field the attitude of European Powers showed itself most clearly in ruthless exploitation of the rubber, ivory and other resources of the tropical forests. The slave trade which had its headquarters in Africa did not terminate until the nineteenth century was far advanced, and the horrors of that episode are not yet forgotten by African peoples.

No man can foresee the part which Africa is likely to play in the world of the future. It can be said with certainty, however, that it will be not passive as in the past, but a dynamic expression of the aspirations of more than 200 million black men and brown men, who, in the past, had little to do with the management and determination of their own affairs.

In its size and compactness, Africa is a much more impressive land mass than the continent of Europe. The greater part of its eleven million square miles is a plateau of remarkable stability, with a foundation of ancient (Archaean) rocks. Within the limits of the African plateau recent folded-mountain systems, such as result from the compression of the earth's crust, are absent. On its flanks, however, there are such folded mountains, in the Atlas and Cape of Good Hope districts, respectively.

The primitive rocks of Africa have been investigated most thoroughly where they outcrop in South Africa. They have great significance because of their valuable minerals, which include the gold of the Transvaal and the copper of the Congo and Northern Rhodesia. The greater part of the African plateau has stood above the sea since earliest geological times, and has been less disturbed by crustal movements than any other of the great continental masses. Parts have been upraised periodically, but the plateau as a whole owes its elevation to the long resistance of its rocks to the processes of erosion. The loftiest summits of all are very scattered, and are, almost invariably, volcanic masses piled high on the surface of an already elevated tableland. Such are the craters of Mts. Kilimanjaro (19,300 feet) and Kenya (17,000 feet), in East Africa.

### River Navigation

A type of land-form which is notably rare in Africa is alluvial lowland; and extensive level areas of deep, fertile soil are fewer than in Asia, Europe and America. Usually the plateau edge is close to the coast, and the great rivers—particularly the Nile and Congo—drop over successive ledges in their descent to the sea. In consequence navigation is impeded at fairly regular intervals. Moreover, the usually straight coast is not well endowed with natural harbours: lack of safe anchorage, together with many difficulties of river navigation, have tended to delay the commercial development of the African interior.

Most extraordinary of the physical features of Africa is the great fissure which

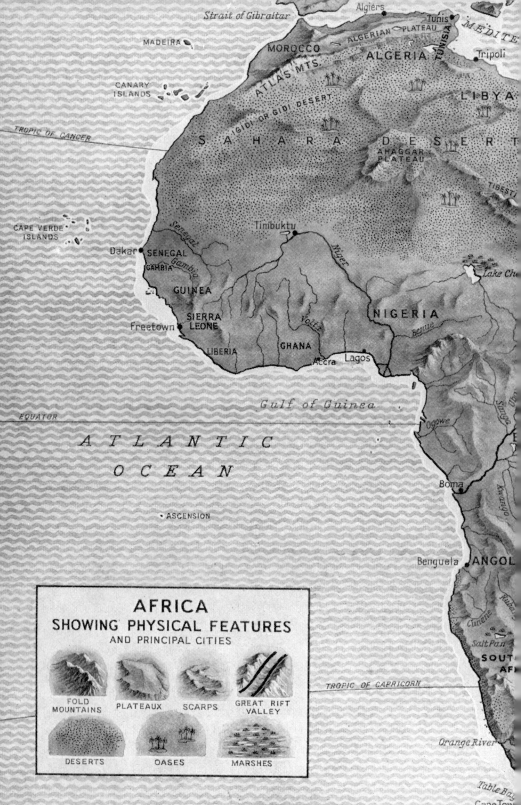

Strait of Gibraltar

Algiers

Tunis

MEDITE

MADEIRA

MOROCCO

ALGERIAN PLATEAU

ALGERIA

TUNISIA

Tripoli

ATLAS MTS.

LIBYA

CANARY
ISLANDS

GIDI OR GIDI DESERT

TROPIC OF CANCER

S A H A R A   D E S E R T

AMAGGAR
PLATEAU

TIBESTI

CAPE VERDE
ISLANDS

Senegal

Tinibuktu

Niger

Dakar

SENEGAL

Gambia

Lake Che

GAMBIA

GUINEA

NIGERIA

SIERRA
LEONE

Freetown

Volta

Benue

LIBERIA

GHANA

Accra

Lagos

Ogowe

Gulf of Guinea

Sanga

EQUATOR

A T L A N T I C

Boma

O C E A N

Kwango

ASCENSION

Benguela

ANGOL

Cunene

Salt Pan

SOUT
AF

AFRICA
SHOWING PHYSICAL FEATURES
AND PRINCIPAL CITIES

FOLD
MOUNTAINS

PLATEAUX

SCARPS

GREAT RIFT
VALLEY

TROPIC OF CAPRICORN

Orange River

DESERTS

OASES

MARSHES

Table Bay

Cape Tow
Cape of Good Hop

can be traced southwards for over 2,000 miles across East Africa, just where the plateau is at its highest. It has been called the Great Rift Valley and extends, so far as Africa is concerned, from Ethiopia, by way of Lake Rudolf and other smaller lakes, southwards to the narrow trench of Lake Nyasa. A deep fissure leads off the main rift, and part of it is occupied by Tanganyika, the largest as well as deepest of the Great Lakes.

### Climate

Climate exerts its close control over all human activities in Africa. The tropical characteristics of excessive temperature and sunlight—combined over large areas with excessive humidity also—are generally unsuited to the health and activity of white settlers. At the north-western and southern extremities of the continent only is climate sufficiently genial to permit Europeans to make extensive settlement.

Climates, with rainfall varying from over one hundred inches, on the one hand, to continuous drought on the other, but with great heat as the common factor of all, determine the three most characteristic vegetation zones of Africa, namely tropical rain forest, tropical grassland (or savanna) and hot desert, respectively. The symmetrical arrangement of the climatic belts and their associated vegetations is notable. With the exception of the equatorial zone, the climates are repeated, so that, going polewards in either direction, a similar distribution is found. It cannot be too strongly emphasized, however, that neither the climatic nor the vegetation belts are sharply divided one from another. In Africa, where relief is not strongly accentuated and great mountain barriers are rare, the climatic and vegetational characteristics of one zone merge almost imperceptibly into the characteristics of a neighbouring zone.

It is necessary briefly to classify the climates of Africa, from the standpoint of the conditions which they offer to life.

We shall begin with the equatorial types of climate, three of which are specially important.

The first is characteristic of Central Africa, and of the vast Congo basin in particular. There is constant and great heat, with a high degree of atmospheric humidity at all times, and rainfall, fairly heavy and well distributed, seasonally. The thermometer registers 80 degrees F. or more, day after day, and there is hardly any relief from the steaming conditions. From the standpoint of the health of Europeans,

FIG. 142. *Locusts which have migrated from breeding-places in the Sudan invading fertile country in East Africa. They fly in vast swarms and devour all vegetation on which they settle.*

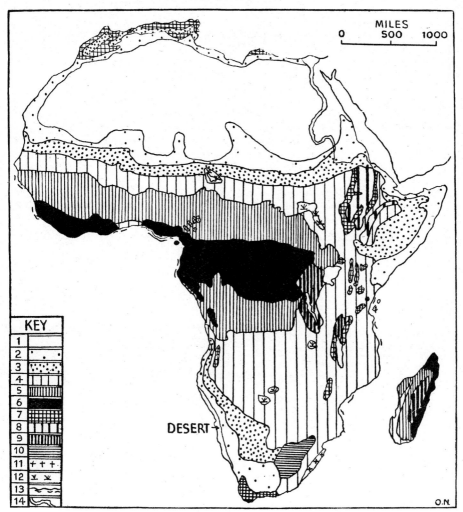

MILES
0 500 1000

KEY
1
2
3
4
5
6
7
8
9
10
11
12
13
14

DESERT →

O.N.

FIG. 143. *Vegetational and climatic regions of Africa. 1, Desert. 2, Semi-desert. 3, Steppe. 4, Savanna. 5, Park savanna. 6, Equatorial rain forest. 7, Temperate evergreen forest (e.g. " mediterranean" type). 8, Tropical highlands. 9, Subtropical highlands (modified savanna). 10, Veldt (modified steppe). 11, Subtropical coast with summer rains. 12, Marshes. 13, Mangrove swamps (see Fig. 68). 14, Nile Valley.*

such a climate is probably more hostile than any in the world.

The second is typical of parts of the Guinea Coast of Africa. Unlike the first, it shows a wide contrast between summer and winter conditions. There is a short winter, when dry but hot north-east winds blow off the Sahara. Rainfall is particularly heavy —usually well over eighty inches—but is confined to eight or nine months of the year, when south-west winds blow regularly off the ocean. Some of the heaviest falls of rain ever measured anywhere in the world have occurred on the West African coast.

Associated with the foregoing types of climate is a particularly luxuriant type of vegetation—a dense forest of tall, hard timber, similar to the *selva* of South America. Where the rainfall is less than fifty inches per annum, near the margins of the equatorial belt, the forest thins out and gives place to grass-and-tree savanna, or park savanna, as it is sometimes appropriately termed.

On the East African plateau, in very low latitudes, the third main equatorial type of climate occurs. It is characteristic of parts of Uganda, Kenya and Tanganyika. The benefit of high altitude is noticeable in the moderate temperatures, but, as usual in equatorial lands, the annual range of temperature is small. Nairobi (Kenya), the main centre of European settlement in equatorial Africa, has no mean monthly temperature higher than 66 degrees F., and no month shows a mean recording lower than 58 degrees. Although the climate of

the East African highlands is popularly regarded as eminently suited to the British settler, the absence of a well-marked seasonal rhythm in temperature means that there is no resting period, such as the peoples of temperate climates are accustomed to expect. Indeed, serious consequences to the mental and physical health of the majority are likely, should residence in these equatorial highlands be prolonged. It is true, however, that a considerable diurnal range permits of cool nights during much of the year, and the relaxation that is possible after sundown is greatly welcomed by the white colonist.

As the relief of the East African plateau is highly diversified, rainfall tends to vary considerably from place to place. It is usually less than in Central Africa or on the Guinea Coast, but the windward slopes of mountains, such as Kenya, catch a heavy

Fig. 144. *A grass hut of the Bakonjo, tribesmen of the bamboo forest on the Ruwenzori Mountains, Uganda. The flexible stems help to determine this form of hut construction.*

FIG. 145. *The Victoria Falls from the air. The falls are, in parts, 343 feet high (Niagara is about 162 feet). The deep slot into which the river tumbles has an outlet barely 100 feet wide, and through this the torrent pours along a gorge in a succession of hair-pin bends.*

precipitation. Vegetation is usually of savanna type, varying in luxuriance, however, in conformity with rainfall. The herding of cattle is characteristic of the local tribesmen, but in well-watered districts the natives undertake agriculture in addition to pastoral activities.

Farther from the equator, both north and south, two other well-recognized types of climate are associated with tropical latitudes. One type, sometimes known as the Sudan type, has temperatures higher even than those of the equatorial zone. Fierce heat prevails almost throughout the year, and is hardest to bear in the summer when the atmosphere is humid. Winter—if really warm conditions may be so described—is a completely dry period which, towards the Sahara, occupies more than half the year; and the amount of rainfall diminishes as the desert is approached.

On the south side of the equatorial zone —in the southern part of the Congo basin, for example—the Sudan type is well represented, though not so widely as it is between the Sahara and the equatorial forests. A luxuriant growth of tall grasses is associated with this type of climate. The savanna is wooded in places, but the long annual period of drought is opposed to the growth of forest. Only those trees capable of storing water are able to survive. Stock-rearing is usually more important than cultivation, for the art of irrigation is hardly known amongst the natives.

Going north from the Sudan, with its summer rains and winter droughts, there is transition to the mostly rainless wilderness of the Sahara, whose arid lands of sand dune, pebble and bare rock cover an area approximately equal to Europe. In southern Africa, the area of hot desert is restricted to the Atlantic side of the sub-continent, whilst towards the Indian Ocean rainfall increases. The Transvaal and Natal, in the Republic of South Africa, are watered by rain-bearing winds from off the Indian Ocean, but in similar latitudes, on the western side of the Republic, the arid Kalahari passes into the completely rainless Namib Desert.

When considering the economic importance of Africa, the precarious and insufficient rainfall of a very large proportion of the continent must be taken fully into account. The possibility of irrigating the Sahara and other large desert areas is remote, except in the close neighbourhood of such great rivers as the Niger and Nile. Although not without inhabitants around scattered oases, the desert has the lowest density of population of any African region. Inevitably, it acts as a barrier to both settlement and communication.

Of the remaining climates of Africa, the "mediterranean" type deserves particular mention. Unlike any other, its rainfall is virtually confined to the winter half-year. The summer is a time, not only of drought, but of excessive heat also, and evaporation leaves the soil parched, and river beds virtually empty. All vegetation, both wild and cultivated, must be able to resist an annual period of drought which may exceed six months. The olive and the vine are well suited to these conditions, and wheat also proves successful.

Africa possesses two widely-separated zones of "mediterranean" climate. One fringes the North African shore from Morocco to Egypt; the other is at the opposite extremity of the continent, and is confined to the district around Cape Town. Both zones have been attractive to European settlers, and their winter conditions with cool-to-warm temperature and occasional rainfall are very agreeable.

All Africa, south of the Sahara, is occupied by peoples of dark skin, in whom the Negro strain varies but is always pronounced. The purest of the Negroes occupy the forests behind the Guinea Coast of West Africa, where they, at an early time, took refuge from lighter-skinned people pressing southwards across the savanna of the Sudan. Typical of the Negroes are the Yoruba of Southern Nigeria and the Kru of the Liberian coast.

The savanna peoples have intermarried with the Negroes and show many negroid traits. They differ from the forest tribes, however, in respect of occupation, organization and outlook. As grassland dwellers, they are herdsmen primarily, but many, such as the great nation of the Hausa of Northern Nigeria, have long practised agriculture, as well as crafts such as textile weaving and leather work. These industries were well established long before European civilization penetrated West Africa.

Central, East and South Africa are the home of the great Bantu family of Africans. The Bantu are Negroes with a considerable admixture of non-negroid blood. In general, the facial features are more refined than those of the West African Negroes. Well-known Bantu types include the Zulu and Basuto of South Africa, the Kikuyu of Kenya and the Barotse of Northern Rhodesia, but the number of tribal groups is large and could not be listed here. Cattle are the main wealth of the Bantu, as of all other grassland peoples of Africa; but, where conditions permit, crops are grown, typical amongst them being millet and maize.

Maize, like manioc, was introduced to Africa after European colonization of the Americas. It has become the staple food of many millions of Africans, and is popular with the native farmer, because of its hardiness and the need for little or no attention during growth. Other plants have also found a new home in Africa: American cotton, rice and sugar from Asia, rubber

FIG. 146. *Kagoro women from the southern foothills of the Bauchi plateau, Nigeria, laden with bananas and rushes for market.*

FIG. 147. *A Hausa town near Kafanchun, Nigeria. The women carrying grain baskets on their heads are Kagoro. The plates which they are shown wearing in this photograph and the preceding one are made of red clay, strengthened with grass and padded with leaves.*

from the Amazon forest, are further instances of the transformation of African agriculture since the continent was first visited by traders from across the Indian and Atlantic Oceans.

Negro standards of agriculture are, unfortunately, very low, and the white man so far has done little to raise them, though the position is slowly improving. There is little knowledge of soil-refertilization, and when a plot of farmed land becomes exhausted it is periodically abandoned. Moreover, farm implements are crude and of low efficiency. For these and other reasons, intensive agriculture is not

practised as it is in the valleys of China and India, and the population is usually very sparse. The Congo basin, one of the most favoured regions of the continent, carries a density of population about as low as that of the coldest and most barren parts of Europe.

Within the Sahara, as well as in the northern parts of the Sudanese savanna and along the northern edge of Africa, where rain occurs in winter, the peoples are mainly non-negroid, and closely resemble the other types of the Mediterranean basin. They are rather more dark-skinned than are southern Europeans, but otherwise, apart

FIG. 148. *Camels in the Egyptian desert.* The rider is protected from sun and sand.

FIG. 149. *Native hut and compound at Somkele, Zululand. In Africa, as elsewhere, dwellings are adapted to environment. They may be rectangular in forest areas where long poles are available, or circular with conical roofs on the savanna (see Fig. 150).*

be able to live, for they perform most, and sometimes all, of the arduous manual toil.

The occupation of East and South African lands by European settlers has often been excused because no native inhabitants were in evidence at the time. Such a defence of white penetration is, however, based either on ignorance or misunderstanding of Bantu conceptions of land tenure. In the agriculture of Negro peoples, a particular plot must be left fallow periodically, in order to recover from the exhaustion involved in long use; so that land which seems to be unoccupied is resting, to be re-occupied in a later year.

To the great majority of African tribes land is not the property of individuals, or even of groups, and cannot therefore be sold. Its occupation by a tribe or family is determined by tradition, and, on behalf of the community, the native chief has the power to allocate the use of particular plots to individuals or families, year by year. When the European, in accordance with his tradition of land-ownership, made African land a marketable thing, he did much to destroy the basis on which tribal society was organized.

The alienation of land has been carried so far under European influence that tribal society in Africa is, almost everywhere, in process of disintegration, and particularly in those districts where the white man attempted to establish a home. Even where land was not alienated to Europeans, the idea of individual ownership in the soil was introduced to the natives themselves. An increasing number of the natives of the

from their dress, they might easily pass for Europeans. The peasants of Egypt, the Berbers of Morocco and Algeria, the Ethiopians—all these, and others, too, belong to the African type known as Hamite. Where conditions are possible for agriculture they make excellent farmers; and the prosperity of the Egyptian cottonfields is as much a tribute to the peasant as it is to the skill of the British engineers who built the great reservoirs on the Nile.

Apart from the borders of the continent, long visited by foreign traders, Black Africa knew no town life, similar to that of Europe and Asia, until the late years of the nineteenth century. Then the vast mineral wealth of the interior, already known to native metal-workers, was first mined by European prospecting companies. Johannesburg, which may soberly be named "the city of gold," began its history as recently as 1886 and, south of Cairo, is now the greatest centre of human activity in Africa. Yet, although the African Negroes, with the possible exception of the Yoruba of Nigeria, have no tradition of urban life, they are able, with remarkable adaptability, to fit into the conditions of European-built towns. South Africa is the land where European interests have spread most widely, but even there, in the towns, the native or other coloured population is as numerous as the European. Moreover, without its natives, no town in Africa would

Gold Coast (now called Ghana) and Uganda, for example, became labourers, working for black employers, who had been granted a title to land.

Before the Portuguese set out, in the fifteenth century, to explore the African coast, only the Mediterranean rim of the continent was known to Europe. Yet an episode of enormous consequence to the interior of Africa had already occurred. This was the penetration of all North Africa and much of East Africa also by Moslems from Arabia. Islam was, until recently, a conquering religion in Africa, as well as in Asia. Of the 240 million Moslems of the world, no fewer than sixty millions are in Africa, and the number of adherents of Islam continues to grow. It recognizes no colour bar, and Negroes, as well as Hamites, find it an attractive faith and code of conduct.

Portugal built a great empire in Africa in the sixteenth century, but gradually lost most of the territories she possessed, north of the equator. Two of her existing colonies, namely Angola and Mozambique, remain of vast size and abundant commercial possibilities. From the sixteenth to the eighteenth century, the Guinea Coast attracted the maritime nations of Europe as a source of gold and slaves. There was a long contest for possession, from which Britain and France emerged with extensive coastal holdings. Yet, vigorous as was the trading activity on the West African coast, neither the French nor the English made a serious effort to explore the interior until the close of the eighteenth century, when the course of the River Niger was discovered.

In the seventeenth century the Dutch chose Table Bay as a harbour for their shipping, roughly half-way between Europe and their possessions in the East Indies. At first only a revictualling station, Cape Town became ultimately the starting-point from which Dutch pioneers trekked inland from the South African coast, as far as the

FIG. 150. *El Dorado, a native village in Rhodesia, showing round and rectangular huts with overhanging eaves and roofs non-continuous with the walls. The absence of a regular alignment is characteristic of this region, as it is of early village sites in Asia and Europe.*

River Limpopo, 1,200 miles to the north. The English annexed Cape Town early in the nineteenth century, but made no important settlement of the interior of South Africa until diamonds and gold were discovered there in the latter half of the century. To this day the Dutch remain a majority of the white population.

The establishment of European spheres of influence in Africa went on apace, especially in the late nineteenth century. This scramble for territory, in which Britain, France and Germany led the field, must be considered in relation to the domestic circumstances of each of the interested Powers. The industrial nations desired the expansion of their overseas markets, not only for the supply of raw

FIG. 151. *Cape Town, showing Table Mountain (3,500 feet), separated from Lion's Head (2,000 feet) by the Kloof, with its road to the suburb of Camps Bay. The city has grown out around the foot of Signal Hill (part of Lion's Head) and up the lower slopes of Table Mountain. Capital and oldest city of Cape Province, and chief port of the Republic of South Africa, Cape Town is also a popular holiday resort.*

Europe's rather doubtful record of exploitation and annexation in Africa in the decades before the First World War was relieved by occasional instances of enlightened interest in the welfare of the natives. In this connexion the humanity and wisdom of the governors of Nigeria, Uganda and the old Cape Colony deserve mention.

By 1914, for good or ill, the entire continent, save Abyssinia and Liberia, had passed under the "protection" of one or other of the European Powers, or been formally annexed by them. Great Britain held in her control much the greater part of the eastern half of Africa; France was dominant in West and Central Africa, as well as in the Sahara and Atlas lands; Belgium, without any desire to become a colonial power, inherited the heart of the Congo basin, a prize which, because of its vast size, on occasion proved an embarrassment to her capacity for colonial enterprise; Germany held four widely-separated territories in tropical Africa, and two of them provided almost unlimited commercial possibilities. Italy, last in the race, had to rest content with several semi-desert stretches along the seaboard of North-East Africa. The Powers were envious or distrustful of each other, and their territorial ambitions in Africa did much to prepare the way for the two devastating world wars of our time.

The First World War eliminated Germany as an African Power. Her former territories, placed, theoretically, in the care of the League of Nations, were shared out, to be administered under mandate by the victorious Powers. Britain and France obtained the lion's share, but Italy's claims to a mandate were rejected—to her great discomfiture. It was expressly laid down

materials and foodstuffs, but also for the sale of the goods manufactured in their factories. The luxuriance of equatorial forest and tropical savanna made the African continent particularly attractive, and European industrialists were quick to measure its resources and possibilities in terms of palm oil, rubber, cotton, cocoa, hemp and other products of the soil.

that government should be primarily in the interests of the native population; but there was no machinery for effective international supervision, and each Power interpreted the terms of its mandate to suit its normal colonial practice.

There was, in consequence, no common standard of mandatory government, though each Power appreciated that it accepted the responsibilities of trusteeship on behalf of the native community placed in its charge.

European settlement is, in aggregate, insignificant. The countries of Europe have great interests in that part of Africa situated between the tropics of Cancer and Capricorn; but within these latitudes, over an area much larger than Europe, there are far less than a million white people all told.

Exposure to tropical sunlight is dangerous to the health of the average European and the excessive temperature and frequently high humidity of the atmosphere render an active life difficult, even for the strongest.

On the highlands of East Africa—in Kenya especially—there are many Europeans, living at an altitude of more than 5,000 feet above sea level. Life at high altitudes brings its own problems for health,

though the settlers claim that the climate is one of perpetual spring. Nevertheless, for work involving manual toil, the Europeans are completely dependent on the native population.

In the Republic of South Africa there is the largest white colony in all Africa, and conditions are subtropical rather than tropical.

As in East Africa, most of the white population live at a very high altitude. Johannesburg, the largest city, stands 6,000 feet above sea level. The climate is certainly agreeable to the tourist, but whether it is satisfactory or not to the health of those who live there is less easy to determine. In sport and mental activity the South Africans—whether of British or of Dutch origin—maintain a high standard, but do not undertake laborious work in field or mine.

As employers they draw freely on the services of ten million Bantu natives, who constitute a permanent reserve of unskilled labour.

At the opposite extremity of Africa, along the Mediterranean, the former French, Italian and Spanish colonies reach an aggregate of about one-and-a-half million European inhabitants.

Up to 1962 Algeria was counted as part oᴧ

Fig. 152. *Mounds of crushed rock, from which the gold has been extracted, at a Johannesburg gold mine. The rock is quartzite and the gold yield is often very small.*

FIG. 153. *A typical sheep farm on the Karroo in Cape Province. There are approximately 44,000,000 sheep in South Africa, which is one of the chief wool-exporting countries. The surface of the Karroo is varied by high ridges such as the one shown in the photograph.*

metropolitan France for purposes of government, and full rights of French citizenship were extended, not only to the settlers, but also to the more numerous Arab and Berber communities, on condition that they attained a minimum standard of French culture.

As regards the acclimatization of French and neighbouring peoples in North Africa, the most significant geographical factor is the similarity of the climate of their adopted home to that of the mother country. Most settlers came from the southern parts of either France or Italy, where conditions of temperature, sunlight and rainfall closely resemble those of the North African seaboard. For example, we find that summer in Naples is almost as hot as it is in Tunis. It was the intention of the Italian Government, at the time of its short-lived conquest of Ethiopia, to send out large peasant colonies to East Africa. The Second World War stopped this new experiment in tropical colonization, but it had already gone so far as to suggest that the hardy Italian peasant is better equipped, both physically and temperamentally, than most Europeans to withstand the rigours of a subtropical climate.

Africa is still in the very early stages of its agricultural and industrial development. Indeed, most of its area awaits a thoroughly-mapped survey of its economic possibilities. Only those districts which are easily accessible from the coast, or whose population is capable of being used as an adequate reserve of labour, have been intensively developed by European enterprise. But whereas, at the close of the nineteenth century, Africa south of the Sahara was represented in the world's raw material markets by what then were wild products of the tropical forest—ivory, rubber and palm-oil for example—nowadays agricultural production is vastly more important.

Certain widely scattered territories are already renowned in commercial agriculture, but over three-quarters of the area of tropical Africa and South Africa farming remains as primitive as ever, serving domestic needs only. We think of Uganda's specialization in cotton for export, and of Ghana's production of more than one-quarter of the world's cocoa, of Senegal's concentration on ground-nuts for the French market, and of a few other territories which specialize in commercial agriculture. In noting their position on the map, we remember that each of these former European dependencies had, prior to commercial development, a higher density of population than was characteristic of the region in which it was situated.

Moreover, in each case transport to the seaboard is convenient (as in Ghana and Senegal), or was modernized early in the period of European penetration (as in the case of Uganda, whose railway to the sea was available at a time when no other East African railway or road had been completed).

These two advantages—abundance of efficient labour, and accessibility to transport—count more than any other geographical factor, and they have much to do with determining the localization of the more important centres of commercial agriculture, although it will be obvious that soil and climate are also important factors.

The mineral wealth of the African interior was legendary in medieval Europe, but was not exploited on a large scale until the second half of the nineteenth century. To the modern industrialist, Africa stands for diamonds, gold, platinum and copper;

and the tendency to regard the continent as a storehouse of minerals, to be exploited, primarily in the interests of European industrialists, did much to bring unhappiness to the lives of African natives and discord to their relations with whites.

The Republic of South Africa has to a large extent built its economic strength on the gold ore mined in the neighbourhood of Johannesburg. The precious metal is not, however, inexhaustible, and South Africa realizes that social and economic health depends on a wider and more varied development of industry and agriculture than it has yet known. No other part of Africa is so dependent on its minerals. Elsewhere in Africa minerals are in an early stage of development. It may well be that, before the close of this century, Central Africa will be one of the most important industrial zones of the world. Already, the district

FIG. 154. *A native guard hut in the Tanganyika maize fields. These huts are used daily by women and children who scare off birds. At night the men keep watch for marauding wild pigs.*

FIG. 155. *Salim Road in Mombasa, Kenya Colony. Situated on an inlet which is a drowned river valley, Mombasa has an important harbour and is the terminus of a railway running up into the interior of the East African plateau as far as Uganda. In addition to a large Swahili population, the town has European and Indian inhabitants.*

lying across the frontiers of the Congo and Northern Rhodesia has gained great significance in the copper markets of the world.

As there can be no mining or commercial agriculture in tropical Africa and South Africa without the labour of the natives, the geographical segregation of the Negroes, such as proposed in the Republic of South Africa, is not practicable; it is quite certain that the white man cannot maintain himself in Africa, south of the Sahara, without the willing co-operation of the Negro.

British administration in tropical Africa freely admitted the right of the natives to retain, and develop in their own way, all that was valuable in their civilization. At the same time, however, the ideas and technique of Western civilization penetrated every part of British Africa, changing the basis of native thought and community life. In the former French dependencies of tropical Africa there was no attempt to preserve native civilization for its own sake, but the desire was to assimilate the Negroes to French culture. France believed that it was not only possible, but also desirable, to make Africans Frenchmen in everything save skin-colour, and was prepared to tolerate—though not to encourage—the marriage of white with black.

Such a policy was unthinkable to the British in Africa, but it had the virtue of extending to Africans, and more than in theory only, the advantage of equality of social and economic opportunity with Europeans.

Each former Colonial Power of the tropical zone of the world followed a policy in harmony with its own ideals and experience; each made its own contribution to the welfare of backward peoples; but international co-operation was needed, as much in Africa as elsewhere.

## Test Yourself

1. In what way did European influence lead to the disintegration of tribal society in Africa?

2. What two factors other than soil and climate have conditioned the development of commercial agriculture in Africa?

3. What difference in attitude towards African native civilizations distinguished French from British colonial policy?

*Answers will be found at the end of the book.*

FIG. 156. *Washed on the east by the waters of the Yellow Sea some hundred miles from Peking, the Great Wall of China stretches for about 1,600 miles into the desert and mountains to the north and west. Parts of it were built before 300 B.C., but it was extended and completed under the Emperor Chin Shih Huang Ti (246-210 B.C.) as a fortification of the northern frontier against marauders from the wilds of Manchuria and Inner Mongolia,*

## CHAPTER XI

# MONSOON LANDS

THE 9,000-mile belt of high mountain and plateau extending from the shores of the Aegean Sea to the Bering Straits cuts the continent of Asia into two distinct, strongly contrasted sections. The north-western section contains Kirgizskaya and Kagakhskaya, and the forested, marshy basin of the Ob. This land bloc of some three million square miles is mostly low-land, and is covered towards the north by a large expanse of forest which gives place to mountain flora along its whole north-ward edge. South of the forest there is steppe and grassland, which merges into steppe-desert with a large desert core over Sinkiang.

### Extremes of Temperature

The great Siberian rivers, Ob, Yenisey, Lena, especially in their lower courses, are ice-bound for several months each year, and flow into the ice-bound Arctic Ocean. There is scanty rainfall, and much inland drainage. The absence of sea influences on the interior, due to the immensity of the continent, makes the Arcto-Atlantic hinter-land a vast, almost uninhabited country, whose population nowhere exceeds twenty-six per square mile. Also, the temperature range between extreme heat and extreme cold is very great. Verkhoyansk, lying in a basin hemmed in by the crescent of the Orulgan, Verkhoyanskiy and Cherskogo heights, has ranged from 90 degrees F. to —94 degrees F., or more than the range from boiling water to ice. Tomsk and Krasnoyarsk, in the latitude of Glasgow, show typical winter temperatures of —2 degrees F. and —12 degrees F. Yakutsk, farther north, shows —46 degrees F.

No great settlement of people could take place of old in interior Asia. The stark, inhospitable, northern steppe, devoid of a granary of economic strength, contained only handfuls of pastoral nomads, whose hardiness and mobility enabled them to overrun, though not overwhelm, prosperous civilizations. But the stimulus of their impact led to renovation rather than destruction. Now, however, the hour of the nomads is past.

South of the immense arc running from the Aegean Sea to the Bering Sea lies the Arabian plateau, the highest and most massive mountain system in the world, radiating from the Pamir, and the lands embraced within the Indo-Pacific belt—Pakistan, India, Burma, Malaya, Indo-nesia, China proper, and the Japanese Islands.

South-east, east, and north-east from the Pamir there radiate the Himalaya to a distance of 1,500 miles, the Karakoram, the Kuon-Lun (about 2,000 miles) and the Tien Shan. These, as well as the height of the Tibetan plateau (over 15,000 feet), the desert basins like the Takla Makan, lying between the long mountain lines, and the jungle-clad hills of Burma, effectually shut out India from any easy direct contact by land with China. But the snows of the Himalaya and Kuon-Lun feed the great rivers—Indus, Ganges, Brahmaputra, Irrawaddy, Salween, Mekong, Si-kiang, Yangtze-kiang and Hwang-Ho—and their great tributaries, which are the life-blood of agricultural populations. These river basins, fed also by monsoon rains, make an ancient home of cultivation of the soil, and of settled, mainly rural, life.

### Agricultural Peoples

Thus the bands of immigrants, whether conquering pastoral nomads or more peaceful traders and settlers, who entered India and China mainly from the north-west and west over a period of several thousand years, found strong inducement to settle in their new homes. Migration by the Indo-Pacific ocean routes did not tempt these confirmed landsmen. Thus India and China collected more and more people whose civilizations were based on agriculture. Today, the monsoon lands of Asia lying between the Indus and Hwang-Ho basins contain a half of mankind

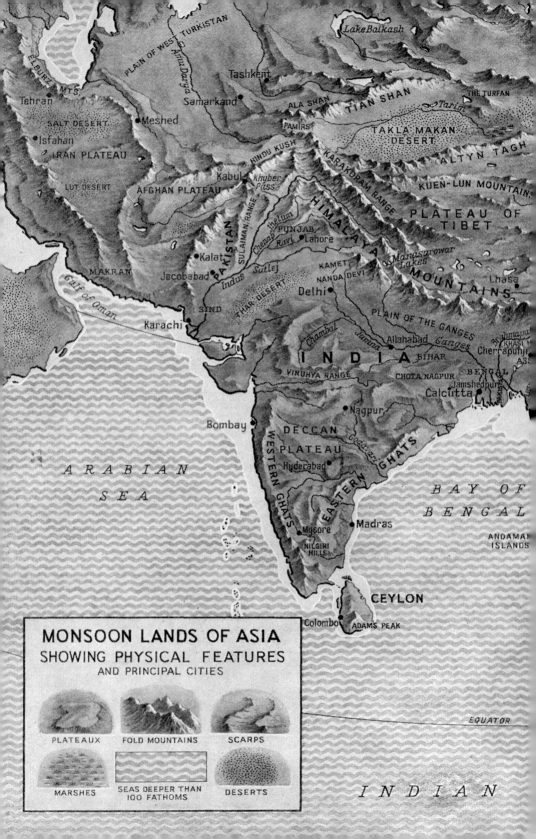

Lake Balkash

Tehran
ELBURZ MTS.
SALT DESERT
Isfahan
Meshed
IRAN PLATEAU
LUT DESERT
MAKRAN
Gulf of Oman

PLAIN OF WEST TURKISTAN
Amu Darya
Tashkent
Samarkand
ALA SHAN
PAMIRS
TIAN SHAN
Tarim
THE TURFAN
TAKLA MAKAN DESERT
ALTYN TAGH
KUEN-LUN MOUNTAINS

HINDU KUSH
Kabul
Khyber Pass
AFGHAN PLATEAU
KARAKORAM RANGE
HIMALAYA
PLATEAU OF TIBET

SULAIMAN RANGE
PAKISTAN
Jhelum
Chenab
PUNJAB
Ravi
Lahore
Indus
Sutlej
KAMET
NANDA DEVI
Manasarowar Lakes
Lhasa
MOUNTAINS

Kalat
Jacobabad
SIND
THAR DESERT
Delhi
PLAIN OF THE GANGES

Karachi
Chambal
Jumna
Allahabad
Ganges
Brahmaputra
KHASI HILLS
Cherrapunji
ASS

I N D I A
BIHAR
VINUHYA RANGE
CHOTA NAGPUR
BENGAL
Jamshedpur
Calcutta

Bombay
Nagpur
DECCAN PLATEAU
Godavari
WESTERN GHATS
Hyderabad
EASTERN GHATS

A R A B I A N
S E A
BAY OF BENGAL
ANDAMAN ISLANDS

Mysore
Madras
NILGIRI HILLS

CEYLON
Colombo
ADAMS PEAK

EQUATOR

## MONSOON LANDS OF ASIA
### SHOWING PHYSICAL FEATURES
#### AND PRINCIPAL CITIES

PLATEAUX      FOLD MOUNTAINS      SCARPS

MARSHES      SEAS DEEPER THAN 100 FATHOMS      DESERTS

I N D I A N

concentrated on only one-twentieth of the world's land surface.

To the north of the Pamir lies the longish strip of the Ala mountains, continued farther eastwards by the Tien Shan. To the south-west lie the Hindu Kush, which pierce into the large, roughly quadrilateral, Afghan plateau. The deep defiles of the Hindu Kush offered paths of entry into the Indo-Pakistan subcontinent to the men from the Central Asian steppes. West of the Afghan and Iranian plateaux lies the fertile Euphrates-Tigris valley, along which route, continued over the Persian Gulf and hugging the coast, came further immigrants.

As with the subcontinent, so with China; mountains decided the routes by which the early peoples entered. Tibet blocked the west; the Gobi Desert stretched for some 1,000 miles along the north, succeeded by forest and swamp up to the Pacific seaboard; and the Pacific itself proved the perfect barrier on the east. Two avenues were available. The less frequented one, used from about 1100 B.C. by Indo-Pacific peoples, lay through Burma and Yunnan; early Roman trade with China was conducted almost entirely along the Irrawaddy-Yangtze route. The more important and earlier one lay through Kansu and Shen-si. All along the line of approach through unforested Kansu there was a long core of steppe and desert flanked by oases, a terrain quite familiar to the dwellers in Sinkiang or in the Central Asian steppe. Such an approach was precisely of the type favourable to nomads.

### Climatic Variations

Northern Indo-Pakistan and China lie within the temperate zone between the tropic of Cancer and the fortieth parallel of latitude, but the dominant influence of the mid-world mountain bloc violently differentiates their climates.

Over all India April is warmer than October, while in the Pacific hinterland, especially to the north, the difference is even greater. Again, in Northern India the mean April temperature rises rapidly above the mean March temperature. In the Turfan basin, east of the Tien Shan, the April mean is 21 degrees F. and even in the Chih-Li (now renamed Hopeh) lowland, in latitude 40 N. and only 150 miles from the Pacific, there is a 10 degrees rise during the first fortnight in March. Asia thus shows a high-pressure system far wider and more intense than that of any other continent.

From the Turfan-Gobi trough icy winds blow to every point of the compass—the dry monsoon. The northern part of the North-West Monsoon is dry till it crosses the 500 miles of the Japan Sea, when it collects moisture, and then deposits much snow on the Japanese mountains, thus protecting the tea bushes. The southern part of the same dry monsoon acquires moisture as it crosses the Yellow Sea and meets eastward-moving whirls formed when cold air from the mountains west of Szechwan meets warmer air in the Red Basin. This provides winter rain for the lower Yangtze basin. (It is interesting to note that geologists find evidence of glaciation here—farther south than anywhere else in the northern hemisphere.) High pressure and low temperature mean a minimum of water vapour. Hence there is a clear sky and rapid radiation, and high solar values. In China, sunburn is actually a winter phenomenon!

Unlike Japan and China which have their strong monsoon in winter and weak monsoon in summer, India and Pakistan have their weak monsoon in winter and strong monsoon in summer. The dry monsoon is divided into two parts, the cool, from December to February, and the hot, from March to May. January and February have a generally low rainfall; there is a heavy deposit of snow on the western Himalaya and Hindu Kush; and there are shallow cyclonic rains, attended with warmth and cloud, but ending in cold, dry north-west winds and clear skies. These rains are valuable for the Punjab wheat.

The hot weather of March to May dissipates the high pressure and by the end of May there is low pressure over the subcontinent accompanied by fierce heat, drought and dust. The relative humidity is very low. But the pressure over the Indian Ocean south of the tropic of Capricorn is high, with the maximum to the south-east of

Fig. 157. *The Khyber Pass. Along the Khyber river valley, north of the Safed Koh range, the historic route from the north-west into the vast Indo-Pakistan subcontinent is now traversed by road and railway.*

Mauritius. This gives India a local rainy indraught from June onwards, the south-east trade winds being drawn across the equator to become south-west winds blowing against the Western Ghats and drawn up the Bay of Bengal to feed the ricefields of Bengal and the tea of Assam.

The air draught up the Bay of Bengal and that coming across the Deccan interfere with one another, turning the latter northwards over Central India and Chota Nagpur where the lifting of the air against high land gives heavy rain and forest development.

The Himalayan wall, in the main, turns the indraughts westwards because the lowlands widen in that direction, and so rain feeds the multitudinous tributaries of the Ganges. But the land becomes drier as the plains expand; the mountains recede northwards, and naked sand becomes conspicuous near Agra, while farther west the over-heated Thar is sheer desert, and the Punjab would be semi-arid were it not for the great modern canal systems draining water across from rivers at a higher level, such as the Jhelum, to rivers at lower levels, such as the Chenab and the Ravi.

The wet monsoon (from the south-west) consists of an Arabian Sea section feeding the Deccan, and to some extent the Indus basin, from the west, and a Bay of Bengal section feeding the Ganges-Brahmaputra basin from the south. The Indian Ocean is the warmest of the oceans, and the wind's three-week journey over it from Mauritius gives the Arabian section about thrice the strength and water load of the Bay of Bengal section. Coming from the south-west it strikes the Western Ghats, which average for many miles a height of 5,000 feet (critical for rainfall in the tropics), deluging the hill crests with almost 300 inches of rain. The north-west is the region of high temperature—Jacobabad can show a shade maximum of 120 degrees F. in May —and the monsoon not only reaches Delhi, but even climbs round Nanda Devi and Kamet to feed the Manasarowar Lakes and the head waters of the Ganges, Brahmaputra, Indus and Sutlej, a region regarded by the Hindus as sacred.

The northern flank of this Arabian Sea section comes past Hadramaut and Makran

FIG. 158. *The Desert of Gobi, 1,000 miles from east to west and 600 miles from north to south, at an elevation of 3,000-5,000 feet, is situated between the northern part of the*

and strikes the Karachi-Gujarat coast in an almost due easterly direction. It has little moisture, considering its high temperature, at which air can easily hold much moisture. Its capacity for moisture is further enhanced as it passes over the hot, dry land beneath the heat-reflectors formed by the mountain sides. Once over the Western Ghats the South-West Monsoon traverses the Deccan slope towards the Bay of Bengal, till it is turned northwards by the air draught up the Bay of Bengal. Conditions of variability arise: rain with a strong, and drought with a weak, monsoon. But heavy downpour on the hill-crests ensures a water supply from the heights of the Ghats, which is conserved by damming streams and providing irrigation tanks.

Part of the Bay of Bengal section feeds Burma. The remainder strikes the Arakan ridge; a part of this, which is deflected into the cul-de-sac between the Lushai and Khasi hills, gives Cherrapunji its annual 460 inches or so of rain, while the other part works up the Ganges valley, producing light rains on the plains and heavier falls on the Himalayan slopes. Occasional heavy cyclones are invaluable for the Jumna rice-fields. The "advance" section (June to September) of the wet monsoon gives the heaviest rainfall of the year; the "retreat" (October to December) produces only light falls; both sections are characterized by "bursts," not steady downpours.

Though northern Indo-Pakistan lies north of the tropic of Cancer, its climate is essentially tropical, heat being the dominant note for the region as a whole. But in China,

whose southern half between the basins of the Yangtze and Si-kiang occupies the same latitudes as Indo-Pakistan, there are greater extremes, coupled with a more bracing climate. Cold is the dominant note in China, for a summer temperature of 80 degrees F. or more and rainfall exceeding forty inches are abnormal here, whereas they are normal in the subcontinent. It is the towering mountain mass of the Himalaya which has deprived northern India and Pakistan of the bracing winters enjoyed in the same latitudes in China.

### Nomadic Groups

Steppe covers one-third of Asia. It is never a rich, permanent pasture, and an exhausted area suffers from over-population in the same way as an area subject to a decrease in moisture becomes over-stimulated and over-populated through an increase of light with the dryness. As the steppe does not invite permanent settlement, groups of people emigrate. These nomads wander over a large area, sometimes having a fixed home to which to return, their movements depending on available food supplies. The steppe is the key to Asia's nomadism and migration, and even emigration.

In contrast, the Indo-Pacific hinterland from the Indus to the Hwang-Ho is the natural home of habitable forest, the more habitable because it lies largely outside the tropic of Cancer. This monsoon forest is the product of warm and wet summers, cool and dry winters, strong winds and great range of temperature. Hence the forest is

*Tibetan massif and the Altai. Mongol nomads have long wandered over its inhospitable surface, and the historic Silk Road lay along its southern edge for many miles.*

open, with much light and space for branching and undergrowth. Such an environment is suitable for man, for it is rich in food, offers good shelter, and provides rich soil.

The abrupt contrasts in Asia, structural, climatic and vegetational, are well reflected in the history of the continent. Swarm after swarm of fierce steppe-men— Huns, Tatars, Kalmucks, Kirghiz, Magyars, Avars, Mongols—make inroads into civilized lands, behaving at times with unparalleled savagery and leaving a trail of destruction to make the gods weep. But on the whole their effect is ephemeral, though stimulating—like a cyclone! On the other hand, tribes and nations enter, millennium after millennium, into India and China, giving rise, with cumulative settlement, to the building of great and complex civilizations, and to rich diversity in thought and culture. Yet the quality common to both the steppe-men and the men of the monsoon lands is the capacity for the gigantic in empire building—witness the vast Tatar empire of Genghis Khan and Ogdai Khan, built in a mere twenty-three years—or for the transcendental in philosophy, like the contemplation of the Eternal and the ineffable bliss of Nirvana in Hinduism and Buddhism.

But the religious and philosophical thought which is the glory of the Hindustan of the pre-Christian millennium was no mushroom growth. Rather, it was the distillate of at least thirty centuries of human experience which was largely the direct interaction between man and the land on which he lived. The land moulded the people, and the people lived as ever-obedient sons and daughters of the soil.

The land was sacred; rivers and mountain peaks were gods and goddesses. To this day, so strong is the sense of organic kinship with the living world of nature that only the unwary may contemptuously fling the epithet "superstitious" at the people of the Indo-Pakistan subcontinent.

At least thirty centuries! For the first inhabitants were probably Negritos. Then came Proto-Australoids from as far west, perhaps, as Palestine; they may be regarded as the true aborigines, since their racial type was ultimately fixed there. The Proto-Australoid type is to be found, not only over all modern India, but also in Malaya and in Indonesia, in all of which lands it is responsible for the dark-skinned elements. Negritos and Proto-Australoids lived in Indo-Pakistan thousands of years before 3500 B.C.

Since it lies south of the great mountain zone of the old world, the subcontinent could receive drifts of groups of people, while the mountain zone was still largely blocked by ice and by deluges of water from the melted ice that accumulated the immense thickness of alluvium in the trough of the Indus and Ganges basins. At this same period, China, lying beyond the mountain zone and having a severer climate, seems to have had far less of these very early drifts. This probably has something to do with the Indian idea of avoidance (developed so much more strongly than in China) of the very dark aboriginals by the lighter-skinned and more civilized peoples who came in after about 3500 B.C. It may not be unreasonable to allow several millennia for the entry of these aboriginals, and their spread and ultimate settlement over the whole subcontinent. Veddahs (of Proto-Australoid stock) are found in Ceylon; the Andamanese (over 700 miles from the Indian coast and over 200 from the south-western tip of Burma) are amongst the purest specimens of Negrito stock; and there are legends among the Kuki and Kachari tribes of Assam of former contact with, and of the extermination of, a dwarf race with bows and spears and living in dense forest. These tribal village communities may have had some form of primitive agriculture, but it is more likely that they depended on food-collecting rather than food-producing. They had no cities.

The Proto-Australoids were followed by a southern branch of the Mediterranean race, resembling the brown race which inhabits North Africa today. It spread eastwards into the Ganges basin, while some drifts penetrated to the extreme south-east of Asia. It is not certain whether these early Mediterraneans brought with them much more than primitive agriculture and navigation. But later immigrations brought a knowledge of metals (but not of iron), and a considerably civilized culture flourished between 3200 and 2800 B.C. in the Indus valley, thence spreading to the Ganges valley.

### Indus Valley Culture

The great discoveries made by Sir John Marshall at Mohenjo-daro and at Harappa in the Indus valley tell us something about this civilization. Yet its origin is still obscure. A figure of Siva, who came to be regarded much later as the Third Person of the Hindu Trinity, was found at Mohenjo-daro, and shows that the beginnings of Hinduism go back at least 5,000 years.

At this period, after 3000 B.C., Sind was apparently less arid than it is now. The Indus valley peoples were irrigators who grew wheat, barley, and a coarse cotton. They had no horses, though they had elephants, camels, sheep, pigs, and fowls.

Oxen drew their two-wheeled carts. Their jewellers were skilled workers in gold, silver, and ivory. The women spun wool and cotton; and children played with toy carts of terra-cotta or copper. There were no swords, but the warriors fought with bows, spears, axes, and daggers. These people were mostly farmers and merchants who, trading as far as Elam and Ur and Kish, preserved contact with the older cultures of Persia and Mesopotamia.

### Urban Civilization

The Mediterraneans were city-builders. The excavations at Mohenjo-daro have revealed that their cities were well planned, having wide streets and two-storied houses (with indoor sanitation) and an efficient drainage system. These cities must have contrasted strongly with the rural settlements of the previous inhabitants, whose villages were probably little clumps of very rude dwellings erected in forest clearings. Both urban growth and rural life, in which agriculture now took the leading part, meant the destruction of virgin forests.

It is difficult to say whether the entries of these and later peoples into the subcontinent were invasions, immigrations on an organized scale, or only drifts of small groups of people. It is likely that most of them, especially the earlier ones, were drifts, and that the advent of the later groups took on the character of immigrations. Be this as it may, the aboriginals were slowly driven out of the fertile plains into the less accessible hill tracts, and in all likelihood were treated as hewers of wood and drawers of water. It is very probable that a distinct barrier lay between them and their supplanters, mainly on cultural and material grounds, and less because of colour differences.

All these peoples literally made a descent into the fertile plains of the Indus basin. They came from less hospitable regions, the mountains and plateaux of Asia Minor and Iran, though the Fertile Crescent (Fig. 221) itself and much of Asia Minor, excepting its core of desert plateau, were favourable for settlement and cultivation. But on the western edge of the Indus basin the mountains ended abruptly. In the vast valley of the five rivers (the Punjab) and in Sind, there was ample living space, with a good living to be obtained from the soil. Through thousands of years this land proved an irresistible magnet to both lesser and higher breeds of men. And century after century the people moved eastward and southward, and south-eastward, to the very ends of the continent of Asia.

Whereas the subcontinent appears to have been first peopled by those who came across the plateau and lowland belt south of the mountain line, it may be that when the northern ice retreated, early drifts moved into Turkistan and the northern steppe.

The lands of that great mid-continental belt from the Ukraine, through Turkistan into China, were loess-covered, subject, however, to an east wind continually driving the soil westward. The soils of the loess lands are of unusual fertility owing to their fine texture, their porous and friable nature, and the presence in them of soluble organic and mineral matter for plant nourishment. Whoever entered the long, fertile ribbon of Kansu from the Tarim, reputed to have cradled a very ancient civilization, entered with some knowledge of loess cultiva-

tion. Archaeological finds show that, even 2,000 years before Christ, the men of Kansu were not warrior herdsmen but a civilized people cultivating the loess.

Civilization reached China, it is agreed, from the west down the valley of the Wei-Ho, that is in East Kansu and in Shen-si. It was the organization of a population of loess and alluvium cultivators of Kansu, the Wei-Ho and the Hwang-Ho, under the lordship of steppe-men, that gave China its characteristic civilization. But here in China the steppe-men had to give up the herding life and became masters of cultivation. This contrasts strongly with the Aryan-speaking warrior herdsmen who, entering India somewhere between 2000 and 1500 B.C., were able to continue with their herding on the Punjab grasslands.

FIG. 159. *Excavations at Mohenjo-daro demonstrate the existence in Pakistan, well before 2500 B.C., of a city with many amenities and much craftsmanship, and indicate links with the civilization of Mesopotamia. Buildings, streets, drainage systems and baths which have been uncovered reveal a high degree of engineering skill. The photograph shows a tank passage which may have been part of the outflow of a sewer.*

Both northern and southern steppe-men based their society on kinship. The family, not the individual, was the unit, and was responsible for each of its members. Associated with this was the rule of the patriarch, succession of authority from father to son, and also the practice of polygamy, which enabled the group to increase both its power and its routine workers. Steppe-men raided the cultivators. But, whereas the loss of a few score steppe-men would decimate a nomad tribe, the loss of scores of thousands of cultivators when the Hwang-Ho surged across a new channel into the sea would by no means wipe out a population.

The early movement of peoples into China was a series of family drifts rather than horde invasions. And the Chinese had two fundamental, though opposed, aptitudes: that of co-operation under patriarchal rule, and that of oasis-gardening on the loess under settled village life. The basis of life was sedentary tillage. Accumulation of goods was easy. As the family achieved a greater and greater hold on the village, "Nation" and "State" were not serious objectives. The family used to be the fundamental unit in China, and the Chinese less a nation than a fusion of family groups united by a common culture. The history of China is rather the record of an expanding culture than that of a conquering empire. Though the floods of the Hwang-Ho ("China's sorrow") caused periodic destruction, the land prospered and culture spread. Music, astronomy, engraving on tortoiseshell, on deer antlers, or on the clavicles of sheep, and the making of fine bronze vessels flourished.

Chinese civilization, beginning perhaps in Kansu or on the Wei-Ho and extending soon to the Hwang-Ho, worked southwards to the Yangtze basin after many

FIG. 160. *Primitive cultivation in Manchuria. The soil is tilled in April. Generally two or three oxen or horses, or even donkeys, are used, though mechanized farming is now being introduced slowly. The old Manchu population has been swamped by the influx of millions of Chinese into the country.*

centuries. Indo-Pacific elements, coming through Burma and Yunnan, had meanwhile spread over the south and up into the Yangtze basin. The Hwang-Ho basin has the most fertile soil, on which there is wheat, slow-growing and not prolific, but the most nutritious of grains. It is, however, a region associated with drought, famine, and steppe-men. The Yangtze basin with its less fertile soil, but with its unfailing rainfall, mud, and a warmer climate, grows rice, a less nutritious grain, but so quick-growing and prolific that two or three crops may be harvested each year. With rice began the supremacy of the Yangtze basin.

But one fundamental object, subsistence agriculture, combined with the fundamental human unit, the family, made for great social stability and coherence. China's ideal was stability rather than progress, the distribution of limited and unexpanding resources among the largest number of human beings rather than obtaining a maximum return for minimum work.

### Collective Effort

The peasant elaborated a special technique. His danger was too much or too little water. Effective control was maintained by an elaborate system of canals, reservoirs, embankments, and irrigation works. That was one aspect of his technique, achieved by state-aided collective effort. The other was his extreme personal care and patience. In time, the Chinese farmer became the world's most skilful market-gardener. His is a primitive agriculture raised to the level of a fine art. But this is a lowland economy, not so successful in the hilly districts of the south-west and south. While the Chinese farmer was exceptionally economical, extremely parsimonious in fact, with space, implements, fuel, fodder, materials and waste products, he was recklessly prodigal with human labour and with the forests he plundered, to the ruin of the soil. In other words, he was under-capitalized and over-manned.

Successive drifts of herders into China were absorbed by the settled cultivators, and themselves became cultivators largely because of the influence of the new environment, and thus grew into one immense, homogeneous society. But the irruption of conquerors into India led to the opposite result, a heterogeneous society rigidly differentiated on a caste basis.

### Warrior Horsemen

About 2600 B.C. the steppe-folk tamed the horse, a native of the snowy slopes between Mongolia and Siberia. They took him, harnessed to the plough of south-west Asiatic origin, into many lands, thus making themselves a dominating factor in the history of civilization. In the second millennium B.C. smelting of iron developed probably among, or near, the Hittites of Anatolia, and towards the end of that millennium it was spreading. The copper dagger became the dirk. The horsemen evolved the sword, first made of bronze and later of iron. Warrior herdsmen armed with horse and sword, driven southwards because their ancient northern home became ice-bound, and still farther by locusts, by hostile tribes, and by drought, split into two sections, one going to Haroyu (Herat) and the other to Kabul and thence to the Punjab. The latter were the Rigvedic Indians, Aryan-speaking peoples. They possessed two outstanding gifts; they were poets, bringing a wonderful language, with all its attendant cultural possibilities; and they were organizers, whose practical intelligence, especially as displayed in their westernmost lands of later settlement, has ineffaceably stamped itself on the world.

In the Punjab the Aryans were safely in the saddle; but farther east, in the Ganges-Jumna basin, Aryans and pre-Aryans interacted on less unequal terms. The balance struck emerged in the course of seven centuries or so as a unique social system, unparalleled in world history, and as philosophic and religious thought which touched the very peaks of spiritual splendour. Intolerant egotists where pride of race was concerned, yet surprisingly tolerant in other respects, the Aryans were experimentalists. They tried various political and social systems, and finally evolved a way of life which for them and their age was good. As with China, so with India, the fundamental unit was the family.

Fig. 161. *A sampan village on the Yangtze. Overcrowding in lowland China has made land-holdings very small, and many families live in boats (sampans) on the River Yangtze and the Si-kiang. The boats are crowded together to form communities. The bamboo huts erected upon them are of the flimsiest construction, and living conditions are primitive.*

Finding various peoples at different cultural levels, with different practices, behaviour and methods of living, and finding no organized kingdoms, the Aryan conquerors, the makers of kingdoms on a large scale, were faced with the problem of organizing their peoples, of producing an efficient, stable, working system in which the highest possible unity could be attained out of such diverse material without offending the susceptibilities of their subjects to an extent prejudicial to their own Aryan over-lordship. A number of families was grouped as a caste, whose main rules were to marry outside the family but within the caste, and not to dine with members of other castes ("to mind their own business"). Partly because of this, and through other causes, the caste system became distressingly complicated as the centuries passed.

As in China the joint family system prevailed. A man and his wife, all the unmarried daughters, and all the sons and their wives and children constituted the joint family living in a single household. The head of the household was responsible for all. All earnings were pooled; and rights and privileges, duties and responsibilities, had relationship, not to individual earnings, but to seniority and family status. Individual initiative and enterprise had place only in harmony with the will of the family. Nothing could be done against the religious and social traditions, or caste rules, of the family, with impunity. The price of non-conformity might even be "excommunication," a very serious social and physical hardship.

But the joint family was the insurance against deprivation—India has never known poor laws, old age pensions, etc.—and against rampant individualism. If there was only a sole surviving member of a family, his caste looked after him. Also, the caste system was responsible for the preservation of that wonderful craftsman's skill which is the pride of India, developed through constant practice generation after generation, for the cultural legacy of India, for that education in the art of living still prized so highly, and for teaching the individual to control self in service of the whole. As against these, it has perpetuated foolish and cruel distinctions between

FIG. 162. *Typical country in central China. The small rectangles of land to be flooded for rice cultivation lie along the stream. The farmhouse stands in the shade of trees; a lake and hill are in the background. Below the slope in the foreground is a pond dammed for irrigation. Skilled cultivation draws rich yields from the alluvial soil.*

group and group—witness "untouchability"—has restrained individuality too far, and has, to some degree at least, prevented caste-ridden people from falling into line with modern world conditions. Further, the caste system today well manifests the inescapable ills of fossilization. In sum, however, it would be hazardous to state that its drawbacks have outweighed its excellences.

The village community was a self-governing institution. Local government always played a very considerable part in India. The task of the king and his officers was to maintain internal order, administer justice, ensure security against foreign aggression, assist villages in need of local security, or in case of drought and famine, and, which concerned the villagers most closely, collect the taxes. This last meant taking a fixed fraction of the produce. Revenues for administration were thus mainly dependent on soil, monsoon, and human labour—on the people's well-being.

The organization of the family and the outlook upon family life in China were largely similar to those in India, except that in China there was no one who corresponded to the Brahmin priest. Indeed there was no exclusive priestly caste, since the Chinese aristocracy were themselves as much priests as they were nobles and rulers. In each family the husband, the patriarchal head, was in theory the supreme authority. But in fact, the mother ruled the household; she decided the children's schooling, she found their marriage partners, she managed all domestic business, she directed all the social and extremely punctilious relations with friends and relatives, and she saw that all ceremonies were properly observed. As proof that she was on an equal footing with the master, the respect and the degree of mourning due to her on her death were equal to those due to the father.

The wonderful sixth century B.C. which saw the rise of the Buddha in India saw the rise of Confucius in China. But whereas Buddha stressed self-knowledge, self-control, and moral and spiritual development, and laid very great emphasis on the true nature and value of individuality, Confucius stressed the supreme necessity for right conduct, not through the compulsion of inward realization or through obedience to the moral law from within, but in unquestioning compliance with correct behaviour as laid down from ancient times. Such, however, was the peculiar greatness of Confucius that his influence has permeated Chinese life through twenty-five centuries; and the Confucianism of China, like the Hinduism of Hindustan, has been a more powerful, vital influence than the Christianity of Christendom. The Chinese are an intensely practical people. Yet how different is the life-wisdom of the practical Chinese from the distinctive abilities of the practical Europeans and Americans!

### Internal Strife

Few major revolutions have taken place in China's long history. In 221 B.C. Shih Huang Ti became the first Emperor of all China by conquest. He destroyed the kingdoms of his rivals, swept away the old social and political system of China, destroyed the great store of Chinese literature (for which he earned the execration of posterity) and even, unintentionally, the heritage of his ancestors and his own family. But he introduced a uniform system of laws and of weights and measures, and he built good roads and part of the Great Wall of China. The roads, constructed primarily for military reasons, extended trade with China's western neighbours, from whom came Buddhism and whose influence showed in Chinese art and literature.

In 1912 Sun Yat-sen and Yuan Shih-k'ai overthrew the Manchu dynasty; and by the mid-twentieth century Communist power was firmly established over China by Mao Tse-tung. Whilst Confucianism, Taoism and Buddhism are still in vogue, whilst reverence for the dead as embodied in family ceremonial is still an expression of religious feeling, at least for the older generation, the Communist régime is bringing about sweeping changes with rapid industrialization and by indoctrination in Chinese Communist philosophy. It remains to be seen what the coming decades hold for this ancient people and for the world at large.

Asia saw the rise of three remarkable personalities in the first half of the seventh century A.D.—Muhammad, founder of Islam in Arabia, Harsha in India, and Li Shih-Min (T'ang T'ai Tsung) in China. Within a hundred years of Muhammad's death Islam was destined to rise to paramount power in South-West Asia and in the Mediterranean, and to provide a great stimulus to learning. Like two other religions, Christianity and Judaism, it was the product of the desert. Its doctrine was simple, puritan, and touched with a flame of devotion which inspired some of the most exquisite lyrical poetry of the Persian and Indian mystics, as also some of the most savage religious wars of history.

### Moslem Invaders

Islam first entered the Indo-Pakistan subcontinent in A.D. 711—a comparatively peaceful intrusion, which petered out in a few years. Under Mahmud of Ghazni, it entered later with ruthless destruction of life and property, and of temples. The clash was less between Afghans and Rajputs; it was between Islam and Hinduism. The settled population of agricultural lands was submerged under the tidal wave of fanatic warrior herdsmen.

But the overlordship of Afghan rulers resulted in their being slowly civilized by the older culture, and so their own Moslem faith reaped advantages by the contact. And when the Mogul dynasty, founded in 1526 by Babur from Kokhand, reached its zenith with Akbar, the contemporary of Elizabeth of England, the subcontinent had reached its peak point. One glaring contrast should, however, be noted. The toiling millions (and Akbar's Empire had about 100 millions) were poor; the nobles lived in luxury and vied with each other in magnificence. The very few rich extorted from the very many poor.

Akbar, like the Mauryan emperors eighteen hundred years before him, had the welfare of his peoples at heart. He identified himself wholly with his empire, and his tact and tolerance, magnanimity, skill and foresight won the goodwill of all, Hindus and Moslems alike. Under his inspiration, art, literature and education

flourished, and a great Hindu-Moslem cultural unity was attained. From the beginning of the seventeenth century, during Akbar's last years, the Dutch and English entered India as traders, a century after the Portuguese. Europeans were the first to use the sea as their main route.

The agricultural system of Akbar's time, as a whole, was pretty much the same as it was for centuries before him, and as it is now. Some changes took place after the advent of the British, but not sufficient to transform the system as a whole. The records of Moslem writers and of European travellers in and around Akbar's time give a picture of the plough and the ox, millets and rice, oilseeds and pulses, barley, wheat, sugar-cane, indigo, cotton and hemp, pepper and spices, and opium. All other details they mention show that the sixteenth century differed little from the sixth, or our own twentieth. Akbar's grandfather, Babur, describes irrigation near Agra in these words: "At the well-edge they set up a fork of wood, having a roller adjusted between the forks, tie a rope to a large bucket, put the rope over the roller, and tie its other end to the bullock. One person must drive the bullock, the other empty the bucket."

The smaller industries were fishing, the pearl trade, silk weaving, the mining of copper, diamonds, gold and iron, and production of jewellery, perfumes, jute, salt, and tobacco.

### Business Machinery

The merchants were experienced business men. Recognized market prices, varying according to supply and demand, rings, combines, credit, exchange, insurance (including overdue market and war risks), and brokers, all formed part of the machinery of business. Of the improvements introduced since the arrival of the British, the most considerable is in irrigation, especially in districts where the annual rainfall averages less than fifty inches. Irrigation works had existed from time immemorial, but by the beginning of the nineteenth century the Mogul works had fallen into ruin. Modern irrigation began in 1819 with the old Delhi

FIG. 163. *Mat-trap fishing in southern India. The flexible bamboo fence (or mat) is placed in position in shallow water, enclosing a large area. The fishermen then diminish the area by moving their mat so that any fish within can be easily taken with hand-nets.*

canal. Four and a half million acres were irrigated in 1879, 19¼ million in 1900; today there are over 75 million acres.

From the middle of the last century the cotton mill industry grew rapidly. Fortunes made in cotton were used by Indian philanthropical merchant princes, like the Tata family, for developing heavy industry, such as steel, and for furthering the cause of education and scientific research. Besides iron and steel, development has taken place in coal, manganese, mica, oil and gold. There has been great development in the use of hydro-electric power—the country's potential is estimated at over 30 million kw. Iron ore of first quality is present, but coal is relatively poor. Bengal and Bihar are the chief districts for coal and iron, the Madhya Pradesh, Madras, Central India and Mysore for manganese, and Mysore for gold.

The jute industry is only a century old, but has assumed huge proportions; most of the jute, however, is grown in Pakistan, whereas the mills are in India. Sugar, lac, and hides and skins are also very important. Mention must also be made of tea from Assam and Bengal and the Nilgiri Hills in the south. The rise of these industries with the advent of the British, together with a vast increase of exports, led to the growth of big cities like Calcutta, Bombay, Karachi, and Madras, which are the counterparts of industrial and shipping centres like Liverpool or London in Britain. These modern centres imply an eversion from a country looking into itself and being almost solely concerned with self-sufficiency to a country becoming related to cash crops for export and to the import of manufactured goods.

### Ceylon

Colombo, a modern town and the capital of Ceylon, owes its importance to its position as a seaport. It has been described as the "Clapham Junction" of the East, an accurate enough description if a magic wand were to convert the squalor of the English railway junction into the tropical charm of the capital city of the "Pearl of the Eastern Seas." Colombo commands the natural relation of the inland hill mass of Ceylon to the most fertile part of the northern plain, and is also central for rubber, tea and coconut exports.

Ceylon has a fairly heavy rainfall, more from the North-East Monsoon than the blustering South-West. There is unfailing alternation of rain and sunshine. Your walking-stick becomes a sturdy plant if left sticking in the garden overnight, when the rains come! The western tracts grow areca-nut palms and large crops of rice; the

FIG. 164. *Checking malaria in Ceylon. During the monsoon season the rivers become flooded; when the rainy season has passed the waters subside, leaving stagnant pools which form favourite breeding-places for malaria-carrying mosquitoes. This picture shows a "fencing-in" device employed to trap silt by palisades of bamboo stakes, buttressed with rocks and concrete. These stakes are planted so as to narrow the river bed to 20 feet. The accumulated silt eventually rises high enough to make permanent banks, thus preventing flooding and the formation of stagnant pools. Regulation of rivers is one of the principal changes man makes in his environment.*

eastern tracts, too, raise large harvests of grain. With proper drainage, more needed than irrigation, these lands could be made into a vast granary.

There is a large amount of good quality iron in Ceylon, but unfortunately there is no coal. There is an important plumbago (graphite) industry, and digging for gems in the alluvial deposits south of Adam's Peak. There is also some pearl-fishing.

### Recent Changes

European control over trade in India was earlier and more complete than over China, where industrialization was slower but cities were larger and more numerous. The diversity between European relations with China and India may be ascribed to Chinese homogeneity and Indian heterogeneity. One may be allowed to say broadly that in China all the people were Chinese whereas in India they were Bengalis, Gujaratis, Rajputs, Malabarese, Tamils, Marathas—and so on. But though it seemed that the impact of Europe had contributed a powerful impetus towards ultimate unification, when, as promised, the British Government granted full self-government to the peoples of British India in 1947, two states emerged. These are now the sovereign independent Republic of India, also called the Indian Union, or Bharat, and the Islamic Republic of Pakistan. Both India and Pakistan are members of the British Commonwealth.

In China little alteration took place in the main, through all her long history, in the use of the plough and the loom, in working in wood, metal and clay, in the basic institutions of the family and property and in the relations between master and apprentice, landlord and tenant, or creditor and debtor. Today, modern industry is entering the country at a steadily increasing pace. Railroads and factories are spreading, partly through Soviet help. China's immense labour force partly compensates for her shortage of machinery. The country is most rich in tungsten and antimony; coal is plentiful; a fair amount of copper and tin, and smaller quantities of zinc, lead, silver and molybdenum are

Fig. 165. *The first skyscraper in Canton, south China. In the cities of the monsoon lands, Asiatic heritages intermingle with ideas brought in from America and Europe. The pole-porter contrasts with the modern building and the man in Western costume.*

worked. Iron, however, is not plentiful. Rice, wheat, millets, soya beans, tea, cotton and silk are important products. Under the Communist régime, co-operation in farming is successfully spreading and moving on to collectivization.

## Burma

There was no fertile Indus-valley land, vast and inviting, to greet those very early drifts of Negritos and Proto-Australoids thrusting across the mountains of eastern Bengal and Assam. They met a mountain focus crushed into a corner of Asia, characterized by feature lines trending north and south, by narrow and tortuous valleys, by violent torrents constantly obstructed by obstacles, and by towering ranges exposed to the full force of the South-West Monsoon. So constricted is the region that the upper waters of the Irrawaddy, Salween and Mekong, the three rivers dominating Burma, converge on a narrow bottle-neck a mere seventy miles wide; and at one point the Salween is only eighteen miles from the Mekong.

*Flag of the new Burma.*

Southwards comes the main mountain spine separating the river basin of the Irrawaddy and Salween from the Menam and Mekong; on either side are several smaller spines; and the long radiating valleys facilitated tribal movements downwards, in ancient times, just as they now facilitate railroad movement upwards. Since the height of the dividing ranges tended to isolate the valleys, the settlers in the valleys tended to political incoherence, and hardly developed any culture or even any agricultural system of their own.

This partly accounts for the sparse population of the area. Only in the rice-growing plains around the river deltas and in the plateau regions did some sort of stable settlement take place. Mon-khmer peoples coming from the north-east spread in the dry, open valley of the Mekong; the Tai-Chinese spread an industrious peasantry over the Shan plateau, pushing the original inhabitants into Siam (Thailand, the land of "the free"), and lastly came the Tibeto-Burmans. Burma's most civilized people are in the Mandalay basin and the lower Irrawaddy. The hill tribes around them still need a paternal trusteeship; many of them belong to ancient drifts into the country.

Buddhism came as the first civilizing agent, to which was added Hindu influence about or soon after the beginning of the Christian era. So profound was the influence of the benevolent doctrine of Buddhism—and Burma is a Buddhist country—helped by the effects of an equatorial climate in the southern and more cultivable part, that the unwarlike Burmese are a peaceable, leisure-loving, kindly people, but somewhat inclined to irresponsible enterprise, and averse from sustained discipline. They have a far higher standard of literacy and greater equality between the sexes than the people of India have; and they have a deep reverence for their religion.

### Modern Amenities

The Burmese have little liking for money-making and less for hard work. Indian labour, Indian, Chinese, and European economic enterprise, and the long period of peace following the establishment in 1886 of British rule, made for the development and slow but steady modernization of Burma and for a growth in population. Increased rice cultivation for export after the opening of the Suez Canal, development in rubber, and the intensive working of petroleum and other mineral resources furnished the revenues necessary for building roads and railways, for hospitals, for irrigation, and for running a modern administration. Teak, tobacco, millet, oil seeds, pulses and ground-nuts contribute to the economic life of the people.

Thus Burma went ahead, securing full independence for her people in 1947. The Burmese are wealthier than in the past, and enjoy a higher standard of living than the

FIG. 166. *The Salween River, Burma, at an altitude of 9,000 feet. The upper courses of the major rivers of South-Eastern Asia—the San Po, Irrawaddy, Salween, Mekong and Yangtze—all lie in corridors between steep and rugged mountain ranges.*

Indians and Chinese. There is, however, much scope for development in the building of motor roads, in water-power, in light and heavy industry, in agriculture, in health and education.

The capital of Burma, Rangoon, a comparatively modern town, owes its importance to the fact that it does some 85 per cent of all the sea trade of Burma, mainly rice, the bulk of which is of comparatively poor quality. It is the one great seaport of the whole country, is the greatest rice shipping port in the world, and also an important exporter of teak. The climate of Burma favours rubber plantation, but Burma is rich in minerals, the granite mountainous core of Tenasserim having mica and wolfram (tungsten) in Tavoy, tin in Mergui and Karathuri. The Shan plateau has sapphires and rubies, lead, silver and zinc in large amounts, copper and nickel in smaller amounts, and the upper Chindwin basin jade and amber. The

Chindwin-Irrawaddy basin is very rich in oil and in brown coal.

Thailand resembles Burma in its scanty population, its climate, its rice and teak, its northern hills and its southern delta. It is an independent state—a buffer state. Both religion (Buddhism) and the absence of any strong sense of political responsibility help to make the Thailanders mainly a peaceable and patient race. Like the Laos of the hilly north, the Thailanders of the lowlands are rice-growers.

The deltaic region round the modern capital, Bangkok, is of considerable importance, producing coconuts, rubber, pepper and cardamoms, and gold, rubies and sapphires. Rice, the main crop, is raised over 90 per cent of the total tilled area. Tobacco of good quality is also grown.

Kaolin, wolfram, coal and, especially, tin constitute the mineral wealth of Malaya, with Perak as its mainland centre. Rice, rubber (especially in Johore), palm-oil, sago, coconuts, and pinappeles are greatly favoured by the high rainfall (over 150 inches in the east) and humidity, and by soil rich in humus and lime. Abundant labour, mainly Chinese for tin, and Tamil for rubber, is easily available.

Singapore, a relatively healthy island on account of its sandstone formation and the steady movement of the air, is situated at a critical point on the longest sea-route of the world, London to Yokohama, and owes its importance to its magnificent harbour. Other ports on the west coast of Malaya include Penang (or Georgetown), which has nearly as good a harbour as Singapore.

Indochina is the peninsula containing the countries of North Vietnam, South Vietnam, Annam, Tonkin, Cochin China, Cambodia and Laos. These came into being after the Second World War, having gained their independence from France.

A mountain spine hugs the coast closely, thus leaving Laos exposed to the South-West Monsoon, while Annam has a cooler climate. Where the range is very close to the coast and runs parallel with it, as at Hué, fertile alluvium has collected in narrow strips, making the really habitable part of Annam.

Whereas the problems of Tonkin, Laos and Annam arise out of the mountain range, those of Cambodia and Cochin China are due to the Mekong basin. A considerable area of Cochin China is very low, and is permanently flooded. The Mekong and the Bassac break up into nine distributaries, which, with their network of canals and cross-channels, provide such efficient transport as to make Cholon one of the greatest river ports in Asia. Saigon, forty-five miles up the Saigon River, is safe from the few typhoons in the early part of the year, and all vessels can use this port, since the tide gives it a depth of over forty feet. Saigon controls the bulk of the foreign trade of the Indo-Chinese Union

FIG. 167. *Pictured here are floating fields on Lake Inlé, the "Lake of Laughter," in Burma. On a strongly interlaced network of roots and twigs several layers of earth are spread and firmly rammed. The artificial islands thus created are tethered with bamboo rods. On these islands the Burmese grow many varieties of fruit and vegetables. The peoples of lowland China, South-Eastern Asia and Japan are among the most expert of gardeners and show their great skill particularly in the utilization of opportunities that are generally neglected in other parts of the world. Planting-out from seed-beds is done with great care.*

FIG. 168. *Paddy-fields in Cochin China. Abundance of labour and the habit of working in long rows, for reasons of control, are features in the monsoon lands. Rice fields are kept flooded for long periods, and the peasants generally suffer from rheumatic troubles.*

(and the whole of the Cambodian foreign trade). It is a very French city, but has a trying climate.

Rice is the main product, but is restricted unfortunately to a single crop per year owing to the permanent wetness of Cochin China. Strenuous efforts are being made to solve this difficult problem of water control. Pepper, sweet potatoes, bananas, sugar and tobacco are also raised. Fish in large quantities are caught and cured, or, when sufficiently decayed, made into sauces and pastes. But none of these products is so important commercially as rice. Cambodia, too, has rice as its main product; also a large fishing industry (the fish being caught by mats stretched on palisades). Pepper, cotton, tobacco and oil-seeds are additional products. Silk is centred on Pnom-Penh, which is the natural capital of Cambodia and the focus for all foreign intercourse, though it is not as interesting as the ancient Khmer capital of Angkor, renowned for its wonderful temples, palaces and monuments, now in ruins.

Luang Prabang is the important centre of Laos, commanding the trade of the whole region, including the products collected by the hill people, the Khas, such as lac, wax, spices and silk.

High grade iron-ore is exported, and rice, sugar, spices, tea and coffee are raised. The Annamese coast has a busy fishery; cattle, drugs, raw silk, spices, and abundant timber are products of the hilly

interior. Hué, the capital, owes its importance mainly to its central position.

The problem confronting Tonkin is the immense load of silt carried down, mostly into the sea, by the Song-Koi (or Red River) and its tributaries. Hanoi, the capital, now sixty miles from the sea, stood by the coast thirteen centuries ago. Embankment only increases the difficulty. Floods, occurring at irregular times in some years, spread ruin far and wide. This partly accounts for the scantiness of the population, and for the export of a surplus of rice, of which there are two crops in the year.

Far more important than rice growing is the silk industry of Nam-dinh, the cotton and paper industries at Nam-dinh, Haiphong and Hanoi, and, above all, mining, for Tonkin is rich in coal, tin, wolfram, zinc, lead and iron.

### Increasing Population

The population of the Indo-Pakistan subcontinent is estimated to have been about 100 millions at the beginning of the seventeenth century. It stood at about 254 millions in 1881, and at 353 millions in 1931. It stands now, in 1962, at about 545 millions, and is increasing by about 6 millions every year. The Chinese population is about 720 millions. In line with the official Communist view (reiterated at the World Population Congress in Rome held in September, 1954) China stated that 12 million a year was a desirable increase in population, for there are lands like Manchuria and Mongolia awaiting settlement. Indonesia has about 90 millions. Japan has about 95 millions, and her rate of increase is about one million a year.

This rate of population increase raises very grave problems. Japan is cautiously taking up the idea of family planning, and the Indian government are doing more than any other government in this connexion.

Great efforts are also being made the world over for increased food production, for widespread education and for raising the standard of living. What effect all this will have upon the problems raised by swiftly increasing population remains to be seen.

### Malay Archipelago

The islands of the Malay Archipelago and Pacific Ocean command the sea-routes between East Africa and South Asia, and between the Far East and Australia, and lie at the crossroads eastwards of Singapore and southwards from Japan. An equatorial climate with a monotonously high temperature is the common pattern, but the presence of the sea and the height of the mountains occasionally exercise a moderating influence, and both Java and Sumatra have pleasantly cool regions. Intense morning heat produces thunderstorms in the afternoon almost every day. "Meet you after the storm" is a standard mode of making an appointment. Eastwards, towards Australia, aridity increases and the dry season is more pronounced. The rainy season associated with the West Monsoon lasts from November to March, when Djakarta gets over fifty inches of rain; the "dry" season associated with the East Monsoon lasts from April to October, when Djakarta gets about twenty inches.

Throughout most of the Archipelago mountain ranges are still in process of formation. Coastal plains occur on the northern side of the Sunda Islands, whose natural alignment in relation to the prevailing winds allows few natural harbours. Surf pounds the steep southern coasts; the river mouths on the north tend to silt up. The only naturally protected harbour is Surabaya in Java, under the lee of Madura Island. But in Borneo, Halmahera and Celebes the ranges radiate from a central knot. The mountain chains are of great importance in producing the climatic differences which are necessary for a variety of crops.

Great mineral wealth exists here, mainly in the older islands of Borneo, Banka and Billiton and the easternmost parts of Sumatra.

Indonesia is today the third greatest producer of tin ore, mainly from Banka, Billiton and Singkep, and the fifth greatest of petroleum, from Sumatra, Java, Borneo and the Moluccas. She produces also bauxite, manganese, gold, and silver from Sumatra and Borneo, platinum, salt, coal, asphalt, sulphur, and phosphates from Borneo.

Agriculture is the main industry of Indonesia, occupying about 70 per cent of the adult male population. The volcanic soil is rich and fertile. Silt brought down by the water from the mountains serves to renew the soil and its fertility. Of the Outer Islands (the islands other than Java and Madura), Sumatra is heavily forested, enjoys possibly the best climate, and has large tracts of very fertile soil in the marshy lowlands. Borneo's mountainous interiors are difficult to penetrate; mangrove swamps cover much of its coasts, but its cultivable lands are in the basins of the rivers flowing into the Java Sea.

### Java and Madura

Java and Madura are specially blessed in that they have extremely rich and fertile volcanic soil and an equable climate. Though comprising only 7 per cent of the total area of Indonesia, they hold about two-thirds of the total population of about 90 millions. The marshy plains of the north coast of Java are built up of alluvium and flood deposits; the thickly peopled south coast plains are suitable for rice, the crop most associated with heavy rainfall, as in the Ganges and Yangtze basins, and the one which best solves the problem of sustenance for dense populations. Added to Nature's beneficence are

FIG. 169. *Kara Battak, a rural settlement (kampoeng) at Kabardjake, Sumatra. These elaborate, high-roofed houses, raised well above the ground on posts, are typical of the dwellings occupied by the Battak, a race inhabiting northern Sumatra.*

the peasants' excellent farming abilities. Under past Dutch administration agriculture was fostered, and experimental stations and irrigation works, which are models of efficiency, were established. Further measures taken by that administration led to a very large increase of rice production in Sumatra.

Java may be divided into four zones: (1) A dense forest or hot zone up to 2,000 feet above sea level, with lofty trees and parasitic plants; (2) A moderate zone up to 4,500 feet—a rich region growing tea, coffee, cinchona, and maize, and with forests rich in ferns, fungi, rattans, and lianas; (3) A cool zone up to 7,500 feet, consisting of volcanic slopes and plateaux, with numerous lakes and swamps, and European vegetation and oaks and chestnuts; (4) The coldest parts, above 7,500 feet. About 44 per cent of the soil of Java is under cultivation.

Though the main part of the agricultural production of Indonesia is for home consumption, exports of certain products are among the world's largest—for example, copra, palm-oil, tea, rubber, quinine, kapok, sisal and pepper. Sugar, tobacco, and tapioca (from the cassava root) are also exported. In addition to rice, mainly native-grown products are maize, peanuts, cinnamon, cocoa, sago, soya-bean, vanilla, cotton, cotton-seed, sweet potatoes, etc. Indonesia is indeed one of the world's richest and loveliest regions, and the whole world has always had access to her great resources.

Of the original people of these islands, the Toalas of Celebes and the Batu of Sumatra seem to be allied to the Veddahs of Ceylon and to the short, dark, broad-nosed people with very curly hair of ancient India. Also, the Andamanese, the Semang in the Malay Peninsula, the Aeta in the Philippines and the Tapiro in Papua are all short and dark with broad noses. With this background of lowly folk there are also hoe-cultivators related to the lowly cultiva-

FIG. 170. *Old Batavia, Java, founded by early Dutch traders and named after their home country, lies inland on low, swampy land. It was originally built in Dutch style.*

tors of India, since small groups from each of the peoples who entered India in very early times trickled down to the extreme ends of South-East Asia.

The sea depth does not exceed 100 fathoms in the region between Farther India and the nearer East Indian islands. A reconstruction of the map (Fig. 216) with the coast line at the present 100-fathom line would join up Palawan, Bali, Borneo, Java, and Sumatra with the mainland, and leave only narrow straits separating the Philippines from Palawan and the other islands in the group from Australia.

In the second century A.D. the Hindus came. Their princes ruled in Java till the fifteenth century; their civilization left an enduring impression on the religion, culture, and art (especially on the dance, in Java and Bali), and on the social and economic systems of the islands. The Javanese have traces of Indian blood. After about A.D. 1450 Hindu power declined, as Arabs and Moslems, who had begun infiltration two centuries previously,

rose to power; and Islam, not too orthodox however, is the faith professed today by the greater part of the population. Chinese traders who came in large numbers kept themselves apart, although many of them, especially in Java, have been settled for many generations. They have done much to promote the development of the islands. The last-comers were Europeans, the Portuguese at the turn of the fifteenth-sixteenth centuries, and the Dutch a century later.

### Japan

The great god Izanagi with his consort Isanami leaned over the bridge of heaven, and stirred the sea with a jewelled spear. The foam flakes which dropped from the spearpoint back on the sea became the Japanese islands. Here lived Izanagi and Isanami with their baby gods and goddesses, and multiplied, and peopled Japan.

So runs tradition, fondly cherished by the Japanese masses. The present emperor traces an unbroken line of descent from the first Japanese emperor, Jimmu (of the seventh century B.C.), who is accepted as divine. So the emperor of Japan traces his descent from the gods. Unquestioning faith in this has been one of the strongest influences shaping Japanese history.

The survivors of the prehistoric population of Japan are called Ainu. They are whitish-skinned men with superabundant wavy hair, contrasting strongly with the yellowish-brown-skinned Japanese with little hair save on their heads. The Ainu are descendants of prehistoric peoples of the Siberian coast, whence they seem to have spread to Sakhalin and Japan. They are still more or less distinct in Yezo. They were expert fishermen occupying the Asiatic coast in the temperate zone.

Malayan seamen from south-east Asia entered, working up northwards along the islands. Then came a succession of invasions from the tenth century B.C. by the daimyo (the great lords) and the samurai soldiers (the knights) from Korea (Chosen) over the "bridge" of the islands of the Korea Strait. Most of the followers were Mongoloid, some Iranian and some perhaps Arabian. These "old Japanese" were fused into a nation in their island home in the south-west of Honshu.

From vast patriarchal grasslands with wide pastures and fertile soil, where their only enemy was drought, came the lank-haired Yamato landsmen. They came to a land where volcanoes and mountains filled most of the islands; where the highlands were heavily forested through unfailing rains; where the little flats were urgently required for agriculture instead of pasture, and where lack of bread would be due to insufficient land on which to grow grain. Even today, only 15 per cent of the land is cultivable, despite the high skill of the people in agriculture.

### Expert Seamen

The imperative necessity for food supplies compelled the Yamatos to learn from the Ainu to be expert fishermen. In the inland sea between Honshu and the large islands Kyushu and Shikoku the relation of the fierce tidal currents and dangerous whirlpools to the intricate channels, reefs and rocks, bays and islands, made the sea a nursery for seamen. The Sea of Japan with its warm and cold currents guaranteed an abundance of fish, and of fish-food like herrings, which could find deep water within five miles of the coast in most parts. The forests supplied

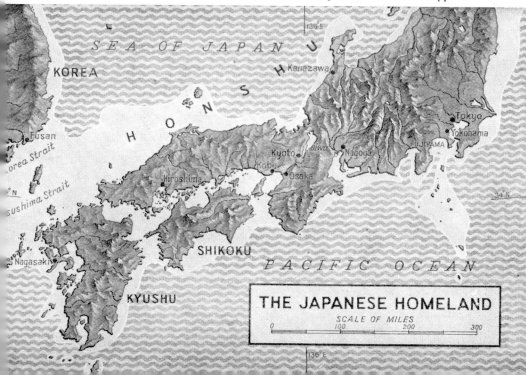

THE JAPANESE HOMELAND

SCALE OF MILES
0    100    200    300

Fig. 171. *Fujiyama, Japan, 12,395 feet high. It is a quiescent volcano of strikingly regular form, and is situated near Suruga Bay, 70 miles W.S.W. of Tokyo. At the summit is a crater 2,000 feet in diameter.*

tion, or a fervent patriotic love and respect) of Japan; of the gods who created it; of the Imperial family (always regarded as sacred because of divine descent); of the heroes who made Japan great; of the sustaining forces of Nature. In the Japanese way of life, the family is regarded in much the same way as in China.

Japan's export trade till the middle of the nineteenth century was limited to a little with Holland. Her industries were fishing and agriculture. Her native arts were porcelain and lacquer, bronze and basket ware. Indeed, in arts and crafts Japan excelled. Temperamentally the people were highly artistic and emotional, chivalrous and romantic, sensitive, courageous and fanatically loyal to personalities and to certain ideals, yet they could compromise when they thought fit.

Except in Yezo Island, both the soil and climate of Japan, especially around the Inland Sea, favour rice cultivation. But a rice civilization means that the cultivators must be industrious, frugal and co-operative, relying upon a strong government for security; and thus a dense but sedentary population grows. The unceasing industry, the skill and intelligence of the Japanese have made good use of the narrow alluvial valleys and coastal plains of the land. Unfortunately, the area is too small, the holdings are tiny, and the soil has been used too much. The steady increase in population, especially in the last fifty years, has raised serious problems. The application of science has enabled the rice output to keep pace with the increase—about 900,000 every year. But now it is almost impossible to get more out of the soil.

Dovetailing various crops on the limited acreage is a triumph of interculture. Lines of vegetables are grown between lines of fruit trees. In northern Honshu wheat and barley are interspersed with oats or rye. On the eastern plains the volcanic soil favours cotton. The belt between the Owari

the wood for shipbuilding. Rice cultivation in the plains, set in a monsoon climate, assured a food supply for a large settled population. Today fish supplies nearly three times the proportion of the people's food that it did in A.D. 1900.

In A.D. 405 an important event took place. Chinese culture entered Japan (as did also the Chinese script), when a Korean scribe became instructor at the Japanese court. Two centuries later, Buddhism entered Japan. Though at first opposed as a rival faith by Shinto, the influence of the pious, scholarly Prince Regent, Shotoku Taishi, established Buddhism firmly, partly by linking it with the Confucian doctrine of loyalty and filial piety, and the cult of ancestor worship—already an integral part of native Shinto belief. Shotoku well said:

Shinto is the source and root of the Way;

Confucianism is the branch and foliage of the Way;

Buddhism is the flower and fruit of the Way.

Shinto, or the Divine Way, the indigenous faith of the land, consisted of the "worship" (understood as religious adora-

and the Suruga bays has a humid, sunny climate, and a moist sandy loam on which an inferior cotton is grown. Green tea is grown over most of the hilly hinterland, except in northern Honshu and Yezo.

The silk industry is one of the oldest in Japan, and one in which the peasant girls through successive generations developed great skill. Production of silk on a large scale was due to the American demand for women's silk wear, and the Japanese export to the U.S.A. has been the chief source of Japan's foreign exchange.

In the application of science Japan proved an amazingly apt learner. The Shogun voluntarily resigned in 1867 in the interests of a united empire; and in 1869 the daimyos voluntarily surrendered their privileges and most of their revenues in order that a strong government might be completely unfettered—an act unparalleled in the annals of history. The old feudal system was swept away.

Careful examination showed how the mineral wealth of the country could best be exploited. There was copper, silver, gold, antimony, petroleum, coal, iron and manganese. Copper and the immense water-power of this steeply mountainous country —a minimum of fourteen million horse-power—were invaluable assets for the development of hydro-electric plants.

Rapid industrialization followed, and the country grew in wealth and power. She modelled her army on that of France first, and on that of Germany after 1871; her navy on that of Great Britain. Her railways were built by British engineers; her banking system was based on that of America,

her political system on that of Germany.

Indeed, in capacity for organization and co-operative effort, in military tradition, in the position of women, Japan resembled Germany closely. From 1934 onwards this German influence steadily increased.

It is sad that copying the Western world should have led to disastrous results. Japan's idealism, especially the patriotism of her people, had been deflected into wrong channels. Imperialism in its evil aspects had seized her. The pernicious falsehood of racial superiority had fouled the Japanese mind—or at least the mind of its ruling group—and filled it with the craze for domination over other people. This could meet, as indeed it did in 1945, but one end—failure.

The Orient is rich in life-wisdom. The Occident is rich in its control over material, and in the art of organization. Both have goodness of heart, the ability to perceive truly, and the power to act rightly. There is no unbridgeable gulf between them. The mind and heart and body of men are those of men everywhere.

It is man's task to learn how to enrich himself with the diversity of appearance, and not be so feeble as to let himself be engulfed in destructive conflict because of these minor (minor because they are not fundamental) differences between man in Europe and man in Asia. Just as man and woman are both needed for the continuance of the human race, even so, the Old World of the monsoon lands of Asia and the New World of Europe and America are indispensable to each other for the building of tomorrow's human world order.

## Test Yourself

1. (a) What inducement would there be to settle in Indo-Pakistan and China to the early nomad immigrants from the west and north-west?
   (b) Explain how the structural characters of the countries concerned affected and controlled those immigrations.
2. What may be said to be the origin of the caste system in India? What was its basis and what advantages could it be said to possess?
3. In view of the history of the economic development of Japan, how far do you think the institutional reforms effected since the Second World War are likely to be effective in solving the problems of the Japanese people?

*Answers will be found at the end of the book.*

FIG. 172. *The Australian House of Parliament, Canberra. Spaciously planned within the federal territory (939 square miles), acquired by the Commonwealth from New South Wales in 1910, Canberra, the federal capital of Australia, stands on a pleasant upland near the River Molonglo. It is not far from the great Burrinjuck dam, from which a large part of the Riverina is irrigated. Canberra's nearest natural seaport is at Jervis Bay.*

## CHAPTER XII

# AUSTRALIA

THE continent of Australia has been described, to suit rigid geographical tenets, as an island or an island-continent. Not so long ago there was a tendency to regard Australia as the largest land-component of the continent of Australasia, which was taken also to include New Zealand, so that its boundaries had to be sought under the sea. Nor was this inadmissible as an exercise in physiography; but the general use of the name of Australasia was deprecated as possibly implying something more than a very remote physical connexion between the two Dominions concerned, and the name is now less often heard than it used to be.

Australia is a continent, and, with its appanages, forms the Commonwealth of Australia, a Dominion of the British Empire—a national commonwealth within a commonwealth of nations.

## Government

The Commonwealth of Australia includes five mainland States—Queensland, New South Wales, Victoria, South Australia, Western Australia—and the island State of Tasmania. The Commonwealth Government controls defence, trade, customs, postal arrangements and a number of other matters common to all the constituent States, while the States retain their powers of legislation in all matters not exclusively under Commonwealth control or inconsistent therewith. A Commonwealth enclave in New South Wales, extending to 939 square miles, contains the federal capital, Canberra. The Commonwealth includes, and the Commonwealth Government administers, the Northern Territory, between South Australia and the north-central coast; also Norfolk Island, and a segment of the Antarctic lands south of 60 degrees S. lat. and between 45 degrees and 160 degrees long. (excepting Adelie Land). The islets of Ashmore and Cartier in the Timor Sea form a territory under Commonwealth authority. The Commonwealth Government administers Papua (British New Guinea), though this is not actually included in the Commonwealth.

A broken oval represents roughly the outline of Australia, the main breaks being represented by the Gulf of Carpentaria in the north and the Great Australian Bight in the south. Apart from these, the coast is not deeply indented, save where, at the eastern end of the Bight, Spencer Gulf and St. Vincent Gulf, separated by Yorke Peninsula, run inland. A five-fold physical division of the continent works out thus:—

1. The high lands of the eastern fringe from Cape York in the north to the mouth of the River Murray in the south.
2. The lowland of the Murray-Darling river system, westward of the southern part of the eastern fringe.
3. The South Australian highland, which parts the Murray-Darling basin from
4. The Lake Eyre basin of the central lowland.
5. The western plateau, which represents rather more than the western half of the continent.

The eastern highlands, extending from Cape York in the north to the mouth of the Murray River in the south, include the highest summits in the continent; but Australia differs from other continents in having no very high mountains. The highest, Mount Kosciusko, reaches only 7,328 feet. The eastern slope of the highlands is generally steeper than the western, but they are not of homogeneous structure throughout. The Queensland highlands in the north reach a height of 5,440 feet in the Bellenden Ker Mountains. They are dissected by a number of valleys, well watered by rivers debouching on a rocky coast fringed with small islands which are the summits of sunken ranges. From thirty to seventy miles seaward from this coast, the Great Barrier Reef protects the waters inshore along a line of 1,200 miles. The Barrier is composed of innumerable coral

BORNEO

CELEBES

NE
GU

JAVA SEA

Batavia

BANDA SEA

JAVA

ARAFURA
SEA

Torres St.
Cape Yo

TIMOR SEA

Darwin

GULF OF
CARPENTARIA

*Daly*

Roper

Norma

INDIAN OCEAN

*Fitzroy*

SELWYN

*Ashburton*

GREAT SANDY
DESERT

MAC DONNELL RANGE

Alice Springs

G
R
E

*L. Macdonald*

A
R
T
B
A
S

*Gascoyne*

*L. Amadeus*

MUSGRAVE RANGE

*Finke*

*Barco*

*Murchison*

Nannine

Cue

DARLING RANGE

GREAT VICTORIA DESERT

L. Eyre

Geraldton

L. Torrens

L.F

Coolgardie

NULLARBOR PLAIN

*L. Gairdner*

S. AUS. HIGHLANDS

Perth

Brok
H

Fremantle

GREAT
AUSTRALIAN BIGHT

Murr

Adelaid

*Spencer Gulf*

Lake
*Alexa*

Albany

*St. Vincent Gulf*

SOUTHERN

EQUATOR
GILBERT IS.
Rabaul
SOLOMON ISLANDS
ELLICE IS.
Moresby
SANTA CRUZ IS.
GREAT BARRIER REEF
CORAL SEA
FIJI IS.
NEW HEBRIDES
Suva
NEW CALEDONIA
Rockhampton
TROPIC OF CAPRICORN
PACIFIC OCEAN
Charleville
Brisbane
DARLING DOWNS
Warrego
Culgoa
Barwan
NEW ENGLAND RANGE
Bourke
Macquarie
BLUE MTS.
Newcastle
Bathurst
Sydney
AUSTRALIAN ALPS
Canberra
MT. KOSCIUSKO
Melbourne
TASMAN SEA
Auckland
Cook Strait
FLINDERS I.
TASMANIA
Hobart
Wellington
Nelson
NEW ZEALAND
SOUTHERN ALPS
Christchurch
Canterbury Bight
Dunedin
OCEAN

islets built, and constantly building, along the line of a former coast, now submerged.

In northern Queensland (Cape York peninsula) the highest land is close to the east coast and the longer rivers drain west to the Gulf of Carpentaria. Farther south the highest land recedes to two or three hundred miles inland, and the east-flowing rivers water wide upland downs before entering the sea through valleys which narrow in their lower parts. In southern Queensland, and all the way southward through New South Wales to the end of the highlands in Victoria, the highest land is again nearer to the coast—somewhat over 100 miles from it on the average. The coastal lowlands therefore are narrow and demarcated more or less clearly into sections which include the northern coastal belt of New South Wales, the valley of the Hunter River, the district around the famous harbour of Port Jackson (on which

stands the city of Sydney), the Illawarra country, the southern coastal belt of New South Wales, the Gippsland district, the district around Port Phillip (where stands the city of Melbourne), and the south-western lowland of Victoria below the ultimate southerly slopes of the eastern highlands. It will presently appear that these lowlands are of first-rate importance in the geography of Australia: though they represent but a small fraction of the whole area of the continent they are fitted by natural riches and climate to welcome the white man's settlement, and the cradle of that settlement was in this part of the Commonwealth.

The highlands in New South Wales and Victoria are complex in form and structure, but they may be divided into four main masses—the New England ranges, the Blue Mountains, the congeries of ranges which culminate in Mount Kosciusko, and the

FIG. 173. *The Great Barrier Reef, off the coast of Queensland. For 1,200 miles this huge coral reef, which actually consists of innumerable islets, protects a navigable channel between it and the mainland of Australia, which is of great value to coastal shipping.*

FIG. 174. *Buckland Valley with, beyond, the Australian Alps, viewed from the Mount Buffalo National Park, Victoria. The cultivated land of the valley floor contrasts with the wooded foothills. The mountains in the far distance have a light covering of snow.*

highlands of Victoria. More or less easy routes to the interior pass between these masses, though the older generations of settlers in south-eastern Australia encountered difficulties in penetrating through the highlands to the interior which seem now to have taken surprisingly long to overcome, even if allowance be made for the rough and inhospitable nature of much of the highland country.

The Blue Mountains, the principal feature of the central mass in New South Wales, behind Sydney, present steep ramparts to the east, deeply cut by gorges which the streams have eroded through a hard escarpment of Triassic sandstone. Within the ramparts, wider but equally deep branching valleys have been hollowed out in softer rocks, providing, from viewpoints on their upper edges, a singular and most impressive landscape. Another notable physical feature of this highland division is the limestone caverns of Jeno-

lan, near the headwaters of the Macquarie River, among the most remarkable examples of their kind known in the world.

Mount Kosciusko is a granite mass, showing much evidence of glaciation in small lake basins, moraine piles and perched blocks. Here alone, in Australia, alpine features of scenery and vegetation are plain to view. Continuing into eastern Victoria we find the granite bosses reaching heights between 6,000 and 7,000 feet. Westward again the Victorian highlands become lower and of plateau form—stumps, really, of old mountain ranges. Rich basaltic soils spread far over the plains below.

A detached part of the eastern highlands constitutes the island of Tasmania, separated from the mainland by Bass Strait, 150 miles wide, shallow (hardly anywhere over fifty fathoms deep), and formed but recently as geological time is counted. The northern highland reaches points over

5,000 feet; in the centre a wide plateau bears many lakes. Two well marked depressions cross the island from north to south. It is a beautiful island, of which some rural sections have been likened, not without an effort of imagination, to England.

The Murray-Darling basin is a lowland (for the most part) watered by rivers which have their sources in the eastern highlands. In the east the basin includes the foothills of the highlands; in the centre the plains, including the tract known as the Riverina; and in the west an area lying still lower, and representing a geologically recent gulf, which several of the rivers entered through separate mouths, but which now receives them all as tributaries of the Murray. Though the Murray alone carries its name to the sea, which it enters through the shallow lagoon of Lake Alexandrina, it is not actually the longest river of the system. It rises not far from Mount Kosciusko. The Darling, rising far to the north of this, in headstreams draining from the Darling Downs in Queensland, is longer. The western rim of the basin is formed by the South Australian highlands; on the north there is no well defined rim; the transition to the dry tract of the Great Artesian Basin is not clear to view.

The South Australian highlands, including the Flinders and other ranges, are composed of old hard rocks standing up boldly from the lowlands on either hand, and scenically striking, despite their modest height, which at the most is between 3,000 and 4,000 feet. To the west and north-west of them a rift valley continues northward from Spencer Gulf, part of its surface lying a little below sea level. In it are Lakes Torrens and Eyre, two of the many lake basins which are found all over the arid parts of the continent, saline and usually

FIG. 175. *The township of Walhalla, Victoria. These rough foothills produced much gold in earlier days. In a dyke of the Long Tunnel mine at Walhalla a single fissure-lode yielded gold to the value of £4,000,000. This region as a whole, however, is sparsely inhabited, the coastal plains to the south proving more attractive.*

dry, covered only with a film of water when sufficient rain has fallen for intermittent streams to flow.

An immense area of Australia has no surface drainage to the sea. The bulk of this area is definable as extending over 25 degrees of longitude and 15 degrees of latitude. Its surface varies, as will presently appear, from scrub and savanna country to desert. The Great Artesian Basin, so called to distinguish it from other such basins of smaller extent, covers more than half of Queensland and even greater parts of New South Wales and South Australia.

In an early geological period there was either a division of what is now the continent into two great islands, eastern and western, with a wide shallow strait between them now represented by the lowland between Spencer Gulf and the Gulf of Carpentaria, or, it may be, an isthmus joined the low land masses in the north, where the land now rises higher than in the south. In this strait or gulf thick beds of sand were laid down and became a porous sandstone, and above them impermeable clays. The sandstones around the basin are exposed, and in New South Wales and Queensland the rain they receive is absorbed and collects below ground in the lower parts of the basin. Many deep wells have been sunk in this region, from which the water either flows under natural pressure, or must be raised by pumping.

The rest of the continent, consisting mainly of older rocks, with a fringe of younger rocks along its western coasts, comprises Western Australia, and much of South, Central and Northern Australia.

### One Quarter Desert

The term desert is not lightly used in Australia, where men have striven, and in many instances with outstanding success, against natural disadvantages of climate in their effort to develop mineral wealth or extend the areas of stock-raising and agriculture. Nevertheless the western plateau, together with the Lake Eyre basin, includes an area more than a quarter of that of the whole continent in extent, in which true desert conditions exist, though these have not wholly excluded man's

activities. The west coastal fringe of this region ranges from the tropical conditions of the north to the temperate conditions of the south-west, in which last division the productive activities of Western Australia are principally focused.

### Climate

Australia is crossed, northward of its centre, by the tropic of Capricorn: it reaches within 12 degrees of the equator, and the fortieth parallel of south latitude passes through Bass Strait. This position implies a climate which may be very hot but is never very cold. In summer (December, January, February), the north (and especially the north-west) is very hot, and there is a season of monsoon winds from some northerly quarter, and much rain. Later in the year, as the sun appears to move northward, there follows higher pressure over the land and dry winds blow from it. South of this northern monsoon belt follows the belt of the south-east trade-winds, which bring rain to the eastern highlands but become dry as they pass inland. To the south, again, the prevalent westerly winds bring rain mostly in winter, but the incurving of the Great Australian Bight carries the land beyond their full influence, and the arid central region of the continent here approaches the coast.

The same thing happens in the middle west. Here the northern region of summer rains and the southern region of winter rains do not adjoin, so that there is a dry area between them. On the other hand these rain seasons overlap in the south-east so that there is a region with rain at all seasons. It may be added here that the rain-shadow effect which helps toward the arid condition of central Australia has a smaller but important parallel in the Murray-Darling basin, much of which is sheltered from a heavy rainfall by the highlands, especially those of South Australia, which slow down the prevalent westerly winds so that they are drained of heavy rain before they reach the plain. Even the Murray River itself has been known to cease flowing in a season of severe drought, and its tributaries commonly do so. Artificial irrigation is important in this region.

FIG. 176. *Mabuiag Island, in the Torres Strait, is one of several under the protection of Queensland. Many of the men find employment with the pearling fleets at Thursday Island.*

Australia, then, may be divided into climatic regions as follows: (1) the northern region of the summer monsoon; (2) the north-eastern division where the south-east trades bring heavy rains, especially in summer; (3) the south-eastern area of rain at all seasons; (4) the dry west-central region; (5) the southern region of winter rains, which consists mainly of two areas, separated by the Great Australian Bight, the south-west (Western Australia), and, in the south, South Australia and Western Victoria. The extreme importance of the rainfall to agriculture, as to quantity and season, will become apparent later.

The visitor to Australia from any other country need be no student of botany or zoology to enable him to see that the flora and fauna of this land are strange to him. This condition is connected with the long isolation of Australia, in geological time, from other lands. We noticed earlier that the western plateau is a very old land mass, and that it was, fairly recently, geologically speaking, separated wholly or in part by sea from eastern Australia. These, briefly, are the facts of physical geography relevant to the distinctions between the flora and fauna of Australia and the rest of the world and between those of western and eastern Australia. The forested areas coincide with those of

F<small>IG</small>. 177. *The paradoxical duck-billed platypus from Australia has a beak like a duck's and lays eggs, but it has fur instead of feathers and suckles its young like a mammal.*

heaviest rainfall—the north, east, south-east, and south-west belts. In the north and north-east a tropical vegetation, characteristic of New Guinea and the eastern Malay Archipelago, has invaded the richer coastal lowlands, notably in Queensland, and has more or less overwhelmed the native Australian vegetation, which, however, asserts itself beyond the limits of the wettest districts. The characteristic Australian trees are the eucalyptus, of which there are many species and many sizes, from the splendid timber trees flourishing in favourable conditions in Western Australia (the south-west), Victoria, and Tasmania to the stunted growth of the mallee scrub which covers great arid tracts in south-central Australia and the Murray-Darling basin.

At its finest development the eucalyptus is a stately tree. Specimens with a height of 300 feet and a girth of 25 feet at 6 feet from the ground have been recorded in Gippsland (Victoria). The eucalyptus is adapted to dry conditions, and so are other typical Australian trees and shrubs, such as myrtles, acacias, casuarinas, and heaths. The evergreen foliage of these plants is commonly dull, but many bear beautiful flowers. The woodlands of Victoria and Tasmania include wide tracts in which the great trees, uncrowded, have beneath them a characteristic undergrowth in which tree ferns (Fig. 185) are prominent. An evergreen beech usurps the dominant position

from the eucalyptus in western Tasmania and in parts of Gippsland, and Tasmania has also a deciduous beech tree: both of these have parallels in South America. In the Tasmanian beechwoods an extraordinary undergrowth appears: masses of beech saplings, ferns and shrubs on a horizontal base of rotting wood make a well-nigh impenetrable thicket.

Inland from the eastern and south-western woodland zones in Australia, there is a transition to savanna, with scattered trees, and to great tracts of grassland valuable for stock, which maintains itself so far as sufficient moisture is available. Below this scale of sufficiency comes the scrub, such as the mallee already mentioned or the mulga, an acacia scrub more typical of the western plateau; then on still drier ground are found the spinifex and porcupine grasses, bushy, and with foliage stiff and sharp enough to wound, until, under extreme desert conditions completely barren tracts appear. Nevertheless, over much of the arid country an unusual rainfall may bring into growth, from seed in which life is latent, a transitory display of vegetation, which in the past has deceived seekers for new pastures.

The long separation of Australia from other continents has already been noticed: to this, in connexion with the fauna, must be added consideration of the division between the Oriental and Australian regions which is known as Wallace's Line

(Fig. 216), after the naturalist Alfred Russel Wallace who worked it out. This, which is much nearer to a sharply drawn line than Nature usually draws, passes through the strait between the islands of Bali and Lombok, only fifteen miles wide, between Borneo and Celebes, and southward of the Philippine Islands. "It separates two faunas more completely different from one another than those of any other two regions in the world," in respect not only of mammals but of birds. In the Australian region placental mammals, born at an advanced stage of development after a relatively long period in the mother's womb, are few and small, whereas marsupials, born at an early stage and nourished in an external pouch, are numerous in species and in some instances large. The kangaroos (Fig. 69) and wallabies are the familiar examples. Flesh-eating marsupials are the Tasmanian tiger and Tasmanian devil. There are marsupial opossums and koalas or native bears (treedwellers), wombats, mice, moles, and many other forms. The marsupials are known from fossils to be an old group, formerly more widely distributed. An ancient link between mammals and reptiles survives in the only two kinds of egg-laying mammals now existing, and that only in Australia. These are the amphibious platypus (Fig. 177) and the native porcupine (echidna). Poisonous snakes are numerous. The introduction of rabbits developed into a scourge.

A large number of bird families are limited to the Australian region; others,

though not so limited, are especially prominent there. Emus, cassowaries, cockatoos, honeysuckers, lyre-birds, and birds of paradise are familiar examples. No visitor can possibly miss the peculiarities and interest of Australian bird life, from the moment when he is greeted by the mocking laughter of the laughing jackass (a big kingfisher), or hears some other loud and unfamiliar bird-call, or sees some brilliant flock of parakeets; though it should be added that most Australian birds have rather inconspicuous plumage.

In Australian waters the lung-fish of Queensland and certain localized freshwater shrimps have been described as living fossils. Native freshwater fishes are not conspicuous, but there are valuable food fishes in the adjacent seas.

### Man in Australia

An aboriginal race of men survives in Australia, to the number perhaps of 47,000. In addition there are some 27,000 or more half-castes. The full-blooded aboriginals have declined in number, like other aboriginal peoples, since white men first came into contact with them, but so far as they now live in reserves, their numbers are believed to be growing again. They are a primitive people, held to have affinities

FIG. 178. *This historic photograph shows the last known family of Tasmanian aborigines, whose race became extinct in 1876. The few survivors, after conflict with settlers and refugees in Tasmania, had been removed to Flinders Island in the year 1832.*

with the Veddahs of Ceylon and with some other Indian peoples low in the scale of civilization, and to be a race of Caucasian origin who moved at a distant prehistoric period through Malaya to Australia.

They live in scattered communities, mainly in the north and in districts untouched by white colonization; but their place-names, adopted by white settlers, remain in many parts. As hunters and trackers they show high skill, and they preserve something of the art of their palæolithic and neolithic ancestry: in Australian museums are many examples of this, such as the barbs of weapons beautifully shaped by chipping glass insulators purloined from telegraph poles in remote districts, as neolithic man chipped stones. Their use of the boomerang as a weapon is well known. Some of them serve white settlers as labourers, and individuals have shown themselves capable of acquiring good standards in education and the arts.

When fitting into the geographical framework the picture of Australian settlement by white men, we meet with the common statement that settlement has been slow. So it was in early days, and for obvious geographical reasons. The western coasts were known from 1616 onward (and very likely earlier, through voyages of which no record remains), but the Dutch navigators who saw them during the ensuing half-century thought nothing of their promise, which is no matter for wonder, for that seaboard offers no prospect of a smiling welcome. The same applies in a measure to Captain Cook, after he had entered Botany Bay in 1770, though his companion Joseph Banks, viewing what he saw of the country with a naturalist's eyes, was more percipient of its future worth. Australia's remoteness from Britain, and from other lands from which colonization proceeded, restricted the flow of settlers, and at the same time justified its use as a dumping ground for deportees. Such was the nature of the first settlement, made in 1788, and for some time free settlement was actually frowned upon by the authorities at home. The establishment of 1788 was set up at first in Botany Bay, but was quickly removed to Port Jackson, destined to become the site of the city of Sydney, on one of the finest natural harbours in the world, entered by no large river and there-

fore free of silting. When in 1813 the Blue Mountains were crossed and the interior grasslands were discovered, it became apparent that Australia was not in fact a difficult country for pioneering, so far as climatic conditions made that possible. The first inland settlement was at Bathurst, reached through the pass to the north of the Blue Mountains.

Movement across the south-eastern mountain barrier from Port Jackson brought explorers into the eastern part of the Murray-Darling basin: wide vistas were opened up, and this territory was to become economically one of the most important in Australia, not only for agricultural and pastoral developments, but also for mining; for it was within the limits of the basin that the first discovery of gold in Australia was made, a discovery which immensely extended the economic horizon, and brought to the country a great influx of settlers. When, in process of political development, the boundaries of the States were laid down, the Murray-Darling basin was divided between three of them—New South Wales, Victoria and South Australia—and some measure of

conflicting interest, in regard to such questions as irrigation and river navigation, not unnaturally arose and has persisted. It is therefore of great interest to find that at the present time there is a movement on foot to plan the basin as a geographical unit under a single authority, on some such lines as those of the Tennessee Valley Authority (T.V.A.), in the United States of America, overriding the powers of the several States and local divisions.

The granting of self-government to the three States just named, and also to Tasmania and Queensland, had been effected by 1860, but Western Australia did not become independent until thirty years later. The early exploration of Western Australia was carried out by seaborne expeditions, and the State remained like an island in relation to the rest of Australia, with a sea voyage of 1,350 miles separating its chief port, Fremantle, from Port Adelaide in South Australia, until the transcontinental railway was completed in 1917.

It needs only a comparison of maps to show the very close relation between climatic conditions and the distribution of population in Australia. The population is about ten millions; of these, over 90 per cent live east of the meridian of 138 degrees, that is to say, on about 40 per cent of the total area including Tasmania. The contrast is more strongly pointed when it is observed that, even within that 40 per cent, there are large sparsely inhabited areas in the north and centre, and that by far the larger proportion of the population of the remaining 60 per cent is found in the south-western fraction of Western Australia. The inhabitants are of European, and primarily of British origin, excepting the aborigines and

FIG. 179. *An air-view of Sydney Harbour, looking east. This shows the seaward half of Port Jackson, which is the harbour, outward to the Heads flanking the entrance from the Pacific Ocean. The central part of the city lies below this view: the suburb of North Sydney is seen across the harbour. There is no finer metropolitan waterway to be found in the world as regards facilities for commerce and for recreational activities.*

about 30,000 non-Europeans or half-castes of whom half are Chinese. The fundamental doctrine well known as the White Australia policy, which has severely limited the introduction of Asiatic immigrants in particular, has been strongly contested on the ground (among others) that in tropical Australia and on its margin the climate is unsuitable for white labour, which moreover is more expensive than coloured labour, and that therefore the development of Australian tropical resources has been backward and will continue so.

### Arid Land

The areas best suited by their climate to white labour in Australia lie, broadly speaking, south of the tropic of Capricorn. In the coastal areas north of this, even though conditions may be otherwise suitable, many if not most white people find the climate trying for at least six months of the year, increasing to nearly the whole year in the farthest north. But south of the tropic there is a larger area than north of it in which dry conditions prohibit any but the most limited settlement—only great mineral wealth accounts for any close concentration of inhabitants in any part of it. This region may be approximately defined as that which receives, on average, less than 10 inches of rain annually. Using figures worked out by Professor Griffith Taylor, it is found that about 42 per cent of the total area of Australia is arid, this portion being divided nearly equally between lands which may provide fair pasture except in drought, and lands which are almost or quite useless for stock; 34 per cent is good pastoral country; 21 per cent "fair temperate farming country, suitable for close settlement," and 3 per cent tropical country in Queensland with rain throughout the year and suited for tropical agriculture.

By way of indicating the relative value of Australian products it may be said that in 1953-54 manufactures represented 52 per cent of the total value, pastoral products 21 per cent, agricultural 13 per cent, dairy 6 per cent, mining 5 per cent, and forestry and fisheries together 2 per cent. The pastoral products are wool and meat, with subsidiaries such as hides, skins, leather,

and tallow. Of the principal agricultural products wheat stands first, with barley prominent among other grains; fruit and sugar rank high, and wine from Australian vines should be mentioned here. The mineral wealth of Australia, as will appear presently, is widespread and varied. So far as concerns agricultural and pastoral products, the output may vary considerably in accordance with seasons favourable or otherwise, apart from economic considerations: crops and pasture may be adversely affected by shortage of rainfall in one locality or another, and sometimes over wide areas. For this among other reasons the relative values of products in these departments fluctuate: as an example, in the year just quoted the chief exports according to values from Australia to Britain were wool, gold, butter, meat, wheat, in that order; in the preceding year the order was wool, wheat, gold, meat, butter. In these two years together, the export value of wool to Britain slightly exceeded that of wheat, flour, meat and butter together.

### Sheep and Cattle

It was through pastoral industries that the major economic development of Australia began. The major sheep-rearing lands are in the south-east and middle east, extending to the coast in the south-east, but inland on the downs in northern New South Wales and Queensland. They extend northward roughly to about 3 degrees north of the tropic, and subject to that limitation, are found mainly on areas receiving from thirty down to ten inches of rainfall annually. The same applies to the sheep-rearing lands in the west of Western Australia. The lower limit of rainfall implies intermittent risk of drought, and from that enemy the sheep industry has from time to time suffered severely, but it has been too vigorous to be set back for long. The use of artesian water has greatly extended the interior lands suitable for stock raising. Artesian water is in some cases fit for use in cultivation also, but is commonly too highly charged with carbonate of soda.

The rearing of beef cattle is confined in

the main to Queensland, Western Australia and the north. Farther south, in the east of Australia, dairying becomes more prominent than the raising of fat cattle. It began in Victoria, and was strong enough, as long as half a century ago, to withstand, and largely to help the area to recover from, a period of severe financial depression. Notably in the western part of the State, where the climate allows the reliable growth of fodder crops for autumn and winter, large landowners became ready to let dairy land to small farmers on a share basis. In the coast lands (especially those of the south) of New South Wales, and on the Darling Downs in Queensland, dairy farming is prosperous. Co-operative methods have strengthened the dairy industry, and the pastoral industries generally have come to support important manufacturers in the preservation of foods and all the other associated activities.

Australia has reached the position of being one of the world's greatest wheat lands through experiment and scientific farming. As against this must be set earlier errors, of which effects are still visible, such as the killing of trees by ring-barking in order to clear land quickly for cultivation. There was never a more dismal form of exploitation, and there are tracts where, in time, this practice let in the desert.

Over large areas wheat is grown with remarkably low annual rainfall, because the rain season coincides with the need of the crop. An example of this can be cited. An area in South Australia has a mean annual rainfall of 17 inches, of which 12 inches falls between May and November, covering the period from seedtime to harvest. And wheat is grown on drier lands than this: broadly it may be said to be limited by a fall of 10 inches during the appropriate season. The most critical period is, generally speaking, October and early November, when the ears should fill.

Such are a few outstanding points in relation to stock farming and wheat growing in Australia; but Australian farming should not be pictured, as sometimes it is, as being clearly cut into these two great divisions. Over large areas where the climate is favourable, notably in the southeast, mixed farming has established itself on the basis of the work of those who brought the experience of generations of farmers from their old homelands, notably Britain, on to which has been grafted the experience and knowledge acquired by their successors through experiment and

FIG. 180. *A street frontage in Kalgoorlie, Western Australia. In its variety of architectural design, the town is not uncharacteristic of similar towns in Australia and elsewhere which have grown up very quickly in order to accommodate a sudden expansion of population and trade.*

FIG. 181. *Perth, capital of Western Australia, on the estuary of the Swan River. As the river cannot receive large ships here, the port of Fremantle has developed at its mouth.*

research. Special reference is due to Tasmania in this connexion; here products and methods approximate nearly, thanks to its geographical position, to those of the mother country; its yield of wheat per acre is above that of the mainland, and its apples rank high in the excellent standard of Australian fruits, which range from the soft fruits of temperate conditions to the oranges and bananas of the sub-tropical lands where the rainfall suffices. In these last Queensland excels, and here also cane sugar is a product of importance, though set back from a higher place by the restriction upon coloured labour.

The ruthless destruction of forests in the course of agricultural development has been mentioned. Forest reserves were indeed created early, but mainly to ensure a supply of timber for the mining industries; not for soil conservation. Destruction brought about a positive shortage of timber in some parts as settlement became closer and precautions began to be taken. Now there are State plantations.

The principal minerals are gold, coal, iron, silver, copper, lead and tin; but there are many others: antimony, zinc, uranium, manganese, wolfram, platinum, mercury, nickel, cobalt, chromium—the range is immense in kind, and no less in distribution. This last cannot be detailed here, but the names of some of the goldfields belong to the history of Australia, and some of the works connected with rich mineral fields in the drier lands are famous, as at Coolgardie, Cue and Broken Hill. Thus the Coolgardie group of gold-mining towns, far in the interior of Western Australia, was supplied with water from the well-watered western land, 400 miles away, by means of a dam across the Helena River, near Perth, a pipeline, and pumps to raise the water over 1,300 feet. Under war conditions the Australian production of gold fell for the time being, but that of coal, and, among metals, notably that of lead, greatly increased. The quest for mineral oil is at the stage of exploration, though some is produced. A variety of gem stones is found, including diamonds, but the gem most familiarly associated with Australia is the opal.

### Room for More

It has been said already that the population of Australia is about ten million: it is estimated that the continent could support a population of twenty millions, even admitting that large areas are uninhabitable or practically so. Well over five millions are town-dwellers, and the great majority of these live in the six capital cities of the States.

The proportion of these to country-dwellers is high, and in the past has caused considerable concern in view of the economic importance of pastoral and agricultural development.

There is less reason now for such concern, for the manufacturing industries of Australia, in process of rapid development before 1939, were immensely expanded during the war years which followed; and though new industries were directed to the purpose of war, and those previously existing were largely converted to such ends, many of them became permanent.

### Cities and Communications

Of the State capitals, Sydney (N.S.W.) and Melbourne (Vic.) are the chief seaports of the continent. Brisbane (Q.) and Hobart (Tas.) also are ports. Adelaide (S.A.) and Perth (W.A.) stand a few miles inland from their ports, Port Adelaide and Fremantle respectively. The next largest town to the mainland capitals is Newcastle (N.S.W.), an exporting centre for an important coalfield. For the rest, Australian towns are not large—there are few populations exceeding 30,000. In all the populous parts of Australia excepting Queensland, these small towns, originating as agricultural or mining centres, are inland, with few exceptions. Queensland shows an opposite geographical distribution. There, in distinction from the rest of Australia, the coast offers a succession of small natural harbours, with an outer protection of little islands, and the majority of the chief towns stand on these inlets.

The towns in all parts of Australia are served by quite effective railway connexions; but so far as concerns the inter-State communications, the railways suffer from the disability that they were originally developed as separate systems of the individual States, which adjudged their own needs in respect of gauges. It results that the 28,000 miles of railway include over 6,000 miles of a gauge of 5 feet 3 inches (mainly in Victoria), 7,400 of the standard gauge of 4 feet 8½ inches (New South Wales, and the Commonwealth transcontinental line from Western to South Australia), and 14,300 of the gauge of 3 feet 6 inches. This last is a gauge usual in areas of scattered settlement where traffic does not call for the standard gauge. So far, however, as concerns inter-State trunk routes, the changes of gauge cause obvious inconveniences at State frontiers, and unification of gauges—an expensive process—has long been under discussion. A standard gauge connexion between the New South Wales lines and Brisbane was opened in 1930, making the first link in a continuous chain between the eastern capitals.

Before the war there were some 29,000 miles of regular air services in Australia, and large extensions have followed. War requirements necessitated active road construction and improvement in many directions—the whole road system is estimated at half-a-million miles—and the improvement of road transport especially benefits those outlying areas beyond the immediate reach of the railways.

## Test Yourself

1. Although the existence of the Australian continent was known to European navigators as early as the first years of the seventeenth century, settlement of the new territory was slow. Account for this in terms of the geographical framework.
2. The population of Australia is unevenly distributed over the land mass. How can this be accounted for in terms of the physical and climatic environment?
3. From your reading of the chapter, try to estimate, giving reasons, the probable lines of future development of Australia, assuming a steady increase of population.

*Answers will be found at the end of the book.*

FIG. 182.  *Sheep farming in North Island, New Zealand.  Early settlers in the New Zealand group of islands found a mild climate with half of the land surface covered with a dense evergreen forest of pine and beech trees, intermingled with palms, ferns and wild vines*

## CHAPTER XIII

# NEW ZEALAND AND
# THE PACIFIC ISLANDS

NEW ZEALAND consists of two main islands, the North Island and the South Island, lying in the Pacific Ocean between 34 degrees and 48 degrees S. Lat. and between 166 degrees and 179 degrees E. Long. The Dominion of New Zealand includes, in addition to these two, Stewart Island, immediately to the south of the South Island, and a number of oceanic islands, among them the Auckland and Cook groups. The Dominion also has under its jurisdiction the Union Islands and Western Samoa, and the Antarctic Ross Dependency.

New Zealand is a single jewel of land in an immense setting of ocean. Australia is 1,200 miles away; the nearest point of South America 5,000 miles distant. The North and South Islands, divided by Cook Strait (rather wider than the English Channel at their respective narrowest points), have a length together of about 1,150 miles and a breadth nowhere exceeding 200. They present an extraordinary variety of very beautiful scenery. By far the greater part of their surface consists of hills or mountains, ranging from the gneisses, schists and palæozoic rocks of the Southern Alps in the South Island to the volcanic cones of Ruapehu, Mount Egmont, Ngauruhoe and others in the North Island. The Southern Alps culminate in Mount Cook, known also by its native name of Aorangi, the cloud-breaker, at 12,347 feet, and in the south they carry extensive glaciers. The western face of these mountains has a heavier snowfall than the eastern: some of the glaciers press down to within 700 feet of sea level, where they terminate in a setting of rich moun-

tains in deep sounds or fjords; and there are also great lakes in a splendid alpine setting. Lowlands are nowhere of great extent: in the South Island the principal of them lie back from the southern and middle eastern coast. The last are well known under the name of the Canterbury Plains, extending south-westward from the city of Christchurch.

The North Island has a wider extension of younger and volcanic rocks than the

FIG. 183. *Maori girls in native dress at the Papakura Geyser, North Island. These geysers, when active, erupt into steam.*

South Island, and its great north-western peninsula is for the most part low. Of the volcanic summits, Ruapehu is the highest at 9,175 feet. Excepting Mount Egmont they show more or less activity, and heavy eruptions, notably of Mount Tarawera, have been recorded during New Zealand's short historical period. One of the world's most wonderful physical features is the volcanic area of Rotorua in the centre of the North Island, with its hot springs and lakes, geysers, and other features of volcanic activity. The North Island lakes, of which there are many, are commonly circular crater-lakes, very beautiful but wholly different from the long narrow lakes in the mountain-valleys of the South Island.

The bold surface-relief in both islands suggests rapid rivers rarely navigable for any considerable distance; but some of them are of great value as sources of hydro-electric power, the use of which, in its applications to railways, industry, lighting and domestic needs has increased over fifty-fold in the present century. Among the major hydro-electric works are those on the Waitaki River in the South Island and those on the Waikato and Mangahao Rivers in the North Island.

The lie of the land does not make for natural harbours, the coasts being little indented save for the sounds in the south-west of the South Island, and the broken shore lines of Auckland peninsula in the North Island. The sheltered waters in these two areas do not give access to developed land of wide extent. Moreover, fast-flowing rivers laden with soil, and strong ocean currents, tend generally to form bars and banks in estuaries, and it results that in the South Island extensive artificial harbour works have been necessary at such important ports as Otago, Bluff, and Lyttelton. In the North Island, however, Wellington, capital of the Dominion, and Auckland, owe their importance to their favourable positions on good natural harbours with relatively easy access from the ports to the interior of the country.

FIG. 184. *The Narrows, Milford Sound, a typical fjord on the west coast of South Island, New Zealand. A close relationship in structure is apparent between this fjord coast and certain other western seaboards, notably in North America and in Norway.*

FIG. 185. *Tree ferns, New Zealand. These plants are characteristic also of some of the well-watered Pacific islands, and of moister parts in the Australian bush country.*

New Zealand is subject to minor earthquakes of frequent occurrence, and there have been seriously damaging shocks. In the hundred years to 1934, sixty-nine earthquakes of destructive force were recorded, though only six of these were of very great intensity. An area covering the south-east of the North Island and the South Island as far south as Hokitika and Christchurch is the most frequently affected, and the southern part of the South Island and the northern part of the North Island are the least so.

The antipodes of the Auckland peninsula are southern Spain, the Strait of Gibraltar, and a bit of Africa adjacent to them, and the antipodean latitude of the south of the South Island is that of north-western France. A substantial range of climatic conditions is thus indicated, and they do range from sub-tropical to temperate; but owing to the oceanic position the mean range of temperature is smaller than this would suggest. The difference of mean annual temperature in the cities of Auckland and Dunedin, over 600 miles apart,

is barely 9 degrees F. Certainly neither great heat nor severe cold is experienced, and no part of the islands is subject to drought, though occasionally in interior areas there are dry seasons long enough to hamper agriculture. The range of temperature is naturally greater in the interior than in coastal areas, owing to the moderating influence of the sea: on the coast, for example, the range between mean temperatures in three summer months (December-February) and the three of winter (June-August), is not more than 12 degrees to 15 degrees F. Broadly speaking, the climate is equable and pleasant, and the average amount of sunshine is high, and these features have an important bearing on human activities.

In the South Island there is a wide range of rainfall as between one locality and another. The west coastal districts, facing prevalent westerly winds from seaward and backed by mountains, have high rainfall—generally an annual average of from 80 to 100 inches, but up to 200 inches in some localities. On the eastward slopes of the island the rainfall is very much less, with an average of 20-30 inches in most of the coast lands, and from 15 to 20 inches in the south-eastern interior (Otago). The distribution is less irregular in the North Island, most parts of which receive from 40 to 70 inches a year on the average, though on the westward slopes of Mount Egmont the figures may be three or four times greater.

In accordance with these climatic conditions and especially those of rainfall, types of evergreen forest, mainly of subtropical character, are natural to most of the country, and large areas of it remain in spite of clearing for agriculture. The Kauri pine is the best-known timber tree, but there are many others. On the volcanic plateau of the North Island, and elsewhere, a natural close-growing covering of ferns and associated plants has been cleared for the most part. Drier areas such as the Canterbury Plains and high ground above the treeline bear native grasses where not brought under cultivation.

The isolation of New Zealand is illustrated by its flora. About 75 per cent of the native flowering plants and ferns are not indigenous anywhere else. The native flora, other than timber, is of no great economic value, excepting the New Zealand flax, whose long leaves yield a useful fibre.

Indigenous mammals are very few in kind: there are native kinds of dog and rat, probably introduced originally, and there are native bats. Several sorts of native birds are flightless, such as the kiwi, parrot, duck and others; nearly all native land birds have become reduced in numbers as settlement has advanced, but introduced birds like sparrows, blackbirds and thrushes are plentiful. Reptiles are few, and there are no snakes. The seas are rich in fish, and trout have been introduced into rivers and lakes with great success.

The population of New Zealand is over 2,000,000. Over nine-tenths of this is British by birth or descent: the foreign immigrant element is very small. There is a native (Maori) population of about 150,000, probably pure-bred and half-caste in roughly equal proportions.

The North Island, though the smaller (its area being 44,000 square miles as against that of 58,000 for the South Island), is the more populous, containing over three-fifths of the total and nearly the whole of the Maori population. This distribution accords with the physical features of the islands, for the high mountains and forested areas, the most difficult for access and settlement, are of greater extent in the South than in the North Island.

The population is urban to the extent of

Fig. 186. *An aerial photograph of Wellington, the capital of New Zealand. This southward view includes the waters of Cook Strait, with the inner waters of Port Nicholson in the foreground to the left; the isthmus separates Lyall and Evans Bays.*

more than one-half of the total, and over one-third of it lives in the four chief cities—Auckland and Wellington in the North Island, both bigger than the two in the South Island, Christchurch and Dunedin. The proportion of rural population to urban in the South Island, however, is rather larger than that in the North Island. The population figures suggest that in a land with so favourable physical characteristics there is room for a large expansion of white settlement; though, as in Australia, this expectation may sometimes have been expressed in exaggerated terms in the past.

The Maoris are a Polynesian native branch of high physical and intellectual standard among coloured peoples. There have been many theories about their origin, including a belief in their Semitic descent. But the commonest view appears to favour a source in India and either an Aryan origin or else Aryan contacts. In the early days of contact with the white settlers in New Zealand they suffered, like many other native peoples in similar circumstances, from acquiring vices and diseases as well as from armed conflicts; but the decay of the race has been at least counteracted in later years, and its natural rate of increase has been greater in proportion than that of the white inhabitants.

Substantial expansion of manufacturing industry has taken place in recent years, but New Zealand is primarily a pastoral and farming country. The pastoral industry began with the extension of grazing sheep for wool over areas of native tussock-grass land, principally in the South Island.

FIG. 187. *A warrior of Ahia, spearing fish on the island of Ulawa, one of the Solomon group of islands.*

of overseas trade was slow —the isolation of the country gave sufficient reason— but improved communications and the introduction of refrigerated ships changed that condition of affairs.

But in both islands there are areas of very fertile land suitable for mixed farming, and also, mainly in the North Island, forest tracts, capable without great difficulty of being cleared and sown with suitable grasses to make some of the finest pasture in existence. This last process is the most valuable, and is capable of expansion even when allowance is made for adequate forest protection.

The outstanding position of the pastoral and agricultural industries is indicated by the fact that over nine-tenths of the value of New Zealand's exports is represented by pastoral products—wool, meat, dairy products and by-products. Wool and butter are the two principal single items, and, as in Australia, cattle products have risen, in some years, to take a place superior to those of sheep, to which in earlier stages they were secondary. For many years after the first white settlement, the development

Mineral wealth is substantial in both islands. Gold has been won for nearly a century: it is obtained now both from reefs and from dredging in river beds. Auckland, Nelson, Otago and Westland are among the more prolific districts. Good bituminous coal is mined chiefly in west-coast fields in the South Island; brown coal is more widely distributed. Oil is known in Taranaki and several other areas, but not in very great quantities. Iron and a number of other minerals, including manganese and antimony, will increase in importance to the country. The phosphatic rock of Otago is of value in agriculture.

There is an efficient State railway system of about 3,400 miles on the 3 feet 6 inch gauge, and road building has kept pace with requirements. Local commercial air services have developed widely since 1935, and regular connexions with Australia and North America were established in 1940.

# THE PACIFIC ISLANDS

THIS section deals summarily with the vast number of islands, some large, most small, which lie in the Pacific Ocean, excluding those which fringe the coasts of North America, Asia and the Malay Archipelago. New Guinea, one of the largest islands in the world, is included. With few exceptions, the oceanic islands of the Pacific (for which the general name Oceania is sometimes used) are found in that part of the ocean which extends over 100 degrees of longitude eastward from the Philippine Islands, and between 30 degrees N. and 30 degrees S. of the equator.

New Guinea is a tropical land in great

part incapable of economic development and little known or explored. Its spine is a series of massive mountain ranges with heights up to 16,000 feet; its northern half is mainly hilly and rugged; in its southern half are vast low plains watered by big rivers, marshy over large areas, with a dense tropical vegetation (extending up to high levels) which makes penetration difficult.

For the rest, there is a broad distinction between high volcanic · and low coral islands. The distinction is not to be pushed too far: in the larger islands eastward of New Guinea, and elsewhere as in Fiji and

Fig. 188. *Papuan children at play in a village on Mailu Island. The terraced, high-gabled homesteads, with their leaf-thatched roofs, are characteristic of the people of this Melanesian race.*

New Caledonia, there are ancient sedimentary rocks. The volcanic rocks, also, are of different ages. Thus, islands of the Marquesas group and Tahiti show no signs of volcanic activity in recent times: on the other hand, the famous volcano of Kilauea in Hawaii and a number of vents in the Bismarck, Tonga, and Solomon Islands are still active.

Corals build their fringing reefs and atolls (rings of islets, or occasionally unbroken rings), wherever conditions of temperature, depth and the slope of the sea floor are favourable, between 30 degrees N. and S. in the western ocean, but over a narrowing range farther east where the seas are cooler. There could not be a more complete contrast than that between the high islands and the low atolls. The rich vegetation of the high islands, replete with flowering plants and ferns, and clothing all but the steepest slopes, is pictured and praised in many books—if any one island may be named in this connexion it is perhaps Tahiti. The low coral islands on the other hand are generally infertile and produce little, with the important exception of coconut palms; yet they possess their own beauty, recognized by Robert Louis Stevenson among others, and described by him as no other could. The coral islands and reefs rise usually only a few feet above sea level, but there are exceptional instances of more elevated islands of coral rock.

There is a threefold division of the oceanic islands, the names of the divisions being Melanesia (the islands of the black peoples), Micronesia (the small islands), and Polynesia (the many islands). This last name is sometimes applied to all the oceanic islands; but the names Melanesians, Micronesians and Polynesians are regularly applied to the three divisions of the native Pacific peoples. The term Papuan is sometimes used synonymously with Melanesian, for New Guinea, a native name of which is Papua, is the principal territory of the black (or dark) Melanesian race, which extends over Bismarck Archipelago, the Solomon Islands, the New Hebrides, New Caledonia and Fiji. The Polynesian, a brown race, occupy Hawaii, Tahiti (Society Islands), Samoa, the Marquesas, Paumotu, Cook, Ellice, Tonga and other groups. The Micronesians, also brown, are found in the Gilbert, Marshall and Caroline Islands. There has naturally been intermingling between these peoples, and, especially in the case of the Micronesians, with others. The Micronesians are, in fact, described as hybrids: the geo-

FIG. 189. *A general view of Hilo, Hawaii, showing Mauna Kea in the background. The mountain rises by gentle slopes from the coastal plain to a height of 13,800 feet.*

graphical positions of their islands have led to intrusions of Malays, Japanese and Chinese, as well as of Melanesians on the one hand and Polynesians on the other. Again, the natives of Fiji, which is grouped with Melanesia, have a strong Polynesian admixture.

The origins of these three races are beyond historical record. The black Melanesians are of African type and there may be relationship with primitive Indian peoples, but their origin is unknown. They are believed to represent an earlier immigration than the others. The Polynesians, light brown in complexion, tall and often handsome, are assigned a Caucasic source, and traditions point to their forebears having come from the west by way of the Malay Archipelago. The Micronesians are of the same general type, though often shorter and darker, and many show their mixed descent; the origin of the race is no less obscure than that of the others. Moreover, in certain islands of the Pacific, for example in Tonga, the Carolines, the Marianas, Pitcairn, and above all in Easter Island, far removed from the rest in the direction of South America, there are evidences of massive building in stone, and in Easter Island of sculptural and pictorial arts of which the natives now know nothing.

The Pacific races, especially the Melanesians, offer an infinite field for anthropological study of customs and primitive arts. There are innumerable variations between the races, as there are between tribe and tribe in the Papuan region. Merely as examples there may be mentioned the distinct inferiority of the Melanesians as seafarers, in comparison with the others, some of whom

FIG. 190. *An outrigger canoe off the Pacific island of Schouten, Dutch New Guinea.*

go immense distances in their canoes; and also the fact that the making of a fermented drink is confined to Micronesians.

As a rough estimate, the total population of the Melanesian Islands apart from the New Guinea territories may be reckoned at 650,000; of Polynesia 260,000 and of Micronesia 100,000. The white population in the two British divisions of New Guinea numbers something over 5,000: the natives in the same territories, so far as enumerated, more than a million. In Fiji, a meeting-place of races, white men number about 6,000, native Fijians 139,000, and Indians slightly more. There are over 7,000 half-breeds, and over 4,000 Chinese. In the American territory of Hawaii, again, there is, or was, a large Japanese immigration which at one time accounted for more than a third of the total population; there are many Chinese, and, among others, people of Portuguese, Spanish, German, and Korean origin.

Climatic conditions naturally affect the distribution of foreign immigrants. The climate of the New Guinea territories is severely tropical and moist: white settlers can only administer, trade and supervise native labour, with cautious restrictions on their own physical activities. But beyond the range of extreme tropical conditions the climate of the Pacific islands is generally pleasant and healthy, the temperature equable and rainfall high, especially on the windward sides of islands within the trade-wind belts; though it should be added that these belts are less well defined than over the Atlantic Ocean, and in the western area between 10 degrees and 30 degrees S., except during June-August, the south-east trade winds alternate with northerly winds and calms.

New Guinea is poor in mammals (as is the Australian sub-region generally), but its bird fauna is rich: among a great variety the birds of paradise are perhaps most famous for their beauty. On the oceanic islands mammalian fauna is as scanty as fish life is plentiful around them: fish form an important part of the native food supply.

Respecting vertebrates, an exception must be made in the case of the Galapagos Islands, a volcanic group far removed from the rest, and only 600 miles from the coast of Ecuador, in South America, to which country they belong. Here are great tortoises and lizards, together with various birds and plants peculiar to the islands and in some instances differing even between one island and the next: the study of these peculiarities by Darwin during his voyage in H.M.S. *Beagle* was part of the groundwork of his views on the origin of species and on variations. It is the more to be regretted that since his time, for lack of conservation, some of the most interesting forms have become far less common, or even extinct.

Among vegetable products of the islands the first place, in regard to its importance in trade, is taken by copra, the dried kernel of the coconut from which oil is extracted. Rubber is among the products of New Guinea, Fiji and the Solomon Islands; sisal is grown in Papua; cotton and coffee in the New Hebrides; sugar in Fiji and elsewhere. Food plants are important to the natives, who live largely on them: yams, breadfruit, bananas and pine-apples are particularly favoured. In the territory of Papua, and especially in the Louisiade Archipelago, gold is worked. Copper is also known in Papua, and pearls are fished. Phosphates are, or have been until worked out, a valuable product of a number of the oceanic islands: Christmas and Nauru are examples. The guano from seabirds, washed by rain, separates into its constituent parts, of which the soluble phosphatize the rock (especially the coral limestone) with which it is brought into contact.

After the voyages of Captain Cook in 1768-79, when he called at many of the islands, they were gradually brought within the ambit of missionaries and traders, while Pitcairn Island became famous in 1790 as the new home of the mutineers of the *Bounty*, some of whose descendants remain as a successful island community. Missionaries did much good in the islands, if occasionally their influence was ill-directed: some of the traders were not impeccable, and those white undesirables, who became known as beachcombers, left nothing to recommend themselves. Well treated or not, the native peoples suffered, as elsewhere, from contacts with white people, proving, especially, non-resistant to introduced diseases. At first there was no formal annexation of islands by European Powers, though France established a pro-tectorate over the Society and Marquesas Islands, with Tahiti as headquarters, in 1842, and annexed New Caledonia as a penal set-tlement in 1853. Australia and New Zealand for some time pressed in vain for the establishment of British rule among the islands, and it was not until 1884 that the agree-ment was made which divided eastern New Guinea and adjacent islands between Germany and Britain—Germany, of course, disappearing from the Pacific as a colonial Power after the First World War. Fiji, as a native kingdom, placed itself under British pro-

FIG. 191. *Members of a family outside their home on the island of Savo, Solomon Islands. The natives pictured here are representative of the higher type of Melanesian.*

FIG. 192. *Fijians making "kava" from the roots of a variety of the pepper plant. The first stage of preparation is chewing the root. The beverage, widely used in the Pacific islands, is not alcoholic, but is intoxicating to those who are unused to it.*

tection and soon became a colony; Tonga also sought British protection and still enjoys it. Hawaii, after an involved history as an independent kingdom and republic, was annexed to the United States of America in 1898, and other annexations date from this period. The possession of the New Hebrides was long in dispute between Britain and France, until at last a condominium was devised, though it has not escaped severe criticism.

The development of air routes across the Pacific brings into importance certain islands otherwise, in some instances, insignificant. San Francisco is the natural starting-point on the eastern Pacific coast, and the flight to Honolulu the first stage of the crossing. Midway Island, at the western extremity of the Hawaiian chain, offers a port of call for diverging routes to Tokyo and to Wake Island, Guam and Manilla. From Honolulu the route to Auckland and to Sydney serves Fiji intermediately, and Canton Island in the Phoenix group has become a stopping-place between Honolulu and the Fiji Islands.

## Test Yourself

1. What are New Zealand's principal products? How has their importance increased in recent years and what steps might be taken to increase it still further?

2. Give a considered estimate of the influences of white men upon the native peoples of the Pacific.

3. Assess the future political value of oceanic islands in the Pacific.

*Answers will be found at the end of the book.*

FIG. 193.   *Weddell seals basking on pack-ice at the base of an Antarctic iceberg. Seals, being air-breathers, break open holes in the ice by means of which they can come up for air, but in fine weather they like to emerge from the water to bask and sleep on the ice.*

## CHAPTER XIV

# POLAR REGIONS

FROM their circumpolar position both the Arctic and Antarctic regions experience the same long daylight in summer and the same long night in winter, culminating at the Poles themselves in six months of continuous daylight followed by six months of night (Fig. 6). But there the close similarity between North and South Polar regions ends. Both, in general terms, have a long cold winter and a short summer, but the intensity of winter and summer are very different at the two ends of the earth.

### The Poles

The North Pole lies in the ice-covered part of the Arctic Ocean which (see pp. 290–291) is surrounded by the northern extensions of the land masses of North America, Europe and Asia. This land circle is broken by one great gap, the Greenland Sea, between Europe and Greenland, and by the minor gaps of the Bering Strait between Asia and North America and the channels of the Canadian Arctic archipelago. The South Pole, on the other hand, lies in the heart of a vast continent of some 5,000,000 square miles, deeply smothered in a sheet of permanent ice and ringed by the drifting pack-ice of the surrounding seas (page 300).

North Polar lands are not all ice-covered and they bear much vegetation, locally luxuriant but all low-growing, to beyond latitude 80 degrees N. Only the interior of Greenland, parts of eastern Spitsbergen, the small islands of Franz Josef Land, Novaya Zemlya, the islands of Northern Land (Severnaya Zemlya) and parts of Ellesmere and Baffin Islands are deep in ice; much land is open and snow-free during summer. But the few South Polar lands, steep slopes and islets mainly, that are not ice-clad, rarely have vegetation of even mosses or lichens, and desert conditions extend from about 60 degrees S. to the South Pole.

North Polar regions have a winter of nine to ten months, with mean monthly temperatures below 32 degrees F., but the short summers have a period of real warmth. If occasional days may be cold and inclement, there are on the other hand some days of blazing warmth, and the mean monthly temperatures frequently exceed 55 degrees F. or even 60 degrees F.

In North Polar lands the snow-line seldom if ever reaches sea level. All low ground is free from snow for two months or more. In summer it may snow, but precipitation is more likely to fall as rain. The wide area of sea, even if covered with drifting ice, prevents temperatures from falling low as a rule, and much mild Atlantic water pours into the Arctic basin between Greenland and Spitsbergen and less Pacific water through Bering Strait. Moreover the Arctic air masses, being only moderately cold and dense, do not always thwart and divert the passage of depressions, or "lows" as they are called, from the Atlantic and Pacific. These "lows" occasionally penetrate the Arctic area, especially by way of the Greenland Sea, and bring milder and stormy conditions.

### Intense Cold

To go to South Polar regions is to go back in geological time to the great Ice Age. The huge ice-smothered land mass is covered throughout the year by a mass of cold dense air into which no "lows" can find a passage and which itself flows over the edge of the continent in southerly winds which may at times move with incredible speeds, sweeping snow before them—the terrible Antarctic blizzards. No place in the Antarctic has a mean temperature above 32 degrees F. in any month, and midwinter months are intensely cold with mean temperatures in some places as low as −40 degrees or −50 degrees F. even at sea level, and absolute minima of −77 degrees F. at sea level. Warm days are very rare, rain never falls, only snow, and the snow-line nearly everywhere is at sea level. Summer in the Antarctic is merely an astronomical conception, not, in fact, a climatic event.

ARCTI

UNEXPLORED REGI

SEAS OPEN ALL THE

No kind of agriculture is possible in any polar regions: poor soil or no soil, lack of humus, and brevity of summer are all factors which render useless any attempt to grow crops out of doors. There are contrasts also in animal life between the north and south. In the north there are many land animals finding sustenance ultimately on the tundra vegetation—reindeer, musk-ox, hare, lemming, and the animals that prey on them, fox, wolf, glutton and ermine. The polar bear, too, is common although it is really a marine animal preying on seals. These animals afford sustenance for man. In the south, on the other hand, there are no land animals, for there is a complete lack of nutriment to sustain them. Nothing, not even a unicellular organism, lives on the vast ice sheets.

The sea, however, both in north and south teems with life, an apparent paradox to those who accept the tradition and belief of lifeless, unproductive polar regions.

In polar seas physical conditions are very favourable to the development of diatoms, a microscopic form of plant life. Great expanses of the Greenland Sea may be coloured bright green with floating diatoms. On this plant life there feed great multitudes of small crustaceans and on them feed fish, seals and whales. The crustaceans and fish provide nutriment for vast flocks of sea birds, which, going north or south for their nesting, animate polar coasts all the summer days. In the north there are fulmars, auks, looms, guillemots, puffins, terns, gulls, skuas, geese, ducks,

etc.; in the south, petrels, gulls, terns and—particularly—penguins, ranging from the fussy small species of sub-Antarctic lands to the rare and lonely Emperor of the far south.

Neither in north nor in south is there much bird life during winter, though the ptarmigan, the gyrfalcon, the Greenland raven, the snowy owl and a few others never leave the Arctic shores where they live, and the Emperor penguin never migrates from the most southern shores of the Antarctic, even laying eggs in mid-winter. Thus both Arctic and Antarctic shores provide man with abundant food in both summer and winter, for many seals do not migrate and fish are always available if the sea ice allows of their being caught.

### Man in the North

In peopling the earth's surface man penetrated but slowly into Arctic regions: he had to learn to protect himself with clothing, to hunt under difficult conditions, and to endure winter darkness, before any attempts promised success. The Eskimos, the only prehistoric peoples in true polar lands, have shown what a full and relatively prosperous life can be lived in these regions. They are perfectly adapted to Arctic conditions. Originally of Asiatic origin, the Eskimos spread into the tundra lands of northern North America, hunting the caribou or reindeer, an occupation which some of them still pursue.

Then the coastal tribes, attracted by the food resources of the sea, spread north-

introduced great herds of reindeer for the tundra Eskimos who were suffering hardship for want of food. The U.S. Government took similar measures in Alaska.

Yet there seems to be no future for the nomadic Eskimos: they are doomed. Their total number now may be about 35,000, of whom the majority live in Alaska and Greenland and the remainder in Labrador, Canada and Siberia.

In Europe and Asia various tribes of Mongoloid stock inhabit the Arctic shores, from the Lapps and Samoyedes in the west to the Chukchi and Koryaks (now called the Luoravetlani) in the east towards Bering Strait. Severe competition for living space probably drove their ancestors north in the first instance, but few of the tribes can be regarded as true polar residents, for most extend into temperate regions. They fish and hunt and herd reindeer with varying degrees of prosperity. Apart from the visits of fur and fossil-ivory traders, they had very little contact (at least in Asia) with Europeans until the Soviet Government began to concern itself with Siberian resources and the care of its Siberian subjects.

### Early Exploration

There was no European interest in Arctic regions until it was realized that, the earth being a globe, the shortest route to the Far East should be across the Pole. And so Arctic exploration started, though some centuries previously the Norsemen were cognizant of the fringes of some polar lands, and in the tenth and eleventh centuries had even tried, with a limited measure of success, to colonize south-west Greenland.

Cabot in 1497, and Willoughby and Chancellor in 1553, began the long searches for the North-West and North-East Pas-

wards to the islands of the American Arctic and turned towards walrus and seal rather than caribou as their staple food. This culture based on the sea gradually replaced the older caribou culture and the majority of the Eskimos have dwelt for long around the Arctic islands and the coasts of Alaska, Greenland and Labrador. They live in small scattered groups in huts built of heaped stones and roofed with driftwood, bones and skins, and they feed on seal and fish supplemented by caribou, musk-ox and salmon in summer. Weapons and fish-hooks, before the European traders came, were made of bone; clothes were made from fur, sewn with sinews. Blubber and driftwood provide fuel. Boats (kayaks) for summer use are made of hides stretched on a bone framework. Sledges and dogs provide transport for winter travel when the familiar snow igloo affords a temporary shelter.

The Eskimo area was much wider in the past than it is today. Exhaustion of game, due largely to the introduction of firearms, and the white man's diseases have wrought havoc. The northern and north-western islands of the Arctic archipelago rarely see an Eskimo today and eastern Greenland was deserted for about a century until the Danes restored settlements in 1894.

In western Greenland the Eskimos have much European blood and live under Danish supervision and tutelage. They call themselves Greenlanders. The Canadian Eskimos, too, live under supervision. In recent years the Canadian Government has

FIG. 195. *Eskimos building an igloo with blocks of snow. These snow houses are used as temporary shelters during winter travel. They can be heated to a remarkably high temperature, which, combined with lack of ventilation, makes them uncomfortable for white men.*

sages respectively, a search which by the middle of the nineteenth century revealed the main features of the distribution of land and water in Arctic regions, but failed to furnish commerce with its hoped-for channels. Barents in 1596 also failed in an attempt to find a short cut across the Pole. Meanwhile, however, the economic possibilities of Arctic regions were becoming known and bringing casual human visitors.

Whalers went in the early seventeenth century to Spitsbergen and the Greenland Sea, in the nineteenth century to Davis Strait and Baffin Bay, and in the latter half of that century to the Beaufort Sea. Fur trappers and sealers, especially the trappers of the Hudson's Bay Company in what is now western and Arctic Canada and Russian trappers in Siberia, Spitsbergen and Alaska, revealed in the seventeenth, eighteenth and early nineteenth centuries much of territories hitherto unknown. The Royal Danish Trading Company in the eighteenth century exploited western Greenland, and seal-catching, for oil and hides, became a widely-spread occupation on the edge of ice-covered seas and, though stocks are now much depleted, persists to this day

While centuries of exploration, trading, and trapping made Arctic regions better known, they did little to reduce the fear of the Arctic climate. Only economic stress and adventurous spirit overcame what were considered grave dangers, for men learned only slowly to live in the Arctic conditions and take full advantage of the most healthy and only germ-free atmosphere in the world. Scurvy was the principal fear: it attacked all expeditions that wintered—and any expedition might be caught in the ice and forced to winter. It was scurvy, mainly, that destroyed the Franklin expedition of 129 men in 1845-48.

For centuries scurvy was supposed to be the outcome of cold and darkness and so unavoidable. Only late in the nineteenth century was it discovered that scurvy is a deficiency disease caused by the lack of something (identified a little later as vitamins) normally eaten in fresh meat, vegetables and fruit. Formerly, polar adventurers lived entirely on salted or tinned meat, etc., and avoided as unpalatable the supplies of seal, bear, fish and birds ready at hand. At best, they took doses of lime-juice of doubtful efficacy as an antiscorbutic. Now that the facts are known the traveller or dweller in polar regions uses what fresh meat he can find, and, like the Eskimo, avoids scurvy in any form. Experience has also taught travellers how to clothe themselves, using close-knit fabric rather than heavy cumbrous furs to exclude wind, and to move and work in the severest cold rather than stagnate and cower in overheated shelters.

There are now few parts of the Arctic that have no interest to Europe and America, and none that has not been claimed as the territory of one or other power, even if in many areas sovereignty is rather nominal than real. And since about 1895 tourist vessels have visited the Arctic every summer (excluding the war years).

The great island of Greenland, with an extent of nearly twenty-five degrees of latitude and an area of about 840,000 square miles, or about seven times the area of the British Isles, is covered by a vast ice sheet, except for a rugged coastal area of bare rock varying in width from one mile to two hundred miles. Only in a few places does the outflow of the ice sheet ride over this bare rim to the sea. The ice sheet rises to two domes, each of an altitude of some ten thou-

sand feet, and is probably at least a thousand feet thick in the interior.

Several exploring expeditions have made the difficult and risky crossing of the ice. The ice-free rim is much dissected by fjords and girdled in parts by islands. Most of it bears a scattered tundra vegetation, but in the south-west there are some copses of birch, willow and juniper, the only trees which grow in Arctic regions. It was in this less inclement south-west that in the tenth century Norse colonies were founded and persisted until at least the thirteenth century. Then they were lost sight of, and by the eighteenth century, when communications between Denmark and Greenland were reopened, had completely disappeared—possibly from lack of nutriment, or perhaps by absorption in the Eskimo stock. Their disappearance remains a mystery.

When rediscovered, Greenland passed under Danish control. In recent times, it

FIG. 196. *An Eskimo fishing for small cod through a hole cut in the ice. Seas within the Arctic Circle abound with fish and there is no difficulty in obtaining a rich haul in an hour. Many of these holes in the ice are also breathing holes for seals, and the Eskimos patiently wait for one to climb out, and then shoot and seize it.*

has been a closed country, no visitors being allowed to land without permission. The growing population of 16,000 Greenlanders and 400 Danes dwells mainly in about a dozen small settlements of wooden houses on the southern part of the west coast. Each settlement has its wharf, warehouses and stores; many have church, school and hospital. Clergymen and doctors are Danes, but a few Eskimos have taken orders. Trade is a government monopoly, and the local stores sell hardware, crockery, ironmongery, cloth, tobacco, sugar, etc., at fixed prices. No private trading is allowed. The produce of the hunt—blubber, skins, eider-down and salted fish—is bought for export to Denmark, possible only during the summer season of open navigation.

### Settlements

The settlements have their radio connexions, postal services, and even a monthly newspaper. There is some sheep-rearing and a few horses and dairy cows are kept. Local supply of fodder has to be supplemented with seaweed and imported hay. A little poor coal is dug at Disco for local use, but the only mineral of importance is cryolite, which is used in the manufacture of aluminium. It is mined by Danish labour at Ivigtut, and sent to Canada and the United States. Royalties on the export of cryolite are an important source of revenue to Greenland. On the east coast there are now no Eskimos except those settled there by the Danes, and probably the virtual extinction of the musk-ox and the decrease in reindeer exterminated the past population. The Danes have two small trading stations, of which Angmagssalik, founded in 1894, is the larger, with a population of a few Danes and three hundred Greenlanders.

Most of the Greenlanders profess Christianity and have adopted the Danish way of life, but the natives are encouraged to use their own language. There is some measure of self-government, but control is centred mainly in the Danish inspectors, at Godthaab, the capital for the south, and at Godhavn for the north. The chief aim of Denmark is to stimulate economic life, especially sealing and fishing, in the interest of the well-being of the native peoples.

The small tribe of some two hundred Polar Eskimos north of Cape York is little Europeanized. The trading settlement there is Thule.

The German occupation of Denmark in April, 1940, led to the severance of all relations with Greenland. The United States took over the protection of the country and the care of its inhabitants for the duration of hostilities.

### Spitsbergen

Some three hundred miles north of Norway lie the Spitsbergen group, now known as Svalbard, a Norwegian possession since 1925. After its discovery in 1596 it was the resort of English, Dutch, Danish and other whalers for half a century, and then, the whales being exhausted, Spitsbergen was left alone for many years, until (in the eighteenth century) it became the haunt of Russian trappers of reindeer, bears, and Arctic foxes. They were followed, as game decreased, by Norwegian trappers who, in diminished numbers, still persist. Lastly, towards the end of the nineteenth century, came the seekers for coal and other minerals, and the fishing around Bear Island (Björnöya) by British and other trawlers.

This partly glaciated land with easy access on the west (due to a warm current, a branch of the North Atlantic drift) was for centuries a no-man's-land, so that claims to mining estates were simple. But so also was claim-jumping. The early twentieth century saw a spate of claims and counterclaims, of reports of rich mines, of booms in land, and of several genuine attempts to mine and export coal. There is an abundance of high-grade coal in the central parts of the country around Icefjord, and less elsewhere. There were in 1940, when a British Expeditionary Force removed the inhabitants and destroyed the mines and coal stocks, three or four active coal-mines, and others whose activity was in abeyance. The working mines, which were the property of two Norwegian companies (Longyearbyen, Sverdrupbyen, Ny Aalesund and Sveagruva), and the Soviet Union (Barentsburg and Grumant),

FIG. 197. *Angmagssalik settlement, Greenland.* *One of the few Danish trading stations on the east coast, it has a small population of Greenlanders and Danes. The settlers are visited once a year by a Danish government vessel, but they rarely see other ships.*

between them employed some 2,200 men, and exported (between May and October each year) about 600,000 metric tons of coal to Norway and Arctic Russia, which are lands without any coal resources of their own. In 1945 the restoration of the mines was put in hand.

The coal is easily reached in horizontal adits into the hillsides, and frozen soil minimizes risk of flooding and collapse of roof. Deep water and good harbourage near-by facilitate export. On the other hand, all labour, food and materials must be imported, and export, but not mining, ceases for six or seven months of winter when ice and darkness make it impossible. The miners live in wooden towns, the larger of which are provided with church, school, cinema and hospital. There are radio stations and, in summer, postal services. The only other mineral occurring in large quantities is gypsum, abundant and pure.

Spitsbergen, and the more southerly isolated islands of Bear Island (Björnöya) and Jan Mayen (also Norwegian possessions), are the sites of meteorological observatories, most important in relation to weather study in Western Europe.

The Canadian Arctic islands became known during the attempts of the nineteenth century to find a North-West Passage to the Far East. The passage was gradually pieced together but found to be useless for trade on account of ice, though a few exploring vessels have made the course since R. Amundsen in 1903-04 took the *Gjöa* through to San Francisco. The islands are rugged, but only those on the east have permanent ice; the others are covered with tundra vegetation. The intervening channels are relatively shallow and frozen in winter, and are much frequented by seals. The scattered Eskimo population (about 9,000) of today is in contact with a

FIG. 198. *A coal wharf at Braganza Bay, Spitsbergen. The mine here was Swedish until sold a few years ago to the Norwegians, who have already done a great deal to develop it, and talk of building a railway to carry the coal to a better harbour.*

few posts of the Hudson's Bay Company, which are visited every summer, and half a dozen outposts of the Royal Canadian Mounted Police, who maintain long patrols by dogs and sledge during the winter to guard the welfare of the natives. The islands are included within the North-West Territories of the Dominion of Canada.

One trade route of some importance traverses this Arctic archipelago, namely the summer route by which wheat is carried from the Hudson Bay port of Churchill by Hudson Strait to Europe. It greatly shortens the amount of land transport for the wheat of the prairie provinces in reaching the sea, but serves only in August and September.

Russian, like Canadian, lands extend into Arctic regions, and the islands north of Russian territory have always been considered as belonging to Russia and no serious counterclaims have been made.

These island groups, where not heavily glaciated, are very barren, and except for Novaya Zemlya almost wholly unproductive in fur-bearing animals. Most have never been inhabited, and many of the groups are only partly explored. All are outside the range of the Eskimos and the existence of Northern or Lenin Land (Severnaya Zemlya) was quite unknown until 1914. Although the Russian Government tried to colonize Novaya Zemlya with Samoyedes and reindeer, fifty years ago, the most striking development in these Arctic areas has been the opening in recent years of the commercial route along the north of Europe and Asia to link the

FIG. 199. *Longyear City and Advent Bay, Spitsbergen, showing the funicular railway which carries the miners up to the opening of the mine. The coal is transported to the wharf by chute and cable conveyor.*

great Siberian rivers with the world's trade routes.

The voyage of the Swedish vessel *Vega* in 1878-79, from Europe to Japan via the North-East Passage, established the unsuitability of the route for commerce on account of drifting ice floes. Since then, only one or two ice-breakers have made the course. The occurrence of ice obstruction cannot be obviated, but its danger can be reduced by a study of weather, ice and current movements, and by reconnaissance and transmission of warnings to ships.

It is on these lines, and by a re-survey of the badly charted coasts of Arctic Asia, that the Soviet Government has made possible—and even relatively safe—the export of great quantities of timber from the new town of Igarka on the Yenisei River by ordinary steamers every summer. Radio stations, observatories, and air patrols have been instituted along this coast and on adjacent islands. Already the dread of the Kara Sea and its ice pressure is decreasing, even if the eastern end of the "passage" is still formidable. Minerals, too, are being prospected, and seaports are being planned in the far north. Air routes have been established, and settlements are well-built and regularly provisioned by both local and introduced supplies. The Soviet Arctic is losing its isolation and ill repute.

Only the northern part of Alaska can be included within the area of the Arctic regions; the greater part of this United States territory has more genial conditions even if much of it has a hard winter. From the summits of the lofty Brooks Range tundra stretches northward to the Arctic Sea, and there only caribou and a few small fur-bearing animals can find sustenance. The musk-ox has been exterminated, but along the coast are seals and polar bears.

Whaling in the Beaufort Sea brought scores of American whalers to these coasts in the second half of the nineteenth century, but these have now ceased to come. The scanty population lives in a few trading posts and missionary stations, but there are no larger settlements. The Eskimos live in turf and driftwood huts partly excavated below ground level, and they cannot be termed prosperous though the introduced reindeer promise to enable them to survive. The navigation season is practically confined to August and part of September and may even be shorter. No roads or railways touch the Arctic parts of Alaska, but the new Alcan Highway (Alaska Military Highway) from British Columbia reaches Fairbanks, which is situated at the end of a railway from Seward on the western coast.

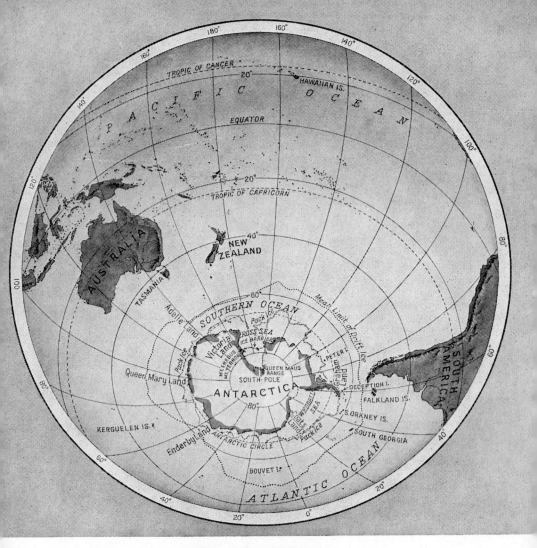

# THE ANTARCTIC

OUR knowledge of the Antarctic regions dates back to little over a century ago. Separated from the great oceans and other land areas of the world by the stormiest seas, far removed from trade routes and on no obvious road to anywhere, the southern end of the earth's axis evoked no interest until recent times. There had, however, been a belief in the existence of a southern continent since the early Greek astronomers had argued that it must exist in order to balance the land of the Northern Hemisphere. For several centuries every new landfall in high southern latitudes was

hailed as part of this hypothetical *Terra Australis*. At length, in 1772, Captain J. Cook was sent by the British Government to find the southern continent and to open up trade with the inhabitants. In spite of spirited attempts he failed to find land in high latitudes, and his failure put a stop to the search for many years; the belief was shattered.

It was the enterprise of sealers looking for new grounds that, in the early decades of the last century, led to the discovery of land in the far south. E. Bransfield, in 1820, sighted land which has since proved to be part of the continent. And thus, slowly, a few isolated landfalls appeared on the blank map. But the fur seals, never numerous, were soon exhausted, and interest in the south lapsed except on the part of a few whalers. It was not until late in the nineteenth century, and particularly in the twentieth century, that exploration was undertaken systematically and scientifically. Although a good deal is now known, much remains to be done.

There is a huge continent of which the greater part is a plateau of very ancient rocks, scored with upheaved fault-ranges rising to 10,000 feet or more, and standing several thousand feet above the shrinking ice-covering. The loftiest is that of Victoria Land and the Queen Maud range. Associated with the eastern edge of this vast plateau are the active volcanoes of Erebus and Terror. Close pressed against the Pacific side of the plateau are tertiary foldings of a structure comparable with that of the foldings of the Andes, and forming lofty mountain ranges with some volcanic peaks in Graham Land or West Antarctica. Parts of these ranges are either worn down or depressed, but there is evidence of their continuity across the Southern Ocean to New Zealand and round the Scotia Sea to South America.

The vast ice sheet, with a surface elevation in the interior of over 10,000 feet, meets the sea with a floating edge 100 to 200 feet in height, making a wall of ice broken only by rare exposures of underlying rock and the occurrence of beaches. The floating faces of the ice may extend for many miles before calving off as the huge tabular bergs which are characteristic of Antarctic seas (Fig. 201). On a few coasts valley glaciers discharge the ice between the mountain ranges to the sea (Fig. 37). The outflow of such huge glaciers from east, south and west would seem to be responsible for the vast Ross Barrier or Great Ice Barrier, which, with an area equal to that of the British Isles, fills the southern half of the great inlet known as the Ross Sea with a level plain of snow-

FIG. 200. *Rear-Admiral Richard E. Byrd, American explorer and scientist, who has led many aerial expeditions into the South Polar wastes, has stated that the world's greatest geographical puzzle is whether an ice-choked channel links the Weddell Sea and the Ross Sea, or whether Antarctica is really one continent. The U.S. naval expedition to the Antarctic, which he led in 1947, discovered by aerial survey a hitherto unknown range of mountains, pictured here. This range is believed to be an extension of the South American Andes and Graham Land ranges. One peak, at least, reaches to approximately 15,000 feet.*

covered floating ice. The southern end of the Weddell Sea has a comparable but smaller ice barrier.

Around its edges the continent of Antarctica is girdled by floating pack-ice and drifting icebergs. Thus a belt of obstructed seas hinders easy penetration to the continent and impedes exploration. Here and there, however, access is less difficult by reason of wind and currents. In the Weddell Sea, the great bight south of the South Atlantic, navigation is particularly hazardous on account of currents sweeping the ice against the south-western shores. Several ships have been nipped there and at least one destroyed.

There is no possibility of human habitation in Antarctica and no inducement, except scientific exploration, to take man there. A few outlying islands which may be termed sub-Antarctic have been used for whaling stations, such as Deception Island in the South Shetlands, South Georgia and Kerguelen, but no mainland site has been used for this purpose. The Argentine Republic has maintained a meteorological observatory at Scotia Bay, South Orkneys, since the station was founded by the Scottish Antarctic Expedition in 1903. There are now also British stations at the South Shetlands and Graham Land.

Beyond the wealth of whales in sub-Antarctic and Antarctic seas there are as yet no products of economic value there. The fur seal has been virtually exterminated and the numerous hair seals have little or no value. Traces of mineral wealth have been reported, but so far no prospect of valuable deposits even if mining were possible on the ice-covered land and export could be safely organized. The Antarctic remains a vast reserve of scenic splendour and scientific research.

In spite of the lack of commercial value of Antarctic seas and lands, almost the whole area has been proclaimed the territory of one or other state, although no state exercises even nominal jurisdiction. The motive in these claims was whaling interest but latterly whalers have abandoned shore stations and work from floating factories on the high seas beyond the jurisdiction of any state.

The first claimant was Great Britain, which in 1908 claimed the area known as the Falkland Islands Dependencies, and in 1923 the Ross Dependency of New Zealand. In 1924 France made a more modest claim to Adelie Land. In 1930, after a harmless diplomatic dispute with Great Britain, Norway claimed the useless Bouvet Island. In 1931, she claimed the lonely, unscalable Peter I Island, and in 1939 a vast Norwegian Dependency on the continent of Antarctica. The Commonwealth of Australia, in 1936, claimed another vast area of the continent south of the Indian Ocean as the Australian Antarctic Territory. The United States has a vague but unproclaimed interest in that part of Antarctica which lies south of the Pacific Ocean and Chile and the Argentine have made claims which came into the news in 1948. All claims involve sectors, so all must meet at the South Pole, and not a single claim has any real political significance.

The discovery of the North Pole by Peary in 1909, and of the South Pole by Amundsen in 1911 and Scott in 1912, did not put an end to polar exploration but rather diverted the energies of explorers to more useful ends. Except as a triumph of human skill and endurance in the attainment of a difficult goal, nothing is gained by reaching the Pole. The Poles have been incentives to explorers but have diverted much enterprise from more valuable exploration. By the end of 1947 the North Pole had been reached seventeen times by land and by air.

Once the nature and cause of scurvy had been discovered, the chief remaining obstacle to the penetration of the polar seas was the floating pack-ice, which, under pressure of wind and current, has often crushed the strongest vessels. Auxiliary steam, introduced by the middle of the nineteenth century, helped the sailing vessel of old. Later still, the powerful steel-built ice-breaker was tried, but with very limited success in heavy polar ice. A newer way of attack is by the use of aircraft. S. A. Andrée tried, with fatal results, a dirigible balloon in the North in 1897. In 1926 a dirigible was flown successfully by R. Amundsen across the Pole, but two years later disaster befell U. Nobile's similar attempt. Modern planes, however, have done good work in the South, where vast unknown areas remain to be mapped, and also have been helpful in the North. R. E. Byrd, who in 1926 had flown to the North Pole, flew easily to the South Pole and back in 1929, L. Ellsworth revealed vast Antarctic territories in 1935, and Byrd made many discoveries in the South in flights in 1940-41 and 1947.

### Recent Antarctic Exploration

Late in 1955 a period of important Antarctic exploration began, in preparation for the commencement of the International Geophysical Year in July, 1957. Thirty stations were established in Antarctica, and eleven nations took part in the work. In November, 1955, the Russian ship *Ob* and later the *Lena* left the U.S.S.R., and established bases on Australian Antarctic Territory early in 1956. At the same time the U.S. ice-breaker *Glacier* and other ships set up American stations, including three in the Ross Sea area. The United States, the U.S.S.R. and Great Britain were responsible, in fact, for the majority of the I.G.Y. stations, others being established by Argentine, Australia, Belgium, Chile, France, Japan, New Zealand and Norway.

Meanwhile, a party of the Commonwealth Trans-Antarctic Expedition under Sir Vivian Fuchs had left England (November, 1955) in the *Theron*, and, in spite of delays due to pack-ice in the Weddell Sea, began to prepare Shackleton Base by February, 1956, ready for the arrival of the main party. The *Magga Dan*, carrying the main parties of both the Trans-Antarctic Expedition and the I.G.Y. Expedition of the Royal Society, sailed from London in November, 1956, and reached Antarctica in January, 1957. From Shackleton Base Fuchs carried out air reconnaissance of the route to the South Pole, in preparation for his later crossing of the continent. Sir Edmund Hillary and his New Zealand party, who had established Scott Base on McMurdo Sound, were to explore the second stage of the trans-continental route which Fuchs was to take. In November, 1957, Sir Vivian Fuchs set out from Shackleton Base on his great 2,100-mile journey across Antarctica, and Hillary left Scott Base, both parties making for the Pole from opposite sides of the continent.

Hillary and his party arrived at the South Pole in January, 1958, having first established a base, Depot 700, 470 miles from the Pole. Fuchs and his party encountered exceptional difficulties during their journey, especially in the crevassed area of the plateau between Shackleton Base and the advanced base known as South Ice, but they eventually reached the South Pole later in January, 1958. They left the Pole again within a few days, were met by Hillary at Depot 700, and completed the crossing of Antarctica, arriving at Scott Base, McMurdo Sound, at the end of February, 1958.

While Sir Vivian Fuchs was triumphantly leading the Trans-Antarctic Expedition, important though less spectacular work was being done in another part of the continent. During the Antarctic summers (November-April) of 1955-57, an expedition carried out a survey of Graham Land for the Falkland Islands Dependencies Survey, which involved a great deal of aerial photography and the establishment of eleven bases near the coast of Graham Land.

## Test Yourself

1. Apart from hazards of climate and weather, what was the early Polar explorers' chief fear, and how was the danger eventually overcome?
2. Where do Eskimos live and how do they feed?
3. Contrast the principal motives in (1) Arctic and (2) Antarctic exploration.

*Answers will be found at the end of the book.*

Fig. 202. *A curious house in the Central Arfak Mountains, Dutch New Guinea. Houses in New Guinea are often built on platforms on piles as a means of protection. They are usually rectangular and made mainly of bamboo, with roofing of sago haulm, leaves or grass thatch. The balcony under the projecting gable roof is a characteristic feature. In a few coastal districts, conical huts with round bases are built directly on the ground.*

CHAPTER XV

# MAN AND HIS ENVIRONMENT

MAN is a part of the realm of nature, but he has developed the special power to describe nature around him as well as in himself.

Other forms of life do little to adjust their environment in any serious way, but man does alter his surroundings in seeking advantages, and his alterations may be for better or for worse.

Moreover, in meeting circumstances he exercises a much more deliberate choice, and with more foresight, than do any other living beings. That choice and that foresight are both largely conditioned by previous experience of his own, or by that of a previous generation imparted to him by training. Further, man's deliberation and foresight in meeting circumstances depend considerably on his vigour of body and mind. This, again, depends upon the environment in which the body lives, which may influence its functional efficiency, as well as upon innate conditions of strength and resistance. These, in their turn, may be the product of past conditions of life, or of combinations of items of biological or social inheritance. If we penetrate below the surface, we find that heredity and environment cannot be disentangled from one another; they must be studied together.

While forms of living and of non-living things change in the course of time, in all probability of and by themselves, living and non-living also are always affecting one another. Neither environment nor forms of life are fixed in character; the universe may be likened to a stream changing as it flows.

Changes in environment, apart from influences of life, are plain enough. The chalk of the Downs of southern England is built up largely of minute shells that fell on a fairly deep sea-floor; the deposit has been lifted up. Again, the floor of the North Sea has yielded evidence that, in the days of early man, portions of it were above sea level; the land has sunk, or the sea level has risen, or both. And these changes around Britain have provided the anchorage of Southampton Water, the beauty of the Devonshire estuaries.

Land and sea have altered their junctions one with another. (See pages 44, 45.) When the ice sheets of the days of early man were very large the level of the sea may have been lower, many believe, by perhaps one hundred fathoms. Under shallow water off some coasts there are accumulations of material dropped by melting ice sheets or glaciers.

As the ice sheets shrank, more and more water poured into the oceans, and sea level rose so that such regions as the East Indies, in which Sumatra, Java and Borneo, at least, had probably been part of the peninsula of South-East Asia, became the complicated archipelagos we know, while New Guinea became separated from Australia (Fig. 216).

### Britain Isolated

In Northern Europe, however, the rise of sea level was balanced to some extent by a rise of the land as the immense weight of the ice sheets was reduced. When sea level was low, Britain was a part of the European continent (Fig. 203); but as the waters rose she gained her saving grace, the silver streak of the Strait of Dover, the English Channel, and the grey North Sea. It is probable, too, that the width of the Strait of Gibraltar (Fig. 99) may at one time have been much less than it now is.

There is thus the probability that men were able to drift between Spain and North Africa, and also between Britain and northern France before they possessed boats.

It seems fairly certain that, in the days of the ice sheets, more moisture-bearing winds blew over the Mediterranean and even farther south, giving light rain to the northern Sahara west of its central highland plateau.

### Water in the Desert

Remains of many animals and of the tools of early man suggest that, at some periods in man's early story, parts of the western Sahara were not desert, though we must not picture it as a rich or well-watered land. Underground water now beneath the Sahara may be in part a remnant of what it had in those far-off times.

These few points might be amplified and multiplied indefinitely, but enough has been said to show that the earth has gone through dramatic changes that affect climate, vegetation, relations of land and sea, and therefore, since the appearance of mankind, the life and work of mankind.

On the human side we can hardly speak of alterations made independently of the influence of environment. Nearly every change that *seems* man-made has some trace of environmental factors in its story. Perhaps the inventions of the internal combustion engine, radio, and radar, and the discovery of atomic energy are not very directly traceable to environment, save that they arose among people with a strong tradition of inquiry and experiment. At any rate they demonstrate in a unique fashion man's power to alter his environment, social organization, commercial and political possibilities in myriad ways.

Broadly, however, while man-made changes do undoubtedly alter his environment it is nearly always possible to trace back these man-made changes to opportunities offered by the environment. These may be seized upon or neglected by man largely according to his knowledge; and this knowledge is based upon experience, sometimes brought from afar, sometimes handed down from a long past. The contrast, for example, between the utilization of Australia by the pre-European peoples and by the British colonists is a dramatic illustration of this; but the British colonists brought with them a heritage of experience from the mother country.

Even the power of choice between the using and the neglecting of opportunity may be said to have environmental factors behind it; that power may depend on vigour, which is often a result of climate, or on initiative, which some earlier environment may have encouraged.

What is important for the study of man and nature is to have an idea of man's power to alter his environment, sometimes deliberately, sometimes without much thought. Native cultivators of Madagascar hack and burn forest and bush to make clearings which they use for cultivation for a few years. The discarded patches later get covered with inferior bush that may be burnt and cleared again after a time. Repetition of this process may result in a growth of grass over which fires may spread and, in time, little save coarse grasses with underground storage organs can resist the fire and thus persist. Worse than this, patches of nearly bare soil may be left exposed after a fire, and the strong sun of Madagascar then draws up quantities of moisture and leaves dissolved salts, including salts of iron, in the surface soil. If there is a good deal of iron and lime, this forms a hard crust that prevents plants from growing.

### Hidden Soil

A hard iron-crust may be formed in this way in many regions with a long dry season; and visitors to some Mediterranean lands have seen peasants, pick-axe in hand, trying to break the crust in order to use the soil beneath, a disheartening task that accounts for some weaknesses of the social life and organization of peasantries in these regions.

In warm regions with a long dry season, also, sharp thunderstorm rain may wash away the soil (Fig. 23), or create gullies that make erosion still more disastrous;

or again a dry season or two may give the winds an opportunity to blow soil away hundreds of miles. The dust storms which swept the American prairies in 1933 and 1934 carried soil even as far as Buffalo and New Orleans (Fig. 204; see also Fig. 126).

Before man laid hold on it, the flood land on either side of the Egyptian Nile (the base of a "slot" cut in the African plateau) was a maze of rushes and reeds, with pools and cut-offs. By patient work and the digging of canals it became a ribbon of fertility, and for thousands of years yielded crops planted after subsidence of the annual summer flood from the monsoon rains of the Abyssinian heights. The building of the great dam below Cairo spread cultivation well into the Nile delta; and the dam built under

British direction at Assuan has made it possible to have water supplied to the field ditches all the year, and thus to grow two or three crops in twelve months. But this dam has also greatly reduced flooding and the resulting deposition of silt, so that Egypt's largest import is now fertilizers for its fields.

Even more remarkable, if possible, than man's transformation of the Nile valley, is the achievement of groups of determined men here and there on the borders of the Sahara, who, by digging wells to tap underground stores of water, have created garden-oases with climbing figs and other plants to shade the soil. There may be unceasing work to shovel away the desert sand that always threatens the hedge of tamarisk and the date palms

FIG. 203.    *During major phases of glaciation the damming up of rivers lowered the ocean level.   This artist's impression shows how the English Channel and the south part of the North Sea might have appeared during one of the early ice ages.   As the huge ice sheets gradually shrank, more and more water poured into the oceans.   The resultant rise of the sea level was, however, offset to some extent by the uplifting of the land masses, which occurred over a long period as the great weight of the ice sheets was reduced.*

THE ENGLISH CHANNEL

FIG. 204. *Large areas of desert have been created in the United States by the ploughing and over-grazing of land which should have been allowed to retain its protective grass covering. This photograph shows an over-grazed area at Pennington, South Dakota, and the bleached ox skull is a grim warning of the consequences that follow upon man's wasteful use of his environment. See also Chapter VIII.*

around the hardly-won oasis home (Fig. 73).

It is not without significance that some of these oases have been created by refugees from religious persecution. We have but to think of the achievements of the Pilgrim Fathers, Mormons, Mennonites and many other groups to realize what religious enthusiasm can do in the organization of collective power, and how long it may continue to animate a community. Holland owes an immense debt to Jewish refugees from Spain and Portugal, and Germany and Britain profited enormously from their reception of persecuted Huguenots. The refugees from twentieth-century wars and persecutions are likely to have pronounced effects on the lands that receive them.

It is interesting to reflect upon the changes man has wrought in the landscape of the British Isles, and especially of England itself. At some stage, long after the disappearance of the ice sheets, the Arctic vegetation gave place over much of the land to coniferous forests, as we know from the study of tree stumps preserved in such places as the low-tide beaches around the west coasts, and from a census of

pollen grains preserved in the lower layers of some peat bogs. Later on, deciduous forests spread over the lowlands, with great oaks as a dominant element.

Before man acquired tools sufficiently strong, and with sufficiently sharp edges, he could not do much with the great oaks, though he might hack the rather small pines and birches near the upper edge of the woodland, which was somewhere near 1,250 feet above sea level in the Pennine Chain. Man was therefore, for a time, almost restricted to the more exposed lands, cliffs and shores, kept free from dense woodland by sea winds or bleakness on the heights.

Probably chalk and limestone surfaces in south and east England also had a woodland covering, fairly thin except for the thicker hanger woods on scarp slopes, where the water that has seeped down through the porous rock emerges and feeds the beech roots.

As population increased in England with the development of agriculture and trade and metal, before and after 2000 B.C., we accordingly find traces of men of that time most abundantly on the chalk and limestone surfaces in south and east England and along the coasts. The peninsulas of Cornwall, Pembrokeshire and Caernarvonshire, and Anglesey, are especially notable.

A wet, cold phase some seven centuries before our era spread bogs in place of woodland on some high ground in the north and west, but the lowland forest remained dominant even during the Roman occupation, though the Roman civil engineers did cut roads through it and begin to reduce it (Fig. 205). By Anglo-Saxon times (Fig. 206) the use of iron had become more general and so had the iron ploughshare on the heavy wheeled plough pulled by a team of oxen or horses. It could turn the soil over and so bring within reach of the grain roots the salts that tended to be washed down in the cool, damp climate of England, a state of affairs contrasting conspicuously with the drawing up of materials in solution in warm climates as described above.

### Strip Cultivation

The large plough with its team was not of great value on broken hillsides, but iron axes could now cut the large trees of the lowland plains. We accordingly find a great forest-clearing effort in what are called the Dark Ages, and with it the spread of the idea of large fields in which peasants owned or held strips (Fig. 207).

This change of the European scene went on apace until well into the thirteenth century, before which time most ploughs had become fitted with a mould-board, a projection at the side above the ploughshare to help to lay the soil that the share had turned up. Later on, shortage of labour resulting from the Black Death, insecurity of harvests in the variable climate, with its frequent St. Swithin's rains from winds off the warm July seas, and an increasing demand for wool, led to the wide development of sheep farming.

Later still, in the seventeenth and eighteenth centuries, the cultivation of root crops spread and helped to undermine the old system of communally cultivating small parallel strips held by different people. A feature of this old system had been the turning of the animals into the big fields after harvest so that they might eat the aftergrowth and manure the land. Now, however, root crops were kept in the ground until the autumn, so this custom of common pasture on the stubble died out.

### Lowland Development

But these same root crops gave the animals winter fodder, so more and, incidentally, better animals could be kept. The stock farmer needed a compact farm with hedged fields, and often chose to live near his beasts. In this way dispersed farm houses spread away from the old villages, and hedgerows added to the beauty of England (Fig. 208). Man had conquered the lowlands; the higher lands occupied some 4,000 years earlier were left almost empty.

In early times man had looked down from a hill brow on to a vast expanse of trees, vivid green in spring and a rich brown in autumn, and his calendar had been dominated by this fact. May Day and All Souls—before the eighteenth-century calendar reform these were what are now May 12 and November 12—were the great festivals of life and death of vegetation.

In the Middle Ages, on the other hand, men in many districts could look down from a hill brow upon great open fields full of folk at work, peasants who lived in village clusters dotting the countryside. In the next phase, the view from the hill brow gave a chequer of fields enclosed by hedgerows, and in the fields would be a varied assortment of crops: grain crops, root crops, and beans; while many patches would be under grass for the animals.

### Sprawling Cities

In the late nineteenth and early twentieth centuries, the importation of cheap grain made England still more a grass land, with a rural population barely able to maintain itself, and not a little of the farm land deteriorating for want of economic returns from its cultivation. Market gardening (Fig. 209) has developed considerably and is some compensation; but it might have been very much more valuable had not so much of the best land been covered by sprawling over-growth from the cities.

Thus has the English rural scene changed from age to age under man's influence; and much might be added, were there space, about the growth of manufacturing towns into what have been well called "smoke-overs" (Fig. 210).

### Changing Aspects

The foregoing examples—from Madagascar, the American grasslands, the Nile, the Sahara, the Mediterranean and Britain—make it clear that man radically changes the aspect of the country he occupies, and sometimes the results recoil to his serious detriment. In every case man has been seen trying to get the benefit of some opportunity presented by the environment; it may have offered itself for ages before he has acquired the equipment to tackle it or even the vision to see it. And the motive force to utilize it may have come from people with experience of some other land, as in the case of Europeans in America, Australia, New Zealand and South Africa.

But the power to adjust a countryside to our needs, as we understand them, is specially enhanced when immigrants come to it armed with an idea, a faith, and its attendant enthusiasm. "We are such stuff as dreams are made on."

We have seen that man's relations with nature around him are ever changing, now slowly, now faster, here more rapidly, there with a great time-lag. It will help our picture if we next review briefly some of the general facts of this evolutionary change.

Obviously man in his earliest days was not very abundant, and, as he was a land animal, his bones have not often been

FIG. 205. *An artist's impression of the great extent of damp oak woods which were a feature of the clay lowlands of south Britain in very early days. Signs of occupation at various periods are to be found mainly on the higher land—ridgeways with early huts near them; a circle of standing stones; a neolithic "barrow" (grave, or store of "spirit-essence"); a "camp" or fortification of the pre-Roman Iron Age; and the straight Roman road across the countryside, linking the Roman camps and their attendant villas.*

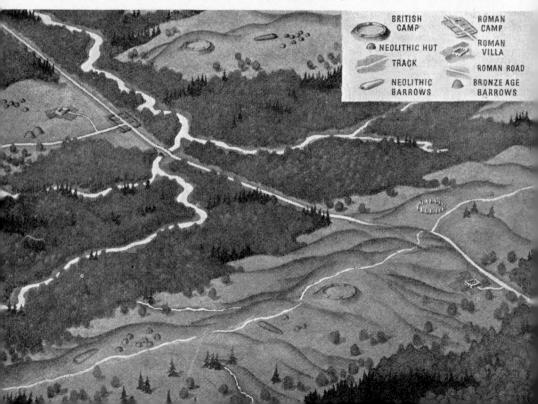

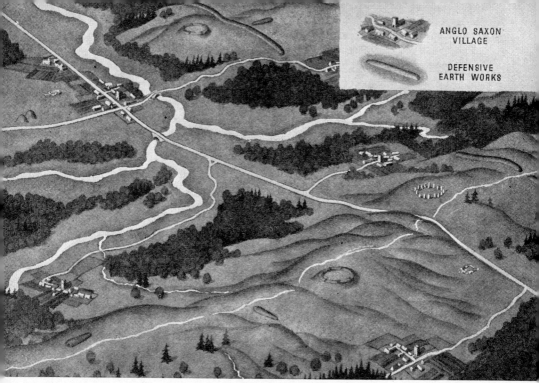

Fig. 206. *The artist's reconstruction of the same countryside in post-Roman times. The spread of iron axes and the need for self-dependence in matters of food led to much cutting of woodland. New settlements developed, often with earthworks for defence and to mark boundaries. The improved iron plough fostered the development of agriculture.*

preserved; but we can nevertheless deduce a few points concerning him from the meagre evidence available. His animal relatives all use their hands to hold on with, and often to climb; they live typically in and near the warm forests. Man also has learned, as every human baby still has to learn, to walk erect on the ground. He has, for the most part, left the trees (but see Fig. 202), though he can climb them at need. It is fair to infer that this implies a shift from the forest edge to more open grassland.

Men's animal relatives all have strong jaws held in place by powerful muscles, so that the skull is as much an attachment for these muscles as it is the brain-holder. Man's hands, especially after he took to using tools, can do much of the work of breaking up and crushing of food, so that our jaws need not be so strongly developed. The muscles holding them in place are weaker, and the erect head is thereby balanced more easily on the backbone,

with the eyes looking forward and together making one picture. Parallel specializations of hand and eye, coupled with longer maternal care, have made larger brains necessary and possible, and the growth of the brain has been so adjusted as to improve the balance of the skull on the backbone. These changes are largely consequent upon the adoption of a grassland environment.

### Man a Social Being

Man does not live alone, and practically never in isolated pairs with their own children only. Group life is the general rule. And group life is also widespread among the monkeys. It is therefore highly probable that we have from our beginnings been social beings.

In the beginning was society, and it is within society that individuality has struggled painfully towards freer expression. Indeed, it is not yet recognized in some current philosophies that one of the

FIG. 207. *Villages developed towards and during the Middle Ages with church and, later, windmill (sometimes replacing water-mill). Ordinary householders held strips of land in large (common) fields. Often they had a small garden or paddock near the house and enjoyed rights of pasture for their animals on the common land at the edge of the village.*

main functions of society is the promotion of individuality, so as to guard against the fossilization of its ideas and consequent degeneracy.

### Effect of Temperature

Finally, we should note that mankind in general is most comfortable when the temperature around him is somewhere between 60 and 75 degrees Fahrenheit. The people of inter-tropical Africa love the cooler evenings after temperatures reaching 100 at midday. The Amazonians seem to be comforted by the cooling influence of the rain on their skins in the steamy climate of that region. Many a poor peasant in the interior of Eurasia has tried to sleep away as much of the winter as possible near a stove. Tolstoi's *Anna Karenina* tells us of the gap the winter makes in social effort, and we have had glimpses of the attempts of the

Russian Soviet Government to overcome the attendant problems.

Now, if these temperatures suit mankind in general, it is a fair inference that our race went through some important stage of approach to its present status in a region in which these temperatures ruled for at least a part of the year.

So far, then, we have man as a sociable groundling, walking with head more or less erect, in all probability on grasslands which enjoyed, at least for considerable seasons, temperatures of the kind noted. But references earlier in this chapter warn us not to argue that the human race must belong by origin to what are now grasslands. Our race came into being in a very long period during which ice sheets alternately grew and shrank time after time, and so temperature, rainfall and vegetation altered strikingly. This was especially true in middle and high latitudes.

On what grasslands of ancient days did our ancestors attain a human level? Any attempt to answer this question would take us into studies—too intricate for our purpose in this volume—of ancient climates and their effects on the one hand, and of evidences of early man on the other— two lines of study which have become closely interwoven.

Skeletal remains of very early men are exceedingly rare; there was not much population, and a groundling in grassland country would not be very likely to leave his skeleton in such a situation as would promote preservation, at any rate until ideas of burial developed.

On the other hand, he would leave such of his tools as were of imperishable material, such as stone, though tools of wood or bone would be preserved in exceptional circumstances.

Stone tools are found in many deposits, some of which suggest very cold conditions, others milder climates. So we get on the one hand a succession of deposits which give us ideas of oscillations of climate, and on the other hand, a succession of fashions in the stone tools men used.

### Primitive Survivals

What is important for us is to realize that, though there are, for example, close resemblances between certain English and certain South African early tools, it does not by any means follow that they are contemporary in the two regions. "Maria Theresa" dollars of an eighteenth-century central European fashion have continued in use in Ethiopia (Abyssinia), and Australian Blackfellows have seized eagerly on broken beer bottles to flake the glass into tools similar in many respects to those of the Old Stone Age, from which these Australians derive much of their technique

FIG. 208. *Here the artist has pictured a later development than the system illustrated on the previous page. At this period stock-raising predominated. Woodland was preserved, the farmhouses were dispersed and the fields acquired hedge boundaries.*

FIG. 209. *The process of modern intensive cultivation often involves the use of elaborate systems of strips in a large field. This photograph shows market gardens at Cobham, Surrey. Near cities, such market gardens are an important feature, but the area available has been much reduced by the appropriation of land for building purposes.*

of tool-making. The Stone Age—even, in a partial sense, the Old Stone Age—may be said to be lingering on in some remote and isolated areas, but never in an unaltered state (Fig. 211).

The parallel must not be pushed too far; and it is especially misleading to speak of a particular people who still live by hunting and collecting as the surviving representatives of some particular phase or period in the Old Stone Age; all such survivors have been affected by subsequent changes, and all are in process of decline.

### Craftsmanship in Stone

The stone tools of early man were mostly of flint, chert, a volcanic glass called obsidian, or a few other materials mostly with a vitreous fracture, but some crystalline rocks were used in cases of need. A blow will knock off a sharp-edged flake and leave a sharp edge on the core. Man may use either the core or the flake, and it is a strange fact that, during the period marked by recurrent ice ages, some groups used mainly cores and some mainly flakes.

When finer methods of shaping cores had spread, the tools acquired an artistic character, if one may use such a term; at any rate the craftsmanship was often of a high order. That they were the work of beings of human status admits of no doubt,

but they show only very slow changes through an immense period.

We thus get a strong impression of widespread uniformity and of the domination of established habit; the mind was not yet playing freely on the methods of fashioning tools. Nor are we impressed with the value of these tools for hunting. Probably food-gathering was still the major means of supply, though pitfalls appear to have been made for trapping animals.

If we venture a provisional linking of core tools with early and fully human types, we may ask where the core tools had their birthplace, or at any rate their home of large development. It looks as though they had penetrated north through Spain and France to England. It seems, too, that they had penetrated south through East Africa right away to the south of what is now the Republic of South Africa. Eastwards they appear to have spread to India and Java. Following these lines back, they meet in North Africa; and in what is now the western Sahara, as well as on either side of the Nile, core tools are found. Very early flake tools were used especially by people of the colder regions. Those who used mainly cores and those who used mainly rough flakes eventually met and influenced one another, especially in western and central Europe. The core users applied to flakes their skilled methods of chipping.

As the last major retreat of the ice sheets progressed, an immense development occurred and from this phase onwards only human skeletons of modern types (*Homo sapiens*) are found. The regions of Europe between the dwindling Northern and Alpine ice sheets became more habitable for man and beast; and large animals such as the bison, wild horse, mammoth, reindeer, and others roamed over them. A kill provided food for quite a number of people. And, once man had learned to chip finely-pointed flint flakes and to haft them, he had a hunting weapon for striking from a distance. The pointed flake could be fitted into a wooden shaft to be thrown or shot at the prey.

It is very probable that people lived mostly in caves in the still bitter winters, but hunted over the grassy plains in summer. Women, less able to stand very prolonged strenuous physical exertion, took less part in hunting and carried on the older habit of food-collecting within a small range of movement. So they formed a focus to which the men returned, and we have many indications of the development of community life among these ancient hunters in Europe, the Mediterranean lands and Africa, with suggestions of their penetration through Inner Asia to northern China.

The climate had begun to improve, and man, now better equipped, could spread into lands north of the mountain belt that stretches from the Alps to the Himalaya.

The hunters observed their prey carefully and have left us many a painting and engraving of bisons, horses, reindeer,

FIG. 210. *Smoke diminishes our supply of sunlight, especially the ultra-violet rays, to the detriment of our health. Smoke-abatement is a primary need if we are to have better, healthier towns. Here are chimneys belching smoke at Stoke-on-Trent. Scientific principles incorporated in the design of furnaces and the adoption of mechanical stoking have contributed towards smokeless combustion, but much remains to be done.*

mammoths and other animals, some at bay, some dead and ready to be cut up, and occasionally a male animal courting his mate. Some of these artistic productions are scratched on ivory or bone, and we also have cases in which little figures, especially of pregnant women, are carved in ivory. An art with a good many resemblances to this has persisted to modern times among the Bushmen of South Africa.

### Belief in Spirits

The hunter-collectors of the later part of the Old Stone Age in a number of cases buried their dead with tokens that show they had some belief in power exercised by the dead over the living; in other words, some idea of spirits or perhaps of reincarnation. These burials, together with the figures of pregnant women, show that life and its generation had become a subject for reflection; and, if we may judge from a rather confused mass of evidence from lowly folk at the present day, men were puzzled by the fact that mating did not lead to the production of young in humanity with anything like the regularity with which this occurred among many kinds of animals.

### Magical Practices

It is clear that the little group desired sons to add to its strength; and it probably noted likenesses between ancestors and descendants and made this a basis of the very widespread idea of reincarnation. The obvious insistence on, and presumably magical practices connected with, securing birth of children are reminders of population conditions. Whereas, nowadays, we count population in terms of so many people, often hundreds, sometimes thousands, per square mile, among hunter-collectors the density of population is better expressed as one person per ten, twenty, or more square miles.

It seems that the hunter-collectors drifted over immense distances, and their descendants still form part of the population of most lands. They certainly form a specially important part of such populations as still live by hunting and collecting.

that is, without cultivation or herding for food production.

Hunter-collectors in the Old World of the present day are mere lingering remnants. Some inhabit the remoter recesses of the equatorial forests in Africa and Malaya. These are generally of pygmy size and apparently short-lived; and some of them have been brought into relation with other peoples who cultivate clearings in the forest; a few remain in India. The main survivals are the Bushmen of south-west Africa, the Australian Blackfellows and some peoples of north-east Asia. The hunter-collectors of the New World will be dealt with later; they are a somewhat different case.

### Work of Women

The fate of those who found their way to the edges of the flood plains of such rivers as the Nile and Euphrates was a very different one from that of the then impoverished peoples of Europe. Here, especially in northern Mesopotamia, grasses grew after the annual flood in the fresh silt; and among these grasses were the ancestors of millet, barley and wheat. They could be husked, stored and pounded for use; and it was worth while to stay in one place to clear weeds, to dig channels to drain the water, and so to look after the flood plain, that more and more of it might become useful.

Thus the woman-collector became the cultivator, personified as Eve; and the man helped to dig the channels and thus to begin irrigation. The more settled life led to better moulding of clay, hardened by fire, to make receptacles for grain, and to the shaping of sun-dried bricks for the building of huts. These lasted a few years before they crumbled and were replaced by new ones set on the debris of the old.

### Irrigation

By these means the villagers were able to live on the resulting artificial mounds near the river banks instead of on the dry edges of the flood plains; and they invented means of raising water from the river and pouring it on the land (Figs. 102, 105, 212).

FIG. 211. *An Australian aboriginal camp on a sandspit in the bed of the Stewart River, Cape York Peninsula. The shelters are covered with sheets obtained from the Paper Bark, or Paper Mulberry tree, a plant which has many uses. These primitive people have no agriculture or domestic animals. Their weapons and tools are fashioned from wood or stone, and in some parts clothing is unknown. About 46,000 aborigines survive.*

Digging with stone tools soon wore their edges away, and the art of stone rubbing, especially to produce a transverse edge for hoes and spades, came into being. Many kinds of fine-grained and very hard crystalline rocks could be shaped by rubbing, and man could therefore spread to new regions and could prospect for new materials. He had, no doubt, already learned to heat water in a clay trough by throwing hot stones from a fire down into the water. The stones would usually crack and this fact might well have helped him to get pieces suitable for rubbing.

But some stones softened in a very hot fire instead of cracking and the use of rubbed or polished stone was doubtless followed in this way by the discovery of metal. Copper, often impure, would almost certainly be the first metal to be smelted.

This phase of invention and discovery has still another aspect. The wild cow about to calve, and the ass about to give birth, could be followed and even controlled, and the calf or foal kept by the captor in the certainty .hat the mother would return to it. She could be made to give some of her milk to her new masters, and she might pull his hoe for him and so lead to the invention of the little plough for repeated scratching of the surface of the silt, lest it should cake too hard as it dried in the strong sun after the flood subsided.

What to do with the male young was, however, a problem. The bull calves might be killed for meat, but this was an expensive luxury; on the other hand, if too many were allowed to grow up they would fight and kill one another. Man found a way out of this problem by castrating such young males as he did not keep for breeding; and so he got the bullock, growing into the patient ox, which could be made to work hard, thanks to his immense strength, or could be kept for food, especially as castration seems to encourage the development of fat, a valuable heat-giving food, especially for those penetrating into colder regions.

### Herders and Cultivators

In Mesopotamia, but less so in Egypt, men differentiated, specializing more on cultivation near the rivers, and more on herding on the rather drier belts of the nearby hills, which nevertheless had grass. So we have the story of Cain and Abel

FIG. 212. *As Egypt is a river oasis in a desert, irrigation has been practised from very early times. In this photograph of a date-palm grove near the site of Memphis, capital of the country in ancient times, water is being raised from a ditch by one of the earliest devices invented by man and still widely used—the Archimedes screw.*

told from the point of view of Abel's friends and a little prejudiced, for it is nearly always the herders, mo ile and energetic and ready for defence of their beasts, who fall upon the cultivators. Often, of course, the cultivator-men would be spared and would become serfs or slaves.

Egypt had less of the herder element, because the desert begins suddenly at the edge of the flood plains, but there were some in the upper parts of the delta, the east side of which was Goshen, accessible from Asia to rough herdsmen, who became a danger at several periods to ancient Egypt. They were especially dangerous when they got hold of the horse, which had been domesticated somewhere in Central Asia, and the dromedary or one-humped camel, which could be used for transport, but which, for its health, needs to be bred away from the mud of rivers.

## Test Yourself

1. Why was it that the men who lived in Britain in very early times were restricted to exposed heights and coastal districts?

2. What was a major factor in the breaking up of the system of cultivating large fields in which different families held small strips?

3. In which parts of the Old World are hunter-collectors still to be found?

4. When man used stone tools, two basic types were evolved. What were these types?

*Answers will be found at the end of the book.*

# CHAPTER XVI
# PATHS TO CIVILIZATION

As we have seen, the gradual advance to something approaching durable villages and cities was accompanied by the cultivation of new crops and the domestication of what we now regard as farm stock—cattle, sheep, goats and eventually camels and horses. Such composite communities, with their craftsmen, merchants, priests, treasures, calendars and records, implied a standard of behaviour and of activity in regard to the timetables of cultivation. Increasing organization doubtless brought new strength, with increased birth-rates and the tendency to expand and to spread through daughter communities equally self-sufficing.

This spread of the complex of ideas represented by community organization was of immense consequence in human affairs. It was an expansion in many directions, some of which had probably already been lines of expansion of lowly types of cultivation of grain from Mesopotamia or Egypt; but very probably hunter-collectors still lingered in several of the areas concerned.

### Caste System

India, south of the great line of mountains, has preserved in its forested hills vestiges of early modes of life. Its first inhabitants were hunter-collectors for the most part, influenced to some extent by neighbours who cultivated the soil; and some of the descendants of those early drifts of mankind into India have become hangers-on around the more highly-equipped communities. Some may be known to the law as criminal tribes. The idea of avoidance of these backward and often dirty people has been one factor in the growth of what has eventually become the caste system.

In Inner and Northern Asia it is probable that descendants of the earlier drifts of mankind were fewer in number, and that the region was of very minor consequence

until irrigation and domestic animals were established as parts of social equipment.

The climate of Inner Asia includes strong seasonal contrasts that make cultivation difficult, except where rivers are available. But melt-water from mountain snows keeps a good deal of pasture green in summer on the slopes, and here have wandered herds of cattle, goats and sheep, uphill for the summer, downhill for the winter. On the lower lands the movement has, of course, been rather northwards for the summer and southwards for winter.

### Two Modes of Life

Man has learned to follow the flocks and herds and, with the help of the dog and, ultimately, the horse, to control them. Therefore, in Inner Asia two modes of life, with many intermediate gradations, are widely spread: the settled cultivator, often an irrigator, lives near the rivers; the nomad herdsman ranges far and wide. The nomad herdsman may be looked upon, broadly, as a rather specialized social type which has rarely shaken itself entirely free from dependence on cultivated vegetable food.

In a climate of extremes comparatively small variations of seasons could be highly significant; a warm, dry summer may mean a loss of crops for the cultivators near the rivers and the death of herds on the grasslands that are not directly watered by melting snow. Damp summers in such regions, on the other hand, may mean better crops and more widespread pasture.

While there is still need for a great deal of research, it seems that there was a good deal of life on the steppes of Eurasia in the third millennium B.C., and that man had already acquired the use of the Asiatic horse for riding, and so was able to control larger flocks and herds.

In the second millennium B.C., at any rate in its later part, it seems (at present) that there was less population on the steppe, and there are indications of emigra-

FIG. 213. *In the last centuries B.C. China was brought into communication with Western Asia through the Tarim basin, and silk became known to the western world. Towns sprang up along the Silk Road. This photograph shows a street in Aqsu, largest town in the northern half of the Tarim basin, on the Old Silk Road through central Sinkiang, China. It lies south of the Tian Shan and about 300 miles north-east of Kashgar.*

tions such as that of the Indo-Aryan speaking peoples into India, of the Shang and the Chou conquests in China, as well as dimmer indications of invasions of Iran and Europe.

In the last millennium B.C., during a period of cool damp summers, the steppes were inhabited by Scythian and other warriors, and, towards the end of that millennium, social organization had produced trading cities and communications, and these became a feature of Inner Asia for a time.

### Trading Towns

But here was a country that had profited by water from its stores of ancient ice on the mountains, and these stores were melting away, so that water supply tended to diminish; and, in a very dry land, watercourses are changeable and undisciplined. It thus happened that trading towns rose and fell, sometimes with longer and sometimes with shorter histories. Samarkand, Bukhara and Kashgar may perhaps be cited as instances of cities of Central Asia whose fame long continued.

Whatever may have happened in Tibet in earlier times, it was with the diminution of ice sheets and the development of communications that trading stations in and around this highest region acquired importance. Lhasa, Shigatse, Gyangtse, Manasarowar and Leh are all famous centres and all gathered around great monasteries (lamaseries), illustrating the widespread feature of the association of religious authority with stations on a long-distance trade-route. Lamaseries spread on the Mongolian plateau, but not into the lands as far west as Turkistan, where one finds Moslem centres of learning at, for example, Samarkand and Bukhara.

Northwards from Central Asia, in Siberia, is spread the greatest forest in the world, the taiga, mainly of pine and birch, a region of small attraction to pre-industrial populations and offering opportunities for cultivators along its southern border only. Herders who were pressed northward might wander along down the riversides, but, moving into colder regions, would have to reduce, and finally give up,

their flocks and herds of Central Asiatic animals. They would depend more and more on fishing and hunting (Fig. 92).

### Reindeer Hunters

Towards the Arctic Circle the reindeer becomes available, and west of the Yenisei there is enough food for fair numbers of these animals. The result is that in the Arctic there are reindeer-herders such as Samoyedes and Lapps, who, in many features, demonstrate their Central Asiatic relationships. In the Arctic east of the Yenisei conditions become more severe and herding of reindeer more difficult, and, in far north-eastern Siberia, some of the people do not have herds, but fish, and hunt the reindeer. It is a region hostile to both herding and cultivation; and it was mainly through it that America was populated by drifts before the time of Christopher Columbus.

Among the earlier drifts to America were hunter-collectors with lowly equipment; but even the later groups which drifted across, equipped with polished stone axes and flint arrow-heads, reached America without cultivable plants or domestic animals, except the dog. They had passed, over the centuries, through and into regions inhospitable to food crops.

### Ancient America

In Mexico they ultimately found maize, tomatoes, agaves and other plants and cultivated them, while in South America the potato, sweet potato and manioc lent themselves to cultivation. At a later stage the llama (Fig. 76) became a beast of burden in parts of the Andes, and it and its relatives a source of wool supply.

In Mexico and in the Cordillera of South America were centres of a primitive cultivation, which, though without the plough or animals for farm work, often reached a high level of skill and organization. Lowlier cultivation, of manioc, earthnuts and sweet and other potatoes, was fairly widespread in South America, while maize cultivation spread into parts of what are now the United States of America. But over large areas, the prairies and the pampas for instance, men long

F<sub>IG</sub>. 214. *A camel caravan passing along a dusty road through the loess country of northern China. In the vertical walls of the great masses of loess (illustrated here) men hollow out dwellings. Whole villages are carved out of the loess cliffs in this area.*

depended entirely on hunting and collecting for a livelihood.

In their physique, the first inhabitants of America—the "American Indian" peoples—show a gradation from the very narrow long-headed types known from the later part of the Old Stone Age in Europe to types with the broad heads and broad, flattish faces characteristic of some peoples of Mongolia. This gradation is what would be expected if, as has been suggested, successive drifts reached America from Asia via north-east Siberia.

There seems no doubt that irrigation and cultivation of wheat spread through Inner Asia to north China, while the cultivation of rice may have reached south and central China from the south-west. The northern nucleus of Chinese civilization in the lower Hwang-ho and the Wei-ho valleys was in an environment that demanded irrigated cultivation and that had few or none of the lowly and back-

ward peoples who lingered, indeed still linger, in parts of India. China developed as a collection of families of irrigators with little of the idea of avoidance and aloofness that has been so influential in moulding Indian life.

Japan has more or less amalgamated, in the south-west of Honshu and parts of Shikoku and Kyushu, elements of population drifting by sea, some from South-East Asia, with elements that have come across from Korea and northern China. The former, apparently interested in maritime life, found special opportunities around what Europeans call the Inland Sea of Japan.

The people around the Inland Sea appear to have made the larger contribution to social organization. The long struggle against the earlier hunting peoples who preceded them, some of whom have become known as Ainu, gave Japanese life a military complexion contrasting dramatically with the pacific organization of almost autonomous families in China and with the caste systems of India.

From the borders of the steppes of Turkistan and south Russia, the expansion we are tracing affected not only northern China on the east, but also Europe on the west. Here, from Russia, there stretched both into Rumania south of the Transylvanian Alps and into Western Europe north of the Carpathians, Tatra and Sudetes, as well as into Hungary, Moravia, Bohemia, Bavaria, and isolated regions farther west, the subsoil called "loess" (see page 26), well aerated and fertile, but too friable to allow great forests to grow easily on it (Fig. 81).

### Loess Areas

Where the soil was rearranged by water there might be more woodland, but loess areas were not often thickly forested with great trees. Man could thus occupy them with relative ease, even when his best tools were of stone and not yet very effective in dealing with massive tree trunks.

The fertility of these areas was another attraction, and the soil over the loess was fairly easy to work, but irrigation did not develop much. It was unnecessary in some districts and impossible in others. It is a notable fact that, though grain cultivation spread very early into the loess areas of Europe and carried the germs of civilization westward right away to Britain, the centre of Europe east of the Rhine and north of the Danube was almost without anything that could be called a city until A.D. 1000 or later. It was, and long remained, a rural area, and when the idea of the city reached east-central Europe it came from the west.

### Differing Cultures

The estrangement between urban and rural cultures in the region immediately west of the U.S.S.R. is to this day a source of political, social, and even religious difficulties. The migration of the urban idea eastward in Central Europe is picturesquely crystallized for us in the story of the "Pied Piper of Hamelin," the young

progressive who led a break-away from the die-hard conservative rulers of his native town in north-western Germany.

The contrast between the expansion of cultivation to India and China on the one hand and to Central Europe on the other is dramatic, and interprets much of the subsequent life of Europe; it was hardly before the Machine Age that Europe, at any rate north of the Alps, was able to go far ahead of other lands in the equipment of its peoples.

But matters went otherwise in Mediterranean Europe. Here the acclimatization of the crops of Mesopotamia was easy, but on the islands and coastlands of the Aegean there were other advantages, too. Somewhere, the migrants found and improved the wild olive and vine. Olives are most useful as a source of fat in a region where the summer sun beats down on limestone hills and turns the grass brown, causing a shortage of pasture for cattle which are, therefore, often replaced by goats. The vine served as a substitute for the date palms of Mesopotamia, providing like the fig, not only fruit but protective shade for both plants and soil against the strong sun.

### Mediterranean Life

The persistent north winds of summer helped navigation among islands that so often lay in sight of one another, standing out of a relatively well-stocked sea which yielded even tunny. Hills, often of limestone overlooking a bay fit for anchorage, made defensible sites for habitation, and the sward on the cliffs is rich in drought-resisting plants, such as the heaths, favoured by millions of honey bees. Honey, and the sugar of the grape and fig, have been essential contributors to Mediterranean life.

Here, then, the basis is the rural life, repeatedly confronted by the growth of cities, some of which have been too apt to decline once the original social inspiration has died down, but which revive and try to renew old memories, as Athens and Rome show us so strikingly today.

It is probable that the aridity from El Alamein to Tunisia limited early

expansions from Egypt westwards. Southwards in Africa the rock-cut slot of the
Nile, with cataracts in its bed and desert
on either hand, limited opportunities of
southward spread of civilized schemes of
life from the northern Nile, though
Ethiopia among its mountains developed
further than the rest of Africa south of the
Sahara, thanks largely to the penetration
of ideas from across the Red Sea.

Hardly any useful food plants were
native south of the Sahara, and barley and
wheat did not succeed well; so millets,
introduced long ago, were the chief grains.
Other long-established non-native plants
include the banana, and, since the discovery of America, maize, manioc, earthnuts and sweet and other potatoes. Insect
pests and coarseness of grass, poor in
vitamin C, have limited the quality of
African cattle, which have not been used
by African people south of the Sahara for
farm work; and the plough was unknown
until Europeans introduced it. Some parts
of Abyssinia and northern Nigeria provide exceptions to this generalization.

The people of inter-tropical Africa have
found little opportunity to use boats or to
develop seamanship; and waterborne commerce was almost absent until Arab
traders and Europeans intervened. Neither
horse nor camel could thrive under native
conditions in the region, so land trade was
limited to objects that could be carried by
men and women.

Factors, therefore, which promoted the
development of organization and initiative
in regions farther north hardly affected
men's lives in inter-tropical Africa until
the nineteenth century. It thus has come
to pass that many African peoples of our
time have to try to step in one or two
generations along the road that Europeans
have been making during a pilgrimage of
many centuries.

The south-east of Asia still harbours in
some of its forests and islands survivors of
the pygmy hunter-collectors. The Malay
region and the East Indies also have lowly
hoe-cultivators scattered here and there.

Of lands farther east and south-east we
may first note that, in the Old Stone Age,

FIG. 215. *The reindeer, herded in the west and hunted towards the east, where conditions
become harder, is the mainstay of man's existence in the Arctic regions of Eurasia.*

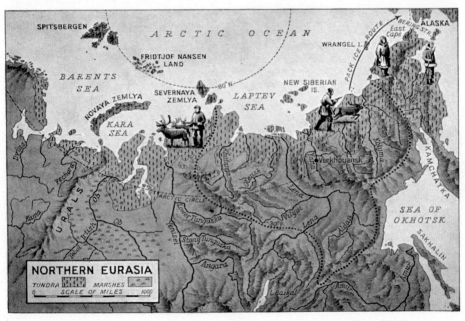

FIG. 216. *In major phases of the Ice Age, sea level may have been nearly one hundred fathoms lower than it is now, making Sumatra, Java and Borneo part of South-East Asia. A deep channel marking Wallace's Line (page 268) has effectively separated the fauna of Australia from that of any other region of the world. (See also Fig. 70.)*

when the sea level lay lower at times because so much water was locked up in ice sheets, Australia was probably continuous with New Guinea (Fig. 216). This in turn was not so widely separated either from the East Indies or from Melanesia as it now is. Hunter-collectors made their way in this direction and reached Australia, surviving now as a forlorn remnant. They were little affected by subsequent migrations because the rise of sea level cut Australia off from New Guinea, and probably the westward flow of the current in the Torres Strait made isolation still more complete.

Hunter-collectors and lowly cultivators reached the Melanesian archipelagos (the "islands of the black people"), boats being used during some stages of the drift. But metallurgy did not spread in this direction, nor was it carried by the later and far more highly skilled and organized Polynesians,

who reached the Sandwich Islands, New Zealand, and the remote islands farther east in their marvellous voyages, some of which seem to have been undertaken during our Middle Ages.

**High Adventure**

Some of these seafarers contributed to the life of the Melanesian archipelagos which lay on the way from the East Indies to the far Pacific. Some of them, again, settling in small islands, lost various skills as the practitioners died out; others had to adapt themselves to special conditions, notably in New Zealand. We thus have a complex of survivals and adaptations of civilization without metals, and with a loss of various arts, in the isles of the Pacific Ocean. There is here a background of high adventure that has made the Maoris of New Zealand one of the most notable of the world's peoples outside the belt of the plough-civilizations.

Hunter-collectors still linger as pygmy peoples in parts of the equatorial forests of Africa, the East Indies, the Philippines and New Guinea, typically with very lowly equipment and organization. Better equipment and great artistic skill have been characteristic of the Bushmen of South-West Africa. The Australian Blackfellows have better equipment than the forest pygmies, but their rock drawings, as well as their general equipment, are cruder than those of the Bushmen.

Forests in India retain some hunter-collectors, often influenced by adjacent cultivators. One-time herdsmen who have been pressed into north-eastern Siberia have in some cases come to depend on hunting, fishing and collecting, and this is broadly true of many American groups, including the Eskimos, but these last are highly skilled in the exploitation of their icy homelands. In most groups characteristics can be found which may be explained as steps towards the art of food production, learned either from more advanced peoples or from occasional migrants who have drifted into the hunter-collector groups.

### Marriage Rules

Typically, the men hunt, and the women, or both men and women, collect. Though very few, if any, women remain unmated, the number of wives a man possesses is small, and many have one only. Infant mortality is thought to be high, and births not as numerous as among grain-producers. Rules concerning marriage seem to be almost universal, and it is

Fig. 217. *in New Guinea and Melanesia the cultivation of starch-producing plants is important. As is usual among peoples lacking ploughs or farm animals, cultivation is woman's work. Papuan natives are here shown cleaning yams and taro. The woman on the left is carrying on her back a net sack in which the edible roots are gathered.*

Fɪɢ. 218. *Yam mounds in a partly cleared forest in the Mount Hagen area on the central plateau of New Guinea. After the men have provided partial clearings, the soil is gathered into mounds and used by the women for cultivating these edible tuberous plants.*

difficult to avoid the surmise that these peoples know a little of the dangers of continuous inbreeding.

Among lowly cultivators one may broadly distinguish several grades. In some groups the men hunt, do rough clearing of the land, cut down fruit trees or seek them out and put a proprietary mark on them, while women do the main work of cultivation. Men carry weapons for fighting when that may be necessary, and women accordingly carry most of the burdens.

Each woman has her cultivation-allotment and a man with many wives may thus gain a large reserve of food, which gives opportunities of patronage and power. The land is vaguely thought to belong to the group and the holder retains a patch so long as it is in use. It reverts to the wild state when neglected or exhausted and later on may be allotted afresh. Women use the digging stick, or may have acquired the hoe. but in any case. work with their hands.

The hoe-cultivator groups typically live in compact villages. which may have a

headman or chief; and a mother-village may have daughter-villages created by its surplus population. The village may have a stockade and something of a general plan. It may be built to last only a few years, after which a move, sometimes attended with special ceremony, is made to a new site.

### Houses

Among some peoples, for example in Borneo, the local group builds a long house in which the different families have sleeping cubicles, while, in the wider centre, there may be a dancing floor. The long house may be raised on a platform beneath which the animals are sheltered overnight. Population is still sparse among lowly cultivators, but not nearly as sparse as among hunter-collectors.

Native cities with organized markets and specialized craft groups are absent from Africa south of the Sahara and Abyssinia, save in the western Sudan. Various households may acquire a reputation for making special objects and there may be exchanges of gifts, sometimes with

FIG. 219.  *The family grave, Philippine Islands.  Built of timber and roofed with rice straw, the coffin house or grave is analogous to the dwellings built on platforms above the ground (see Fig. 202).  The dead are first enclosed in wooden coffins of heavy construction, which are afterwards deposited inside these huts.*

ceremonial accompaniments, and these exchanges take place within a village or between one village and another.

In inter-tropical Africa the village may have dormitories for the boys for whom there is no longer room in their mothers' huts, and even for the girls, though the latter may be allocated to the huts of widows whose children have married. Schemes of this kind seem, indeed, to be a widespread feature of the villages of lowly cultivators. There may also be a guard-house or club-house for the men.

### No Domestic Animals

Lowly cultivators, especially near the equatorial forests, may have no domestic animals at all, or—in the East Indies and Melanesia—a few dogs, or half-wild pigs. They may have chickens and goats; while most grassland folk in Africa south of the Sahara have cattle. These, however, are not used for farm work, but are a mark of social prestige, exchangeable as "lobola" for wives.

The lowly cultivators are without horses, asses or camels; human—often female—porterage has been the rule, and trackways are little developed. The wheel is practically absent except here and there where it may have come in from better-equipped groups.

Language among lowly cultivators is very multifarious in forest lands with impeded communications, but there are notable resemblances between the various Bantu languages spoken over wide areas in grassland Africa south of the Sudan. The lowly cultivators may send messages by means of notches cut on sticks, but they have no writing; and their memorized records are slight or non-existent.

Generally speaking, they lack institutions such as a priesthood with rules of succession, though chieftainship is widely recognized. The problem of succession is in fact at a very early stage of comprehension. Correlated with the lack of a priestly order, and of a scheme of training and succession of priests, is the importance of the individual who is supposed to possess special powers—the medicine man, witch doctor, or magician. His position is often a personal one, but the people may be accustomed by long tradition to the prestige of such a person, and in this there are germs of the idea of succession.

On the African grasslands, especially among the Zulu of the south-east, there have arisen military despotisms based mainly on the predacious habits of herders, but they have been poor in constructive ideas. Generally speaking, administration remains rudimentary among lowly cultivators; communications are poor, records are non-existent, and most wants are supplied locally. Even under the despotisms mentioned, the local group has largely managed its own affairs, subject to payment of tribute. The local leader was, and is, often rather the first among equals than an overlord with full authority backed by organized force.

While Africa south of the Sahara is the main area of lowly cultivation, because it has a climate in which few of the early cultivated food-plants would grow, and in which pasture is poor in vitamin C and cattle suffer from the tsetse fly, ticks and other pests, there are also survivals of lowly cultivators elsewhere.

### British Influence

India has a number of such groups. The Baiga live in central India in villages that have houses in rows or around a square; their tradition is to cut a clearing in the forest, burn the timber, and sow seeds in the ashes before the season of the rainy monsoon. It is needless to add that British influence has tried to spread among them the use of the plough in order to discourage their war against the valuable forests. The plough is an old established feature of all but the lowliest groups in India.

This gives us one of many great contrasts between India and inter-tropical Africa.

FIG. 220. *Australian aborigines have many elaborate ceremonies, some of which concern food supplies. Here they are performing a ritual believed to increase the wild plum harvest. Other rituals in the same category are observed for the welfare of animals or the totem of the tribe. The different rituals of these peoples are rich in myths and legends, and in addition to the type of ceremony referred to above, many varieties of complicated initiation rites and burial rites are performed.*

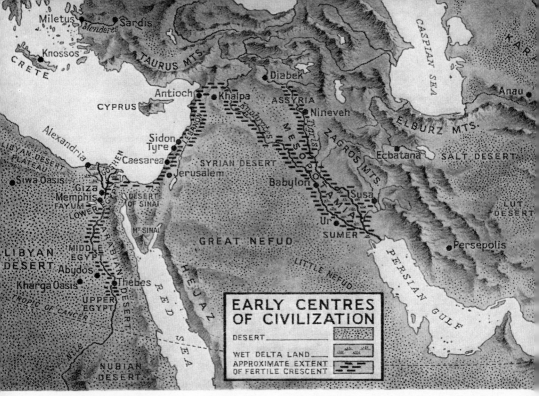

EARLY CENTRES
OF CIVILIZATION

DESERT

WET DELTA LAND

APPROXIMATE EXTENT
OF FERTILE CRESCENT

Both have lowly peoples in considerable numbers, but in India, with its richer possibilities of crops, its working animals and irrigation, there is every gradation from the hunter-collector to the organized villager who is a plough-cultivator.

The Murut of North Borneo plant rice on hill-slopes from which they have cleared the trees; and they choose a fresh patch each year, thereby wasting a great deal of valuable timber. As usual among lowly folk, the men clear the ground and the women make holes, digging with sticks, drop the seeds in the holes, and then weed the land from time to time.

### Starch-producing Plants

Some of the more advanced peoples of New Guinea, and of many other parts of the East Indian islands, use the starch accumulated in the pith of the sago-palm, which provides a large amount of food from comparatively little labour. Other plants of this region also store starch in the pith of their trunks, or in the root, as in the case of taro and yams (Figs. 217, 218). Partial dependence on cereals is also found, but they are less important than among

the millet and maize cultivators of inter-tropical Africa. One should contrast this partial dependence on roots and trees with the much greater dependence on cereals for food in early Mesopotamia and Egypt. In those early days the cultivators had to build up a much more elaborate routine; and it is from their achievements that civilization has grown.

Another important feature of the East Indies and the part of the Pacific near to them, as well as of Eastern Asia, is the adoption of the pig as a domestic or semi-domesticated animal.

The coconut palm flourishes on and near the coast in West and East Africa, South India, Ceylon, Farther India, the East Indies, the Pacific Islands within the tropics, and the American inter-tropical lands. There is no problem about its wide distribution, as the fruit is wonderfully suited to distribution by sea, with its fibrous husk light enough to float and its tough shell impervious to sea-water.

Lowly agriculturists spreading eastwards through the East Indies to the Pacific have therefore found cultivable plants of considerable value for food as well as for other

FIG. 221. *As the major phases of the Ice Age passed away the desert became more extensive and habitation-sites were maintained only if they were near water. Euphrates-Tigris, Syria-Palestine and the Nile gave special opportunities, particularly as wild ancestors of emmer wheat, barley and probably millet grew here. It is likely that parts of Persia participated with the Fertile Crescent in the early development of cultivation, and that the land between the Taurus Mountains and the Mediterranean was also concerned. These areas were, in very early days of food-production, cultivated with the plough. Irrigation was characteristic. The more settled mode of life which resulted from habits of cultivation led, first to village societies, and then to the evolution of cities. These urban communities possessed a military and priestly aristocracy, craftsmen, markets, and a sacred ritual centre where the records and treasures of the group were kept.*

purposes. The coconut palm is specially famous for its many uses, such as roofing (leaves), matting (husk fibres), drinking vessels (the fruit shell), intoxicating toddy (from the flower-spathes), and a milky drink (from inside the nuts).

Even among hunter-collectors ceremonial plays an important part in binding a social group together, and ritual, typically including dancing, is generally elaborated in connexion with the main phases of the work of cultivation (Fig. 220). There is thus among most cultivators a calendar of festivals, linked with the alternation of rainy and drier seasons, of seedtime and harvest; and that calendar has undergone remarkable elaboration among peoples of European and Asiatic civilizations.

Ritual, and what may be broadly called religion, are difficult subjects for short treatment; the outward and visible form of ritual may survive a radical change of meaning. Boys in Britain burn "Guy Fawkes" without knowing that, for ages before the Gunpowder Plot, the effigy represented the dying vegetation-year. The effigy is still called the "Bout-de-l'an" in the Channel Islands. An item of ritual

may be borrowed and adapted by one people from another, and may spread with change or loss of meaning; it may be found in process of slow decay and its original meaning may be lost.

It seems obvious that we should not look for any one general beginning of ceremonial or religion. Children, even in civilized communities, readily ascribe personality to objects outside the animal kingdom, to inanimate objects, to wind, thunder, rain; and so apparently have lowly peoples from time immemorial. This is one basis of the idea of spirits.

### Spirit-idea

Another may be that lowly folk, interested in the fact that human mating leads less regularly to a birth than is the case among animals, have thought the entry of a "spirit," sometimes an ancestral spirit, into the prospective mother is a part of the scheme of reproduction. This spirit-idea has almost certainly been much strengthened by noting hereditary resemblances.

The tombs of ancestors, or the skull collections in some cases, may become

FIG. 222. *These holes cut in the rock face are entrances to primitive cliff-dwellings in New Mexico. At one time it was believed that the former inhabitants of the caves belonged to a mysterious race of people who had completely vanished from the American scene. It is now recognized, however, that the dwellings once sheltered pre-historic ancestors of the Pueblo Indians who are still found in parts of the south-western United States. This ancient people was probably driven to such inaccessible refuges by the pressure of hostile tribes. This photograph was taken in the Bandelier National Monument, a reservation named after the famous American archæologist and maintained by the U. S. Government.*

repositories of spirits awaiting rebirth, and ceremonial at or near those tombs, or skull houses, with dancing and general excitement, may be held to be a help in securing offspring. It is probable that the tombs made from huge unhewn stones near the seaboard of so many parts of Atlantic Europe were held to be such repositories.

The association of members of a group with some type of animal, plant, object or power is widespread among lowly cultivators, and some hunter-collectors also have this idea. There may, too, be an idea of powerful spirits, who may rank as gods to be propitiated. Certainly it is widely the case that lowly folk cherish the idea of a ritual which will compel the unseen powers to give them their desires.

The prosperous growth of seeds laid in a grave as food for the dead has helped the idea of a fertility-sacrifice, in many cases a human sacrifice, with distribution of parts of the body for burial in different fields. The victim has often been almost royally treated for a while before sacrifice.

### Plough Cultivation

Cultivation with a small plough, sometimes accompanied by irrigation, is characteristic of the area of earliest food-production, i.e. the Fertile Crescent from Ur of the Chaldees around the north of the Arabian desert to Gaza, and the lower Nile (Fig. 221). It has spread thence to the lands of mainland Asia affected by warm summer monsoon rains, and to Sumatra, Java, Formosa and Japan. It has also spread via Persia into Inner Asia to the river margins in the steppes, to both Mediterranean and more northerly Europe, along the North African coastlands, and to Abyssinia and parts of Arabia, as well as into the Niger basin to some extent.

Cultivation with the help of animals for farm work, and, in time, for dunging the land, increased men's resources and made life more settled. The privileged folk, often descendants of herders who had conquered cultivators, have typically striven to avoid the work of ploughing, and even of cattle-tending in some cases, and to form a landlord-class with craftsmen gathered around them and some link with the priestly or ritual leaders, even though the latter often belong by tradition to the conquered rather than to the conquering.

Societies of cultivators are, therefore, typically composite, with a good deal of internal strain that needs to be mitigated or repressed by administrative schemes. The success of such schemes is made more assured by the more definitely settled life, and by the possibilities of record-keeping.

From the stage of settled villages, the plough cultivators went on to the evolution of cities with an aristocracy that had both military and priestly elements, with craftsmen, a market, and especially a sacred ritual centre, where records and treasure were kept, and where, often, there was some "mystery" maintained by priests.

Among hunter-collectors a small group of some fifty souls may range over hundreds of square miles. Among lowly hunter-cultivators, where men hunt and clear land, and women do the work of cultivation, a group of fifty to a hundred may get most of its living off ten to twenty square miles, patches of which it clears and cultivates for a year or two, but there is usually an indefinite wild area beyond this into which the hunters range.

Among those who have more organized cultivation, but are still without working animals or ploughs, groups of one or two hundred may consider an area of five or ten square miles as theirs. Plough-cultivators can be much more close-packed even without towns; and a density of over fifty persons per square mile is often reached. On irrigated land, densities reach very high figures indeed.

Among the plough-cultivators a cycle of work keeps pace with the seasons, and high

FIG. 223. *Skyscrapers at Shibam in the Hadramaut province, southern Arabia. The provinces of Yemen, Hadramaut and Oman have some fertile areas and the two last have long enjoyed maritime trade with Malaysia as well as with Africa. Frankincense and myrrh are well-known products. The high buildings, erected long before America experimented with skyscrapers, provide a little freshness for those who live in them, and also supply welcome shade in the narrow streets of this ancient oasis town.*

points are marked by festivals, which have grown out of the desire for fertility of soil, stock and family. One form or another of fertility-religion is, or has been, characteristic and has given rise to the goddesses Demeter, Isis, Hathor, Ishtar, Kali, the "Mother Goddess" statuette recently found by Mr. Leslie Armstrong on the Norfolk-Suffolk border near Brandon, and others, with many variants of each.

The festivals play a large part in marriage arrangements and, thereby, in the birth-rate, which formerly was high, since it had to reach an average of six children for each woman if population was to be maintained against heavy infant mortality, epidemics, famines, and wars. Populations increased at only a very slow rate under such conditions.

### Ancient Philosophers

In China, India, Persia, Israel and Greece, we find within a short space of time, the rise of teachers turning men's minds away from ritual to conduct, teachers with little interest in the many old-time gods and goddesses, but with their attention turned more towards humanity as a whole. Lao Tse, Confucius, Mahavira, Buddha, Zoroaster, the major Hebrew prophets, Xenophanes and the Greek philosophers, all belong to nearly the same period, though there is some doubt about Zoroaster's dates.

But the simpler folk in all these lands kept to their old customs and ritual, changing a name here and there. And the rulers and leaders adopted diverse attitudes towards these hoary traditions. Lao Tse, if we understand his teaching aright, did not wish to hurry people forward, and Confucius was essentially conservative in face of a ritual that emphasized the family, the pivot of his system. It is interesting to note that the long struggle of what became the Japanese Empire against the older peoples of the islands helped to develop reverence for the family (the so-called "ancestor-worship") into reverence for the emperor, the head of the Shinto system.

We have now followed the geographical distributions of the efforts towards a regulated civilized life until we have reached the threshold of what is generally studied as documentary history. It has shown us that a zone from China to Greece and Egypt gives a long sequence of changes more fully worked out, for periods before the beginning of our era, than elsewhere —ploughs, irrigation, cities, social and religious hierarchies, schemes of trade and dominion, ships for the sea, roads for the land, and ethical teaching either as an addition to, or an attempted substitute for, traditional religion.

### "Outer Lands"

We could go on to draw more detailed attention to primary expansions of some of these ideas from the zone just mentioned—to Japan in the east and to the Roman Mediterranean in the west, with, in this last case, a secondary spread over the European continent.

But, on the whole, life long remained on a lower level of equipment in the lands beyond the zone of ancient civilization as discussed above.

The plough reaches into these "outer lands," but there are still many ploughless cultivators and a truly indigenous city is rarely recognizable. Any traces of higher religious thought are obviously importations. The peoples of these "outer lands" in the Old World may be said to fall into three main groups, those of the Arctic North, those of the East Indian archipelago, New Guinea, Melanesia, and the Pacific, and those of Africa south of the Sahara and Abyssinia, and a few areas of the Sudan. The Polynesian islanders are in some ways a special case.

### India's Diversities

Finally, we get back to the peoples of the uttermost regions, of the denser warm wet forests and the wastes of South-West Africa, of Australia, and of north-eastern Siberia, in all of which hunting and collecting peoples still linger. India is unique in that diverse peoples illustrate all stages of the process sketched in broad outline here. Indeed, in that great sub-continent, in spite of an infinite gradation, a unified consciousness is still a far-off ideal.

# RACES OF MANKIND

COMMON usage classifies mankind into white, yellow, brown and black—or sometimes into kinky-haired, wavy-haired and straight-haired peoples. The tacit assumption has been that these groups separated off from a common stock in some very remote epoch and have gone on separately ever since. But the story of the drifts of mankind outlined earlier in this section shows that this view is quite inadequate for the interpretation of the geographical distribution of man's bodily characteristics.

Man, in the modern sense, and his close relatives known to anthropologists as the Neanderthal stock, seem to grade into one another, at any rate in Palestine. They probably did so in Europe as well. There is undoubtedly an overwhelming common inheritance throughout mankind. Many cases have occurred of highly fertile interbreeding between peoples of widely separated regions.

## Persistent Characteristics

In such unions between persons of very diverse characters we notice that neither is the offspring a sort of average between the two, nor does it follow one or other parent exclusively. Some characters, such as head-form, seem to have a great tendency to persist in most circumstances, so that we get, for example, among the peoples of South Africa, southern India, Australia, northern Japan, western Great Britain, and various corners of the New World, an extremely narrow and long form of head linked with a tendency to strong brow ridges, deep-set eyes, broad nostrils, prominence of mouth and strength of teeth. Only in aboriginal Australia do these features characterize whole populations, but they are nevertheless present in samples from many regions, generally from remote and rather isolated spots. They also characterize some populations of the more isolated oases, e.g. Siwa, of the Sahara.

There is a high degree of probability that this bundle of physical characters was carried by an early drift of mankind in all directions from a North African zone of early occupation. And, in the process of drift, some have come to differ in certain characteristics; some are white, some dark brown, some wavy-haired, and some kinky-haired, and so on.

If we classify men according to skin-colour, or hair-texture, or head-forms, the result is a very artificial one, and is of little value. We must link together the study of the drifts of mankind with that of the physical characters of mankind, both as heritages from ancestors and as responses to environment.

As an illustration of the difficulty of the problem we may mention the case of men with very long and narrow skulls. Those which are characterized by these measurements include at least two, and probably more than two groups that are strikingly, contrasted. The very tall, slim, thin-faced, fine-featured type of some state of north-west India is very distinct from the equally narrow-headed Australian Blackfellow, with his rougher features and broad nose.

We cannot take any one character, study its distribution and argue thence concerning the classification of mankind. Each of us is a complex bundle of characteristics of varied origins affected in various ways by our surroundings and our growth.

Skin characters are certainly the most easily observed of all and have been made the basis of prejudice in a unique degree. The skin is our medium of contact with our environment, and its diversity of character in different parts of the earth is largely a result of response to divers circumstances, especially to diversities of climate.

## Tropical Sun

Near the tropics of Cancer and Capricorn, the sun's rays beat down almost vertically for months at a time, and violet and ultra-violet radiation is very strong in these regions that have little protective cloud-cover or rain. Such regions include the Sudan to the south-east of the Sahara, and the dry Angola region on the

Fig. 224. Reading from left to right: **A. European:** Fair, long heads (English and Frisian): various broad heads—S. French, Georgian, Russian Slavs; Spanish, Prussian, Dinaric, Alpine (Tyrol), Mediterranean (Italy). **B. American:** N. American Indian (Algonquin), S. American (Tierra del Fuego), Central America (Yukatan, Mexico), S. American (Peruvian). **C.1. N. African:** Egyptian Fellah, Abyssinian, Arab Egyptian, N. African Arab. Southern Egyptian Fellah, Tuareg (Sahara), light-skinned N. Egyptian type **C.2 African:** Nandi (Kenya), Soudanese (Fuzzy Wuzzy) Zulu Hottentot,

Pygmy, Fula (N. Nigeria); Masai (E. Africa), Bushman (S.W. Africa), West African, Cameroon type (W.C. Africa). **D. Arctic:** Greenland Eskimo, Laplander, Samoyed; Arctic Mongol. **E. Asiatic:** Mongol, Korean, Jap; Afghan, Mongol, Burmese, Jungle type (S. India), N. China, Naga (Assam), N. Indian, Balinese (E. Indies); Veddah (Ceylon), Madras types. **F. S.W. Asiatic:** Jew (Palestine), Armenian (Syria), Iran type, Bedouin. **G. Pacific:** Solomon Islander; Gilbert Islander, Dyak (Borneo), Papuan, Samoan, Australian Blackfellow, Maori (New Zealand)

FIG. 225. *This photograph, taken in Central Africa, of an American, a Congo pygmy, and a Congo Negro, provides a contrast in stature and general build. Note the long trunk and arms and relatively short legs of the Negro. He usually follows an agricultural way of life, dwelling in a village ruled by a chief who in some cases may have extended his domain to other villages. The African pygmy has his counterpart in other regions of the world—the Philippine Islands, Papua, Indonesia, Malaya and the Andaman Islands—where the aborigines are a backward race of very small stature with flat noses, thick lips, woolly hair and other physical characteristics of the Negro.*

tropic of Capricorn facing the Atlantic. Here are found the African peoples with darkest skins, and we know that skin pigment stops the violet and ultra-violet rays, but that these last are apt to set up blisters in tender skin not protected by pigments.

Towards the Gulf of Guinea cloud-cover and thunderstorms with heavy rain are a marked feature; and, in this environment, the rays just mentioned are only sometimes in excess. But the moist heat is very trying. The skin of many peoples of this region is rich in blood vessels; and blood colour combines with brown skin pigment to give a more or less chocolate effect. The blood brought to the surface to cool also gives up moisture through large sweat-glands and the evaporation of sweat helps to cool the body. Protection against an excess of ultra-violet rays is here a little less marked, protection against an excess of moist heat more marked. But in neither case is it a simple and uniform response to climate. In any one region we may find a considerable gradation in these characters probably not entirely explicable by recent migration.

One of the cloudiest regions on earth is North-Western Europe, where the warm Atlantic water driven landwards by the sou'westers gives up to those winds a great deal of moisture that condenses into cloud and rain against the highland coast of Norway and the British Isles. Here, also, the sun is never within 25 degrees of the zenith and is very low in winter. The supply of violet and ultra-violet rays is small. In fact, the deficiency is a serious factor of ill-health and specially affects children of African parents in England.

Now we note that this is the region in which eyes without brown pigment in the iris, blond hair, and pink and white complexions are commonest, along with large but narrow noses and tall stature. We may thus venture the inference that there is less evocation of pigment in this cool, cloudy environment, and the contrast is most marked over against the high evocation of pigment in the Sudan.

Further, we find that as we go south from Britain and the Baltic, blonds become rarer and brunettes become more numerous and darker. Eyes having the iris with brown pigment soon become common, and a brownish tinge appears on the skin, while hair that is very dark becomes the rule. Southern Europe is a region of swarthy whites. North Africa is a region of browns.

So the latitudinal gradation of skin colour from North Cape to the Equator is a striking fact. Blondness becomes rarer as we pass east in northern latitudes, where cloudiness also diminishes, and this contributes further evidence to the general argument.

### British Peoples

It may be that both the blond and the very dark are specializations from a primitive intermediate brownish type of skin, and that, since evolution is generally irreversible, we should not expect blonds to darken if they migrate equatorwards or blacks to lighten in colour if they move polewards.

It is interesting that the British population includes in the west a large element that in bone characters is related to peoples of South-Western Europe and that is on the whole darker than other peoples of these islands. There are abundant archæological and legendary indications of late Neolithic movements from South-Western Europe to the British Isles and the " little dark people " of western Britain were named Iberians by the pioneer anthropologists of the nineteenth century. But, when we compare Spanish and British examples, we find that the British are somewhat less dark and have, especially, less pigment in the iris of the eye. It may well be that, coming north, they have lost some of the primeval pigment. There is at any rate little doubt that the North-Western European blond is bleached from brown.

The hair, again, as a skin-feature, illustrates similar gradations. There is the highest probability that, primevally, human hair was wavy, and that, at some very early stage of its evolution, humanity reduced its hair-covering from causes we shall not attempt to discuss here. The blond peoples of Northern Europe are noted for the quantity of facial and body hair of the males, but body hair becomes sparser southwards and is very much reduced in inter-tropical Africa, save for the downy ("infantile") hair among the pygmies of the equatorial forest who, on many grounds, may be regarded rather as decadent remnants of very ancient stocks. Hair is a valuable protection against cold, but a nuisance in a very hot sunny climate.

But we may go further than this. Not only is there less hair on the body in inter-tropical Africa but the head-hair is, as everyone knows, excessively kinky, being coiled into tight spirals. It emerges from loose follicles so that its growth is very irregular, whereas the European's hair emerges from follicles that have a fairly regular oval shape. The loose follicles of the African skin can be thought of, along with the large sweat-glands, the broad nose with widely open nostrils, and the thick lips, as promoting evaporation of moisture and, when possible, radiation of heat out from the body. It has been suggested by two independent authorities that the hair of at any rate some Africans and Melanesians becomes really kinky only after birth.

### Extremes of Climate

This line of argument is again useful in trying to interpret some of the characters of the people of Inner Asia and the Far East. On the high Mongolian plateau the great climatic problem for man is the change from the fierceness of winter to the strong sunshine of the summer. The brown of the skin is modified by yellow, which is partly due to the density of the skin-tissues and to the fact that the blood vessels are deeper down than they are among either Africans or Europeans.

The hair, too, is modified; it emerges from tight, round follicles which it fills completely, so that little heat radiates out, and little moisture evaporates. The regularity of the follicles gives regularity to the hair growth, and the hair of the head is coarse and straight. There is very little body hair. The conservation of heat by the skin in this region appears to be as remarkable as is its dispersal from many African skins.

This type of skin and hair has spread into north China and beyond but becomes less distinctive towards the south-east of China and in Farther India, though the yellowish tinge is found over a wide area. West of Mongolia the yellow tinge diminishes, but the skin is sometimes dense enough to be dead white. The skin of some western Himalayans is, however, a rosy white in spite of very cold winters. So the yellow or yellow-brown tint is not to be considered a necessary or invariable response to coldness of climate.

Arctic peoples are mostly migrants from Inner Asia, and their skin is typically brownish with a red tinge. In the far north snow-glare is an important factor, and Europeans are apt to get skin troubles if they expose themselves too much.

The American Indian peoples are mainly descendants of migrants who came from Asia through north-eastern Siberia and Alaska or the adjacent islands. It is thus natural that brown colouring with a yellow or red tinge, is widespread among them, along with straight and often coarse hair, and paucity of body hair and beard.

To discuss head-form in any detail would take us too far afield, but we may recall the importance of the very narrow long head in early times (page 335). As has already been stated, it is found in several remote areas at the present day. The less extreme forms of long head, i.e. those with the sides rather more filled out, are most notable in the lands south of the great mountain zone that stretches from the Pyrenees to the Pacific; they also occur north of it in European Atlantic lands. Broad heads are characteristic of most of that highland zone, but small heads of considerable relative breadth occur among the pygmies of the equatorial forests of Africa and South-East Asia (Fig. 225).

To the north of the great highland zone there have penetrated both long heads and broad heads. In the New World the earlier components of the pre-Columbian population seem to have been predominantly long-headed, while later migrants, probably arriving like their predecessors via North-Eastern Asia, are mainly broad-headed.

It may be that a broad- or short-headed element existed on both the northern flank and the southern flank of the main early zone of long heads, which seem to have included North Africa, Arabia, South-West Asia and India. If so, as the ancient ice sheets diminished the broad-headed element in the mountain zone expanded and migrated more to the north than to the south, which was already occupied by long heads in the main—save for the short, small heads of the pygmies.

## Test Yourself

1. Both India and inter-tropical Africa have groups of lowly people who eke out an existence by hunting, collecting or agriculture. What differences are apparent when the lowly peoples of Africa and India are compared?

2. In many countries skin colour is the basis of violent prejudice. Why is this illogical?

3. The use of the plough for cultivation was unknown in Africa south of the Sahara Desert until the advent of Europeans. Which two areas provide exceptions to this generalization?

*Answers will be found at the end of the book.*

# GUIDE TO FURTHER STUDY

SINCE geography is the detailed description of the earth *as an inhabited planet*, it is within the reach of everyone to make a study of some branch of the subject at first hand in his own home area. In fact, the practical pursuit of geography demands little more than a lively and intelligent interest in the immediate world around us, and a knowledge of maps, and does not by any means claim time and leisure for extensive travel.

Travel, or wide reading, is naturally necessary for a knowledge of other lands, and for the study of economic geography in all but very local aspects, and this brief guide includes some recommendations of works well worth consulting. The value of listening to foreign radio broadcasts, though dubious in some instances, should not be overlooked.

### Making a Beginning

One of the best possible ways of getting into the subject of geography is to attempt to answer such questions as the following:

1. Why is my home town situated where it is?
2. How does it manage to support so many inhabitants?
3. What sort of crops are grown locally, and what sort of stock is reared? Why these, and not others?

The answers to such questions will lead you to information about the physical geography, geology, and climate of your district, and even if you have no chance to go farther afield, will provide you with sufficient subject-matter for a lifetime of study.

For example, the answer to Question 1 may turn on one (or both) of two factors. First, the actual position of the town may be its *raison d'être*: it may be situated, like Montreal (see Fig. 115), at the junction of several important routes, it may be an old fortress commanding a pass in the mountains through which road, rail and river all, perforce, must run (for example, Lewes, in Fig. 83), or it may be placed on such a fine harbour that it is worth while transporting goods to it from great distances simply for the ease with which they can there be loaded on to ocean-going vessels (Figs. 88, 179). In the last case, you will be led to a study of the physical geography of the harbour, and its commercial history.

Second, its position may be of little importance, and even inconvenient, but it may owe its existence to some purely local source of wealth. This may take the form of a valuable mineral (Figs. 111, 180), or an area of especially rich and fertile soil. In the case of the old manufacturing towns in the Lancashire cotton districts the local wealth was originally cheap and abundant water-power for driving the mills, though this has since been replaced by coal, which is also found locally. If the town happens to be in an inhospitable or unhealthy country, its wealth may consist simply in a beneficial climate (for example, Simla in northern India), or an abundance of spring water (for example, Alice Springs in Central Australia, and Timbuktu in the Sahara).

However you may succeed in answering Question 1, the information gained is likely to give the key to Question 2. But it sometimes happens that such information is quite inadequate to account for the *size* of the town, and this has to be explained by reference to something other than its situation. The clue you now need will possibly be found in a study of local, or even national, history.

Thus, a town like Cambridge, England, is supported largely by the income derived from the university, and one like Winchester (which is important partly for its position at the northern entrance to the Hampshire basin) is maintained chiefly as the administrative centre of the county and the cathedral city of a large diocese. Other towns live on incomes derived from religious devotion to some shrine or historic event or as a centre for tourists.

Canberra, seat of the Australian government, was sited and built as the federal capital to avoid a dispute between rival claimants, Sydney and Melbourne, to that distinction. Washington, the capital of U.S.A., is a somewhat similar case, but has also become a centre for trade and light industries.

In agricultural and stock-raising districts, the physical geography and geology of the neighbourhood are of great importance, and the answer to Question 3 should be followed by a study of the local rocks, soils (see page 24), water-supply and climate. Much of this information is to be obtained from the local library and archives, and much from conversation with the working inhabitants, but the serious student of geography will need to make constant reference to the best obtainable maps of the district, and will take some pains to become proficient in the art of interpreting maps correctly.

### Surveying Problems

Maps are a statement of geographical fact in graphic form, and as such may follow any agreed convention of symbols to represent places and directions. The South Sea Islanders, for example, made sailing charts of strips of palm leaf, and the first "Maori" colonists of New Zealand were guided in their epic voyages from Tahiti by charts consisting of interlaced twigs.

The first real maps were, however, much older than these crude sailing charts, and arose from the necessity of recording the holdings of land in those "cradles of civilization," Babylon and Egypt, where annual floods frequently obliterated landmarks. In ancient Egyptian sculptures we have bas-reliefs showing men engaged in surveying by means of a measuring chain. The records would have been made on papyrus and therefore have not been preserved; but in Babylon as early as 2000 B.C. plans of estates were made in clay which was then baked to make permanent records, some of which have remained to this day. An old Babylonian map is shown on page vi.

The basic problem of map making is,

of course, accurate measurement of horizontal distances. In a flat country such as Egypt or Mesopotamia, it was an easy matter to measure the distances between various fixed points and to record the results on a plan drawn to scale; and provided some fixed unit of length had been agreed, comparison could be made between one area and another.

Such "chain surveys" are, however, only practicable for small areas, and on level ground which is free from obstructions.

The ancient Greeks discovered the method of *triangulation* based on the sighting of points from the opposite ends of a measured base line. Even though the early map-maker was thus enabled to make a reasonably accurate map of his own district, he had no means of showing its relationship to places outside the range of his own measurements. For this he needed fixed points of reference for both direction and distance. The apparent movements of the sun in its daily course provided an obvious solution of the problem of direction and gave the "cardinal points" east and west, south and north. By observations of the sun and the stars the ancient Greeks learned to determine latitude and longitude and thus to fix the relative positions of any number of points without actually measuring the distances between them. They were thus able to draw large areas with reasonable accuracy in respect of position, size, shape and orientation.

### Medieval Maps

Unfortunately, much of this knowledge was lost or ignored by the Christian world, and medieval world maps are remarkable more for imagery than accuracy.

Nevertheless, the need for maps sufficiently accurate to provide a rough guide to travellers and to fix the ownership of land led to a revival of the art of surveying by such simple instruments as the astrolabe.

By about the middle of the fourteenth century the main roads of England had been mapped, and many detailed plans of monastic and other estates had been compiled. A series of such maps through the centuries shows an interesting development from the pictorial method of representing

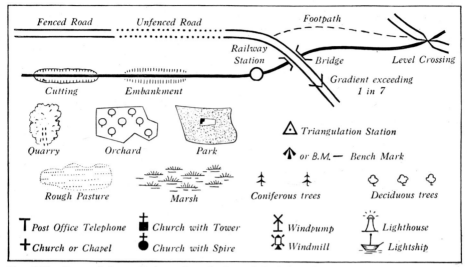

FIG. 226. *Some of the symbols used on the British Ordnance Survey maps. "Bench marks" are usually found carved into milestones, buildings, bridges or rocks. The point of the arrow is crossed by a thin line, or "bench," and a figure gives its height above sea level.*

buildings and other features in elevation to the modern method of representation by symbols shown in plan.

In the sixteenth century the rediscovery of a map by Ptolemy, the spread of the new learning, and the rapid opening up of the world by the voyages of discovery led to a rapid advance in the art of map-making. Triangulation by means of compass directions and the plane table facilitated more accurate surveying, and by the end of the century maps of all the English counties had been engraved and published.

### How to Read Maps

Almost all countries nowadays produce large-scale, accurate maps of their territory. In Britain, for example, the Ordnance Survey Department publishes at very small cost maps showing all the physical features, towns, villages, roads and footpaths in Great Britain. These maps are obtainable in various scales, the principal of which are at a half-inch, one-inch, two-and-a-half inches, and six inches to the mile. The whole of the cultivated districts of Britain are also obtainable in a scale of twenty-five inches to the mile, and the densely populated areas in one of fifty inches to the mile.

Of this abundance the well-known "one-inch" maps are likely to be of greatest use to the amateur student of geography, particularly as geological maps of the country, showing the distribution of rocks and soils, are obtainable on the same scale for easy comparison. On this scale, also, are the "land utilization" maps, which show areas under various crops, pasture, woodland, and so on.

To get as much information as possible on to such maps use is made of conventional symbols which do not differ greatly from country to country. Fig. 226 shows how some of the features given on the British Ordnance Survey maps are indicated, and most of these will be seen in use in the map in Fig. 229.

There are two common ways in which hills and mountains may be represented. The chief of these is by means of "contours," which are lines drawn on the map to connect together places of equal height above sea level. They are generally drawn at intervals of fifty or a hundred feet. In Britain, the official sea level, or "O.D." (Ordnance Datum), is that of the mean sea level at Newlyn, Cornwall, as observed hourly during the six years 1915 to 1921.

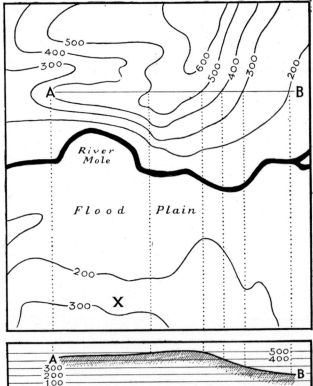

Fig. 227. Above: *A contour map of the valley of the River Mole at Box Hill, Surrey. The view from* x *is looking east towards* A-B, *and the river flows from south to north.* Below: *A section through Box Hill projected from the line* A-B. (See text.)

Where the gradient, or slope, of the land is steep, the contours run close together, as they do between the line A-B and the river. Where the slope is gradual the contours are wide apart, as in the neighbourhood of x. The land occupied by the flood plain of the Mole is so level that it nowhere rises to 200 feet or drops to 100 feet, and therefore contains no contours.

One great advantage of a contour map is that it is quite easy to draw from it a "profile," or section,

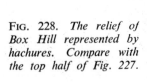

The general appearance of heights as portrayed by contours may be seen in Fig. 227, which shows the valley of the River Mole, in Surrey, with Box Hill at the top of the map. It should be borne in mind that the height above sea level of any given point not exactly on a contour always lies somewhere between the heights of the contours on either side of it. Thus, the point x stands between 200 and 300 feet above sea level, while the point A, lying exactly on the 400-foot contour, is 400 feet above the sea level.

between any two given points. In our example, the section between A and B is shown at the foot of the map, and is arrived at by dropping perpendicular lines from each point of intersection of the line A-B with a contour on to the appropriate line

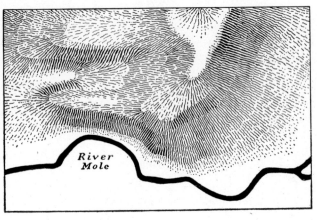

Fig. 228. *The relief of Box Hill represented by hachures. Compare with the top half of Fig. 227.*

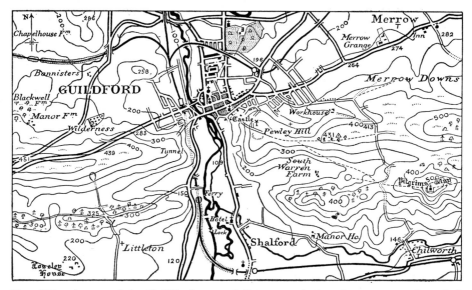

FIG. 229. *A map of the Guildford area of Surrey employing the conventional symbols of the British Ordnance Survey. See Fig. 226. The scale of the map is slightly larger than the standard one inch to a mile to facilitate close examination. Antiquities and places of historic interest are printed in Old English characters (e.g. 𝕮𝖆𝖘𝖙𝖑𝖊 and 𝕻𝖎𝖑𝖌𝖗𝖎𝖒𝖘 𝖂𝖆𝖞).*

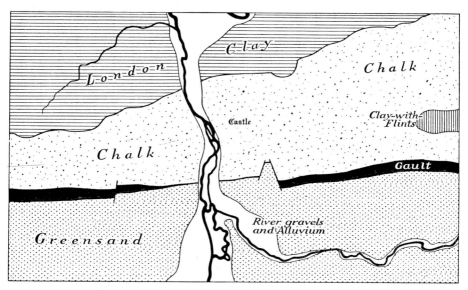

FIG. 230. *A simplified geological map of the area shown in Fig. 229, on the same scale. The river receives tributaries from the spring-lines of both ranges of hills, and has filled its valley with a wide strip of gravel and alluvium within which it meanders from side to side. Note the three faults at the junction of the gault with the chalk.*

in the grill below. This section should be compared with Fig. 231, which is an actual photograph taken from the point x and looking towards A-B. The slight apparent discrepancies are due to the effects of perspective, and the fact that higher land lying behind the line A-B (such as the area within the 600-foot contour) appears in the photograph.

The representation of the relief of the land by hachures is exemplified in Fig. 228, which also shows Box Hill and covers exactly the same area as the upper half of Fig. 227. Hachures, in themselves, do not show heights above sea level, but are designed to show gradients by the frequency and thickness of the lines. They give a more graphic representation of the relief of the land, but have the drawback of showing both low-lying plains and flat mountain-summits in the same way— namely by the entire absence of shading.

Both contours and hachures are widely employed in modern maps, sometimes both together (but in different colours) on the same map. The actual heights above sea level of mountain-summits and other pro- minent physical features are also given as isolated numbers, and those which have been ascertained with great accuracy as standards are known as "trigonometrical stations," and are accompanied on the map by a small triangle. One is shown at Pewley Hill in Fig. 229.

### Interpreting a Map

The reader is advised to study Fig. 229 with great care, and to see how much he can get out of it. He should first look for the "orientation" of the map, which he will find in the top left-hand corner. This usually takes the form of a crossed arrow, the head of which points due north (in the Northern Hemisphere). This pre- liminary inspection is necessary because not all maps have their northerly boundaries at the top of the sheet. In our maps of Box Hill (Figs. 227, 228), for example, we look east towards the top of the page, and north towards the left-hand edge; it is just a matter of convenience.

The principal features in the map we are studying (Fig. 229) are the river, running

from south to north across the centre, and the two areas of high land on the extreme left and right. It is evident that there is a range of hills running from east to west, broken by a river-gap on which stands the town of Guildford. Through this gap run the road and railway to the north, as well as the river, and a closer inspection shows how the wise medieval barons built their castle so as to overlook and guard the gap at its narrowest point.

A careful examination of the contours reveals a second range of hills to the south of the first, and parallel with it, but this range is wooded instead of being grass- covered, and doubtless provided a safe and pleasant path for the old "Pilgrims' Way." The reader should ask himself why the vegetation is different on the two ranges of hills (which are of approximately equal height). The local farmers could tell him of differences in the soils, but a glance at the geological map will prove even more informative.

A simplified geological map is given in Fig. 230. This tells us that the main range consists of chalk on which little more than grass will grow. The second range is greensand, which will support trees, and particularly pines and firs. Note also the patch of wooded land on the chalk hills where they are capped with clay-with- flints (on the extreme right), and the fact that the orchards, farms, and parks occupy the area of low-lying London clay to the north. South Warren Farm is also note- worthy as being one of a chain of farms occupying the narrow clay (gault) vale which separates the two ranges of hills.

The relation between plants and soils is often very strongly marked. One might amuse oneself on a train journey by guessing the changes in the soil and the rocks from the changes in vegetation observed from the carriage window, and it may be possible to verify one's guesses if the train should travel near quarries or through cuttings. Even greater opportuni- ties occur on a holiday ramble, for then it is often possible to trace the passage from one geological formation to another by wild flowers.

For example, the predominance of such

FIG. 231. *Box Hill, Surrey, as seen from Ranmore Common, with the valley of the River Mole in the middle distance. The level top of Box Hill is the post-Pliocene peneplain, and its steep slope is the chalk escarpment. Compare with Fig. 232.*

FIG. 232. *Mt. Eglwyseg, Denbighshire, showing the carboniferous limestone escarpment. Note how the strata of bare rocks outcrop on the scarp-face, and compare with the grass-covered scarp-face in Fig. 231, which is a precisely similar formation but in the softer chalk.*

plants as heather, gorse, broom, sorrel, · bracken, foxglove, and pine trees is a sure sign of sand, either as sandstone or the residue of weathered igneous rocks. The rhododendron, in particular, invariably grows on sandy or gravelly soils, and cannot tolerate lime at all.

On the other hand, limestone and chalky districts are characterized by the growth of sheep's fescue (a fine wiry grass), scabious, bee and fly orchis, wild cherry, dogwood, valerian, deadly-nightshade, etc.—all plants which are absent or very rare in sandstone regions. Sometimes the change from one flora to another is quite abrupt, and can easily be marked on the map with a pencil line. Here and there, however, anomalies may occur, and considerable skill is required in detecting them.

The reader will also have noticed the appearance of cattle in valleys and river-plains, where there is plenty of lush meadow grass, and their replacement on the poorer hills and moors by sheep. (He should make use of this knowledge when studying peasant countries.) Both plant and animal life are so dependent on the rocks and soil that it was possible to trace the line of demarcation between slightly different igneous rocks beneath pasture-lands in Norway by observing the distribution of a deficiency-disease in the cattle!

### Tell-tale Scenery

The interpretation of scenery is another branch of what is called "field geography," and the reader should familiarize himself with the characteristic forms of mountains of igneous rocks (Figs. 38, 189), and of sandstone (Fig. 151), limestone (Figs. 100, 232), and chalk (Fig. 231) hills. He should learn to recognize the signs of glaciation (the work of ice) both by the forms of the valleys (Figs. 39, 40) and the scratched and polished boulders which distinguish glaciated regions.

Compare the steep slope of Box Hill (Fig. 231), which is the chalk escarpment, with the carboniferous limestone escarpment, shown in Fig. 232. Note how the softer chalk has become rounded and grass-covered, whereas the limestone remains bare and craggy. The outcrop of rock at the top is in fact the end of an immense sloping bed of limestone which dips towards the left of the picture. The bed has been cut off in this way by the action of ice and water in the production of the valley on the right. The term "escarpment" is reserved for such precipitous truncations.

The farm in the foreground of Fig. 232 stands on a deposit of boulder-clay, a relic of the last Ice Age. The foot of Box Hill, on the other hand, rests on the alluvium of the River Mole, whose curved course here can be traced by the line of trees. The trees on the top of Box Hill betray the presence of clay-with-flints, a deposit not met with on the carboniferous limestone hills, which are therefore bare.

### The Cycle of Erosion

Just as it is possible to deduce the age of a river from its form (see Fig. 25), so it is possible to detect the stage of development of a tract of land. Fig. 233 illustrates what is known as the "cycle of erosion." The top diagram represents a recently elevated region (for we are obliged to break into the cycle somewhere), and erosion is seen to have begun by the presence of a few swift (and therefore straight) rivers.

In the second diagram the rivers have cut deep gorges, carving up the plateau into a series of mountain ranges, and at the same time weathering has lowered the average height of the mountain-tops. The third stage shows a general planation of the land-surface, and in the last diagram the whole district is shown reduced to a comparatively low, practically level "pene-plain," the mountains having become mere stumps of their former selves, with flat, level tops.

Sooner or later there will be a renewed uplift of the land (for the crust of the earth is never entirely quiescent), and this will result in the restoration of the conditions shown in the top diagram, with the re-juvenation of the rivers (see page 29) and the rest of the story repeated over again, for the cycle of erosion is a continuous performance.

A peneplain is to be distinguished from a river plain by the fact that it is a worn-

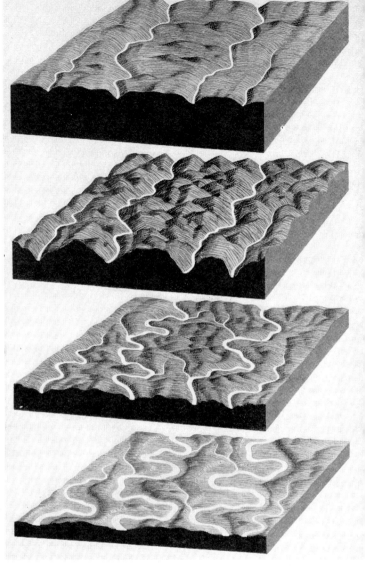

FIG. 233. *The "Cycle of Erosion." Note how the surface of the land passes from a comparatively level state at high altitude (plateau: top) to a similar state at low altitude (peneplain: bottom), through the transitional stages of high mountains and deep valleys, and the widening and levelling of river plains.*

down highland, levelled-off like the flat top of Box Hill (Fig. 231), which represents the post-Pliocene peneplain of southern England. The clay-with-flints which supports the vegetation on the top is actually the insoluble residue of the original highland—relics left behind as the mountains were weathered down to form the peneplain. The clay-with-flints in Fig. 230 is part of the same deposit, on the same peneplain, about ten miles to the west.

These are examples of the sort of study which can be made of any district with the aid of suitable maps. Two examples may be given of geographical phenomena which are interesting in so far as they *differ* from the maps, which may have been printed quite recently.

### The Restless Earth

It is an important fact of geography that the surface features of the earth are always changing, though the changes are usually very slow. But it sometimes happens that large-scale alterations to the landscape are accomplished by nature in a comparatively short time, and then it is of great interest to compare the existing features of a given area with those shown on a recent (if possible, dated) map.

For instance, Fig. 234 shows the Culbin sand-hills, in Morayshire, Scotland, the forms of which are constantly changing. On the left are the tufts of marram grass often planted in such districts because their roots help to bind the sand and prevent its shifting. On the right is the wall of the advancing sand, blown by the prevailing wind. The battle is between grass and wind, and shows on a small scale the cause of many vast migrations of man and beast in the desert regions of Asia and Africa. Whole civilizations have been overwhelmed by sand in just such a manner as this.

Fig. 234. *The Culbin sand-hills, Morayshire, showing the advance of the sand over the marram grass under the influence of the prevailing (westerly) wind.*

Again, the sea is encroaching on the land with such rapidity on some coasts that maps may become out of date within a few years. This is true in East Anglia, and Fig. 235 shows the inroads made by the sea near Lowestoft during the exceptionally high tide of November 30th, 1936. Since then the sea has advanced still further upon the land, and the features shown in the photograph are no more. It is both interesting and instructive to mark on a large-scale map the exact positions of such coast-lines in successive years, and to note particularly the effects of severe storms.

If you possess a camera, it is good practice to make photographic records of all remarkable events, such as any exceptional flood damage, the fall of a great cliff, or the effects of a gale on vegetation. Photographs should also be taken of instructive examples of rock formations (folds, faults, etc.), the erosive action of streams, the growth of alluvial flats, and the shift of river meanders.

### Useful Exercises

Every opportunity should be taken of working at practical exercises of the following types:

Classify the hills in any locality known to you under the headings: (a) escarpments, (b) plateaux, (c) peaks. In each case search for reasons why the hill has its particular shape.

Choose some coastal district and work out, with the aid of maps, the relationships between: (a) the relief of the land and the form of the coast, (b) human activities and the effects of erosion or deposition, (c) the coastal forms and human settlements.

Select some rural area which shows a variety of relief, and try to work out the relationship between: (a) the hills and the outcrops of hard rock, (b) elevation of the land and types of farming, (c) village sites and water-supply (try to find a "spring line").

Select an industrial area and an agricultural area in fairly close proximity to each other, and work out geographical reasons for the difference between the two.

Such exercises are best undertaken "on the spot," and for most people will come under the heading of "holiday geography."

### Weather Work

The reader who desires to become his own weather prophet should, first of all, obtain with absolute regularity the official weather-maps issued daily by the Meteorological Office in Britain, and by the corresponding authority in other countries.

The interpretation of weather-maps, and the use of the international symbols (Fig. 64) and the "station model" (Fig. 63) have been explained in Chapter III, and here we may add a practical example in the form of an actual map showing the advance of a depression over Ireland. Fig. 236 shows the form in which the daily weather information is conveyed, and the reader will at once recognize the "secateurs" formed by the cold and warm fronts (*cf.* Fig. 59).

On studying this map, the reader will note that the cold front has just passed Malin Head, because (1) the clouds in that neighbourhood are towering cumulus [◮], (2) showers [▽̇] are falling, (3) the temperature stands at 44 degrees and it is rising (it stands at 41 degrees on the eastward side of the front), and (4) visibility is good. The same is true of Castle Archdale. It has clearly passed Blacksod Point, where it is fine and the barometer has risen (+ 20) in the last hour. It has just passed Foynes, where the wind is west, the air dry, and the barometer already risen (+ 06), and is passing Valentia, where it is still raining steadily and the wind is south-west.

That the whole system is travelling due east can be ascertained only by reference to the maps for the preceding days, but once the past history of a depression (or other system) is known, it is not beyond the ability of any serious student to forecast the future weather for forty-eight hours at any place included in his maps.

Anyone sufficiently interested in meteorology to invest in a standard rain-gauge, a barometer, thermometer and hygrometer may do really useful observational work, especially if he is situated in a district remote from large towns. The type of observation best suited to his position, and the way in which his results may be made known, may be ascertained by writing to the Meteorological Office, or by joining the Royal Meteorological Society which includes many amateur meteorologists among its members. The small monthly magazine, *Weather*, published by this Society will be found to be useful.

### Books to Read

The subjects dealt with hitherto in this Guide are mainly physical ones, and the student anxious to learn more of the principles of physical geography might read with profit any of the following books: *Britain's Structure and Scenery*, by L. Dudley Stamp; *Geology and Scenery in England and Wales*, by A. E. Trueman; *The Physical Basis of Geography*, by Wooldridge and Morgan; *Principles of*

FIG. 235. *Coast erosion near Lowestoft in 1936. Note how the sea, during a single exceptionally high tide, has undermined the houses on the top of the low cliff, which is of a soft and friable sandstone. The houses have disappeared since this photograph was taken.*

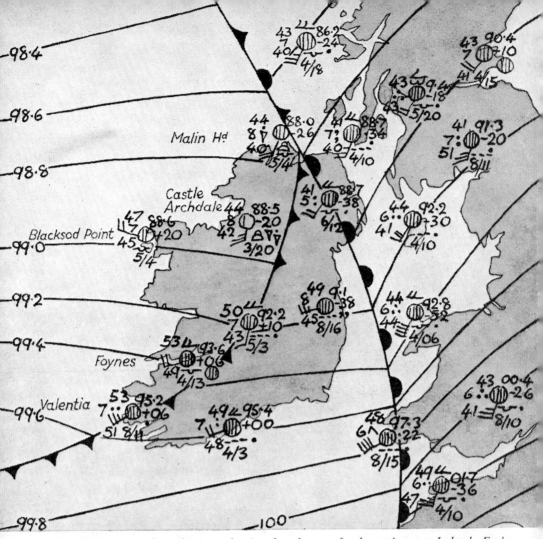

FIG. 236. *A typical weather-map showing the advance of a depression over Ireland. Each of the small circles represents a meteorological station, and the figures and signs surrounding it correspond to the plan of the "station model" illustrated in Fig. 63. (See text)*

*Physical Geography*, by F. J. Monkhouse; *Elements of Geography, Physical and Cultural*, by Finch, Trewartha, Robinson and Hammond; *Understanding Weather*, by Sutton; *Everyday Meteorology*, by Miller and Parry.

### World Geography

We now turn to the wider aspects of human geography, and the study of man and his world on a scale beyond the scope of personal inspection and experiment. For this purpose we need maps of a different kind from those whose purpose it is to portray local details. The maps we now require show vast areas of territory and are therefore on very much smaller scales than those of the British Ordnance Survey. They are the maps we find in any common atlas.

A good atlas is essential to a general study of geography (this cannot be too often repeated), and the reader would do well to provide himself with one which, in addition to the usual physical and political maps, contains special maps showing the climate and vegetation, and, if possible, the products of the various countries.

A feature common to most atlases which may at first sight seem curious is the varying shapes of the maps. There are, possibly, two circular maps showing the eastern and western hemispheres of the world, respectively, several oval maps each containing the whole world, many rectangular ones of the separate continents and countries, and a few of very odd shapes indeed—reminiscent, perhaps, of a badly cut-up orange-peel with one or two stray sections hanging on at the edges. Why this variety?

The answer, of course, is that the earth is a sphere and it is quite impossible to represent accurately any substantial portion of its surface on a flat sheet of paper. If you try to flatten a piece of orange-peel it either stretches or splits, and if you try to draw a map of the world on a flat surface, you have either to distort the shapes of the continents and oceans, or cut them up into odd shapes which cannot be made to fit closely together.

### Varieties of Maps

Various methods of representing—or "projecting"—the round world on flat paper have been worked out mathematically, and different projections have been found useful for different purposes.

Some distort the shapes of countries while maintaining their relative areas; others reduce the distortion to a minimum but, perforce, grossly misrepresent their sizes; others again pay little attention to either shape or area provided only that the compass directions from place to place are preserved as straight lines (as in Mercator's projection—see Fig. 237). These last are particularly useful to pilots and navigators, while equal-area maps are essential to students of political geography and population problems.

It is often necessary to know the shortest route between two places widely separated on the globe, and it is easily proved that this route always lies on a circle whose centre is the centre of the earth. Thus, the shortest distance between London and Vancouver is not a straight line connecting them on the normal map, nor is it the distance along the parallel which passes through the two cities. It is the arc of a circle which runs north-westward from London (Fig. 237) to Iceland, then westward over Greenland and south-westward across Canada to Vancouver.

### Maps for an Air Age

A simple photograph of a globe gives a form of zenithal projection in which all great circles passing through the centre of the map are shown as straight lines, but the land areas towards the edges are fantastically distorted by foreshortening. This distortion can be modified by imagining the camera placed at various distances from the surface of the globe, and even, in one projection, on the centre of the surface of one hemisphere in order to photograph the other hemisphere through the globe itself. The circular maps of the hemispheres given in the early pages of most atlases are on one of these projections.

The chief value of the zenithal projections is that they all show the shortest distance between the centre of the map and any other point on it as a straight line, though not all of them show such lines to scale. Maps of this type have proved of great practical use in the selection of points for the intersection of air and steamship routes, though each such point to be considered requires a separate map of which it is the exact centre. They have demonstrated the importance of polar routes, the proximity of the U.S.A. and the U.S.S.R., the suitability of London as the "air capital" of Europe, of Bathurst in West Africa as the hub of the air routes of the South Atlantic, and of Cairo as the air-focus of the Old World. The position of the air-focus of both hemispheres is shown on a map of this kind in Fig. 80.

If you are studying air routes, therefore, and wish to know which places lie on a straight course from, say, London to Calcutta, you will consult a map on a zenithal projection like those in Fig. 80, and on pp. 290-291 and 300, but centred on London or Calcutta. You can obtain your answer simply by laying a ruler across the map. Such a study may prove of immense interest, for it will show why former great seaports are now

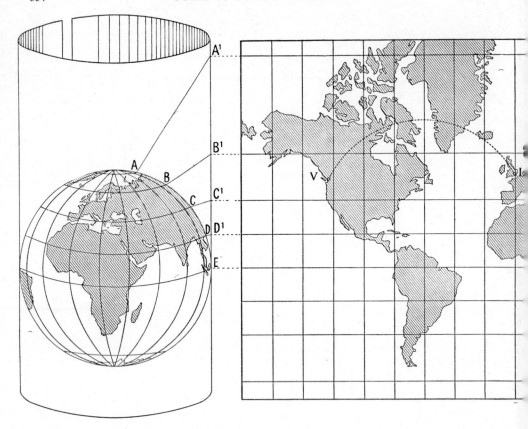

losing some of their importance, and why places which were once insignificant native villages are fast growing into large towns with a Western civilization.

Should your chief interest lie in the political sphere, you may find your best aid in Sanson's, Lambert's, or some other equal-area projection. In such maps you can appreciate at a glance the relative areas of the countries, and may realize for the first time the true comparison between, let us say, U.S.A. (population 182,000,000) and U.S.S.R. (pop. 216,000,000), or between India (pop. 438,000,000) and China (pop. 720,000,000). You would get a quite erroneous impression from comparing these countries on Mercator's projection, or in their separate maps.

From time to time the cry for *Lebensraum* (living space) goes up from some densely populated country or another, and

the atlas will assist you to judge how far the demand is justified, and how the condition of the country in question compares with that of some neighbouring country of similar size which apparently finds no necessity for expansion.

The separate maps of the countries are usually on a conical projection (Fig. 238), which is used for delineating smaller areas of the earth's surface without excessive distortion at any point. Such maps are often reduplicated in the atlas, one map giving the political boundaries and towns, and the other the physical features. The two should be studied together, and are therefore generally printed on opposite pages.

The subjects of study to which appropriate atlas maps should be applied are legion. The distribution of raw materials, for instance, is a barren subject unless the

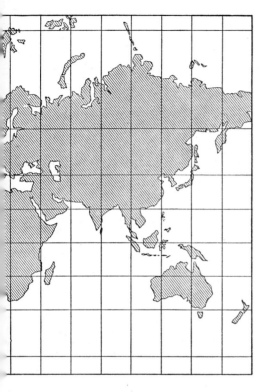

FIG. 237. *Mercator's map is derived from the "cylindrical" projection, which may be simply explained as follows. Imagine a sheet of photographic paper rolled into a cylinder and slipped over the globe, as shown in the diagram on the left. Further, imagine that the globe is transparent and contains a lamp at its centre. The shadows of the continents would appear on the paper, point A at A¹, B at B¹, and so on, and would there print themselves on the sensitive surface. If the paper is now unrolled it will be found to contain the flat map of the world shown in the diagram on the right. One drawback to this type of projection is that the regions round the poles can never be shown, for the cylinder of paper has, of course, open ends. The shadows of the polar regions could be printed on flat sheets of paper laid across the ends of the cylinder, but such maps would be on a different projection. They would be "zenithal" or "polar" maps.*

atlas is employed to show the accessibility of each commodity to the countries which depend upon its supply for their existence or enrichment. The climatic and physical maps, studied in conjunction, reveal the possibilities of home production of essential foodstuffs, and the need for imports, and may explain why it is sometimes found profitable to export materials which are in short supply at home.

Again, the demand of some country for territory belonging to a neighbour on grounds of "security" means little to one who cannot consult an atlas to see where protective mountain ranges or rivers run. In studying such questions the ethnographic map (showing the distribution of races) included in most atlases is an invaluable help, for it often happens that a good natural boundary has been overrun in the past by marauding tribes, so that their

descendants find themselves on the unsafe side of the fence. Are they to retreat into their "natural" territory, or extend their boundaries to the next natural line of defence? The history of the Sudetenland region of Czechoslovakia (studied with the help of an atlas) provides an object-lesson in this sort of problem.

The importance of such places as the Khyber Pass (Fig. 157) and of such outposts of the Commonwealth as Singapore, are clear only on the map, and the reader who has familiarized himself with information gathered from this source is in a far better position to understand why, for example, a country which has boasted some remote possession for centuries may suddenly decide to lease or sell it to a foreign power. It is also possible to discover the truth between the lines of many a puzzling political news item. Does Britain really need Hong Kong? This is an example of a vexed political question which must eventually be solved—on a map.

It might be thought that a model globe of the world is the best possible type of map in which to invest, but while a good globe is a valuable adjunct to an atlas it cannot replace the specialized maps which we have been describing. Even if you could consider a separate globe for each subject of study, you would find it difficult to collate the information on two different globes, and the comparison of measurements on a curved surface is much more difficult than it is on a flat one.

Nevertheless, a small globe (large ones are apt to be very expensive) is extremely instructive in such subjects as physical geography and international time, and should do more than anything else to give the student a view of the world in its proper perspective. If you have a globe to which you have paid but little attention in the past, you will probably be surprised at the answers it will yield to questions such as the following:

1. What country in Europe lies exactly opposite to New Zealand?

2. If you made a flight directly from Cape Horn over the South Pole, what is the first land you would sight after leaving Antarctica?

3. What capital city in Europe is "level" with (i.e. at the same latitude as) New York?

Before leaving the subject of maps we should mention the value of a good gazetteer. Those interested in current political geography often see references in the news to places of which they have never heard, and it is essential to their study to be able to pin-point them on the map. *The Times Atlas of the World*, the index to which contains nearly a quarter of a million names, would be a valuable investment. Many publishers of reference books sell at a moderate price excellent gazetteers as well as atlases. The positions of places are given by reference to their latitude and longitude, and this suffices for pin-pointing them on any map, whether their names are printed or not.

The serious student will find that the best way to check his knowledge and fix it in his memory is to construct simple sketch-maps of any area in which he is particularly interested. In this way he will gradually accumulate an invaluable summary of geographical knowledge to which reference may constantly be made. In this connexion he will benefit from a study of E. G. R. Taylor's *A Sketch Map Geography*, and from the various simplified atlases by J. F. Horrabin.

For statistical material, the *Statesman's*

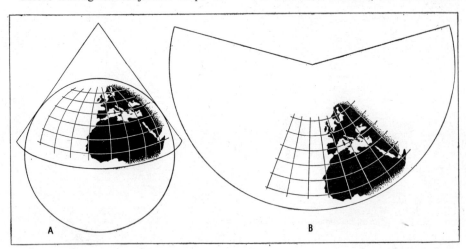

FIG. 238. *The conical projection may be visualized in a similar way to the cylindrical projection described in Fig. 237, except that a cone of flat paper is substituted for the cylinder. The cone is adjusted so that it makes contact with the globe at the parallel of latitude running through the centre of the area to be mapped, as shown on the left. The map which is produced when the cone is unrolled is shown on the right.*

*Year-book* should be consulted, while in *Whitaker's Almanack* will be found a mine of up-to-date information on populations, areas, production statistics, imports, exports, astronomical data, and the like.

Readers interested in the wider aspects of geography will find further guidance in the books mentioned in the following paragraphs. For convenience these paragraphs treat of the subjects included in Section III of this book in their order as chapter-headings (Chapters V to XIV inclusive). There is also a subsidiary bibliography on man in his relation to Nature and his progressive invasion of the land areas of the world, which are the subjects of Chapters XV and XVI.

### Western Europe

The student of geography of western Europe may care to add to his English atlas one or more of the national atlases published officially in many European countries, including France, Finland, Germany, Poland, and Czechoslovakia. These atlases display the physical and human facts of their respective national environments in the form of excellent maps. A more general atlas of this sort, covering the whole of Europe, is the American Geographical Society's Special Publication No. 24, which consists of a series of eighteen maps of *Environment and Conflict in Europe*.

The following books will be found of value in giving a general view of the geography of Europe and the problems springing therefrom: *Europe: a Regional Geography*, by Shackleton; *A Geography of Europe*, by Gottmann; *A Social Geography of Europe*, by Houston.

Fuller accounts of the land forms, climates and economic conditions must be sought in more specialized studies of the different regions of the continent. If he has no predilection for some other country, the reader is advised to begin with a study of France, for France is in many ways a "Europe in miniature," and has contributed so much to the cultural life of the continent. The following short list begins with an excellent book for those who read French: *Tableau de la Géographie de la France*,

by Vidal de la Blache, the introduction to which has been translated by H. C. Brentnall and published in England as *The Personality of France*; *France: a Regional and Economic Geography*, by H. Ormsby; *France, the New Republic*, by R. Aron; *Germany: a General and Regional Geography*, by R. E. Dickinson; *A Regional Geography of Western Europe*, by F. J. Monkhouse; *Food, Land and Manpower in Western Europe*, by P. L. Yates.

### Soviet Lands

One of the great difficulties in studying modern Russia is to obtain good maps and up-to-date information. However, the physical map of Russia remains true, and a study should be made of the structure of the whole of the U.S.S.R. Special attention should be paid to river-drainage, the distribution of highlands and lowlands, and the vegetation zones, with constant reference to the climatic maps. In this way the reader will obtain the necessary basis for the study of Russian civilization.

It should be remembered that the Asiatic parts of Russia are becoming more and more important. The difficult place-names in Siberia and other parts of Inner Asia, and more particularly the new cities which are growing up, should be marked on an outline sketch-map. Keep in mind the scale of distances which is involved, and if possible, study the relations between Russia and neighbouring countries on a map showing the North Pole at the centre. The following books will be found useful and instructive:

*The U.S.S.R.: a Geographical Survey*, by J. S. Gregory and D. W. Shave; *The Basis of Soviet Strength*, by G. B. Cressey; *Soviet Russia; the Land and the People*, by N. Mikhailov; *Physical Geography of Asiatic Russia*, by S. P. Suslov; *Russia and China*, by J. V. Davidson-Houston; *Russia in Flux*, by J. Maynard; *Soviet Communism*, by S. and B. Webb; *Recent Soviet Trends*, edited by G. W. Hoffman.

### The Mediterranean Lands

The same general principles of study which have been suggested for western Europe and the Soviet Lands should be applied to the contiguous region of the Mediterranean countries. In addition to all available guide books, the recommended books for study are:

*The Mediterranean Lands and Southern Europe,* by M. I. Newbigin; *A Geography of Italy,* by D. S. Walker; *Spain: a Geographical Background,* by W. B. Fisher and H. Bowen-Jones; *The Land and People of Greece,* by F. Noel-Baker; *Europa Minor,* by Lord Kinross; *L'Algérie,* by J. Blottière (in French); *Yugoslavia,* edited by R. F. Byrnes.

### English-speaking America

More has been written about North America in the past twenty years than about any other continent, and it is therefore difficult to make a selection of books for study. Many excellent works must be omitted from the list, and the reader who wishes to pursue his studies beyond the books included here is advised to consult his local library for additional reading.

*North America,* by L. R. Jones and R. W. Bryan; *North America,* by J. Russell Smith and M. O. Phillips; *Frontier America: the Story of the Westward Movement,* by T. D. Clark; *Anglo-America: A Regional Geography,* by Earl B. Shaw; *Canada: Tomorrow's Giant,* by B. Hutchinson; *Canadian Regions,* edited by D. F. Putnam; *Inside U.S.A.,* by John Gunther.

### Latin America

Relatively few books on Central and South America used to be available to the student, but in recent years many more have been written, especially by American authors. These include some excellent studies of individual countries in Latin America. Articles on Latin America appear frequently in the American *National Geographic Magazine,* and these are always illustrated by good photographs. The following books are recommended: *Latin America,* by G. J. Butland; *Latin America,* by Preston James; *South America,* by E. W. Shanahan; *Economic Geography of South America,* by R. H. Whitbeck; *Inside Latin America,* by John Gunther; *The Twelve Republics,* by M. Follick; *Argentina and Uruguay,* by G. Pendle; *Town and*

*Country in Brazil,* by M. Harris; *Chile,* by G. J. Butland; *The New Eldorado: Venezuela,* by E. Ward; *Bolivia: A Land Divided,* by H. Osborne.

### Africa

Begin the study of Africa by consulting a good physical map, and if possible a map showing the vegetation regions. These should be compared with an up-to-date political map, and will give the reader a truer and better balanced impression of the characteristic features of the "Dark Continent" than any textbook. It is an excellent practice to prepare your own sketch maps showing the distribution of the population, of rainfall and vegetation, and of coal, iron and other minerals.

If you succeed in tracing the connexion between the distribution of the population and the physical features and natural wealth of the continent, you will have made an excellent start. You may follow this up by tracing the connexions which Africa and the African peoples have with other continents, particularly the links between Africa and Europe both now and in the past. The following books will be found both useful and interesting:

*Africa,* by W. Fitzgerald; *Report on Africa,* by O. Meeker; *Races of Africa,* by C. G. Seligman; *African Economic Development,* by W. A. Hance; *Southern Africa,* by J. H. Wellington; *West Africa,* by R. J. Harrison Church; *A Survey of North West Africa (The Magrib),* edited by Nevill Barbour; *Land and People in Nigeria,* by K. H. Buchanan and J. C. Pugh; *A Geography of Ghana,* by E. A. Boateng; *Handbook of Tanganyika,* edited by J. P. Moffett.

### Monsoon Lands

A similar line of study to that indicated for Africa will be found most profitable for the Monsoon Lands. This should be accompanied by a study of the history of the great Eastern civilizations, which will necessitate a good deal of wisely chosen reading. The following books are recommended:

*Asia,* by L. Dudley Stamp; *The Pattern of Asia,* edited by N. Ginsburg; *The*

*Changing Map of Asia*, edited by W. G. East and O. H. K. Spate; *South-east Asia*, by E. H. G. Dobby; *The Far East: A Social Geography*, by A. D. C. Peterson; *China's Changing Map*, by Th. Shabad; *Land of the 500 Million*, by G. B. Cressey; *India and Pakistan: a General Regional Geography*, by O. H. K. Spate; *The Cambridge Shorter History of India*, edited by H. H. Dodwell; *The Story of Indonesia*, by L. Fischer; *Malaya*, edited by N. Ginsburg and C. F. Roberts; *Return to Japan*, by E. G. Vining.

### Australia, New Zealand and the Pacific Islands

The student of Australian geography should first acquaint himself very thoroughly with the physical geography of the continent, noting the wide diversity of climates and the natural factors tending to isolate large portions of the habitable land. He should then read a short history of the discovery and settlement of Australia, and obtain the official *Year Books* for the Commonwealth and separate States. A similar course should be followed for New Zealand. The following works are, if possible, to be added to his reading:

*Australia: a Study of Warm Environments and their Effect on British Settlement*, by T. Griffith Taylor; *Australia, New Zealand and the Southwest Pacific*, by K. W. Robinson; *The Australian Way of Life*, edited by G. Caiger; *This New Zealand*, by F. L. W. Wood; *Portrait of New Zealand*, by D. O. W. Hall; *The Maori*, by E. Best; *Social Change in the South Pacific*, by E. Beaglehole; *Britain and the South Seas*, by Sir H. Luke; *The Pacific Islands Year Book*, edited by R. W. Robson; *The Pacific Basin: a Human and Economic Geography*, by G. L. Wood.

### Polar Regions

Our main sources of information on the Polar Regions are still the records of explorers. During the twentieth century there have been many expeditions to the Arctic and the Antarctic, and each one has added to our knowledge of the regions—particularly the scientifically planned and well equipped expeditions of recent times. Interest in the Arctic has been stimulated by the establishment of intercontinental air routes over the area, and it is now common-place for airline passengers to cross the North Pole and the Greenland ice-cap on journeys between Europe and North America. Of the many books written by members of Polar expeditions and others, the following are suggested: *The Crossing of Antarctica*, by Sir V. E. Fuchs and Sir E. Hillary; *Antarctica: the Story of a Continent*, by F. Debenham; *Antarctica Today and Tomorrow*, by G. C. L. Bertram; *90° South: the Story of the American South Pole Conquest*, by P. Siple; *The Arctic Year*, by P. Freuchen and F. Salomensen; *The Friendly Arctic*, by V. Stefansson.

### Peopling the Earth

The reader interested in the subject-matter of Chapters XV and XVI is recommended to supplement his reading of the following books by systematic visits to the national museums such as the British Museum, with its unique collection of Romano-British, prehistoric and Oriental antiquities and ethnography, and local museums having sections on these subjects.

*Primitive Civilizations*, by Simcox; *The Corridors of Time*, by Peake and Fleure; *The Races of Mankind*, by H. J. Fleure; *We Europeans*, by Huxley, Haddon and Carr-Sanders; *The Dawn of European Civilization*, by V. Gordon Childe; *Man's Influence on the Earth*, by R. L. Sherlock; *Geographical Background of Modern Problems*, by H. J. Fleure, published by the Workers' Educational Association, is an excellent jumping-off ground for the beginner.

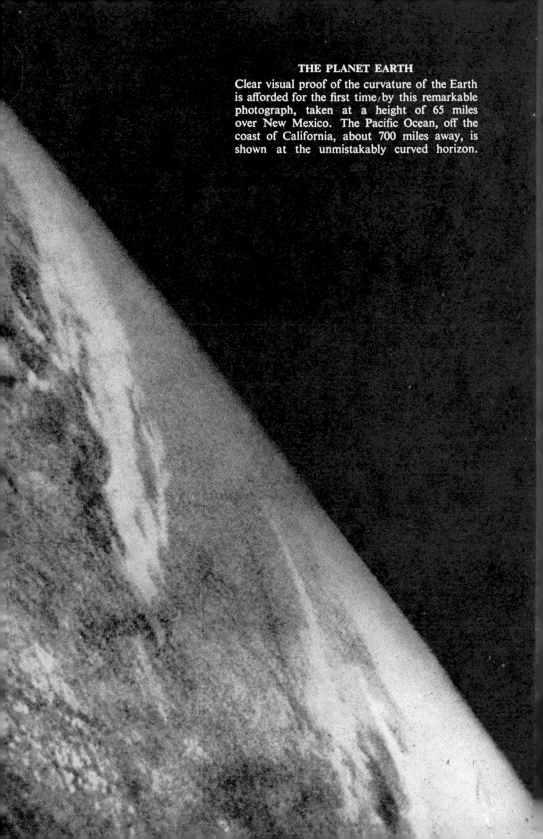

**THE PLANET EARTH**
Clear visual proof of the curvature of the Earth is afforded for the first time by this remarkable photograph, taken at a height of 65 miles over New Mexico. The Pacific Ocean, off the coast of California, about 700 miles away, is shown at the unmistakably curved horizon.

# ANSWERS TO "TEST YOURSELF"

GENERALLY speaking, answers to each set of "Test Yourself" questions will be found embodied in the particular chapter to which the questions refer, and can be deduced without much difficulty by careful reading of the text. The answers given here are, for the most part, capable of more extended treatment, and it is hoped that the interested reader will be stimulated to discover how far, from his own independent reading, he may be able to deal more exhaustively with the questions. The books recommended for further study on pp. 351-359 will furnish much material for this valuable exercise.

## CHAPTER I

1. (a) As the outlet to the Baltic is so narrow, tidal variations in this sea are negligible and the use of ports does not depend upon the periodical rise and fall of the level of the water. Thus a ship's captain could dock at Gdynia at any time. He would also be able to moor his vessel, secure in the knowledge that no matter how long he might remain there, the relative positions of ship and quay would be unchanged. At Liverpool, however, the difference between high and low tide may amount to as much as twenty-nine feet. (Page 12.)

(b) Electrical power can be generated from the tides and it is convenient to tap this source of energy in places where natural formations have already concentrated the power into a small area, for example, in wedge-shaped estuaries. Here the advancing tidal waters converge and their ebb and flow rate is greatly increased between narrowing banks. The Severn estuary is eminently suitable for such a project, and plans for a great hydro-electric station have already been drawn up in detail. The importance of this scheme may be judged from the fact that the electricity generated each year would equal the amount obtained by the combustion of a million tons of coal. (Page 12.) Wind power has also been used to generate electricity, notably in the U.S.S.R. Theorists have also suggested deriving power from absorption of solar radiation in hot countries with little cloud.

2. (a) All around the shores of the Atlantic Ocean we find waterways and easily navigable rivers which drain into this great basin and provide routes into the far interiors of the surrounding land masses. Thus, easy access to the sea over broad fertile plains has encouraged men, since the application of the mariner's compass, to explore, to trade and to build cities, gathering the products of the plains, adventuring ever farther and more daringly over the waters, and establishing new communities along the newly discovered waterways and their hinterlands. (Page 16.)

(b) Mountains affect humanity in two ways. Their direct influence is mainly unfavourable as their characteristic steep slopes and harsh climatic conditions are unsuited to agricultural pursuits, and rugged heights interfere with communications, thus hindering the establishment of central government and the spread of culture. Indirectly, however, mountains are often responsible for the economic wealth of lowland regions. Rock waste provides alluvium, from which the fertile plain may be built, while heavy rain and melting snow feed the rivers which are so essential to human welfare, and provide a stimulus to industry in the form of water-power. Humanity has also benefited when hardy mountain communities have been able to maintain independence on a democratic basis, as in Switzerland. (Page 18.)

## CHAPTER II

1. It is in the vicinity of rivers in the stages of "maturity" and "old age" that increasing populations are to be found. Such rivers, meandering through rich alluvial plains of their own making, are slow-flowing and often navigable, thus providing easy and cheap means of communication by both land and water. (Page 28.) Irrigation is made easy and the fertility of the land is maintained by periodic flooding. (Pages 32, 33.) It is also true,

however, that towns may spring up round the lakes which provide navigable inland waterways in the courses of young rivers. In modern times an advanced society may develop the latent power of parts of rivers in a "youthful" stage in order to provide power for machinery. (Pages 29, 33.)

2. The rapid development of the area round the southern Pennines at the beginning of the Industrial Revolution provides an example of the utilization of rivers in their "youthful" stage. The development was due to the need for cheap and abundant source of power to drive the machinery installed in the new textile factories. This power was provided by the "young" rivers which flowed rapidly through the deep mountain valleys of the district. (Page 33.) The discovery of coal and of iron ore in neighbouring regions later led to increasing concentration of industrial effort as markets for the products expanded both regionally and overseas.

3. One of the greatest examples of a submerged lowland is the sea separating Britain from the continent of Europe and from Ireland. Ports such as Dublin and Belfast in Ireland, Glasgow, Liverpool, Swansea, Cardiff, Newport, Bristol, Plymouth, Southampton, London, Hull, Aberdeen, Havre, Antwerp, Rotterdam, Amsterdam, Bremen, Hamburg, etc. also owe something to inland communications and some of them are helped by being on submerged valleys, by the proximity of coal, etc. The entrance to the River Plate in South America has Buenos Aires, Montevideo, etc.

## CHAPTER III

1. The Trade Winds and the Doldrums (page 63) ceased to be important when mechanical power replaced the sail as a means of propelling ships. Until this change had been effected, seamen welcomed the regular and predictable Trade Winds and learned to fear the Doldrums in which a vessel might be becalmed for weeks at a time.

2. (a) There is no real difference between fog and cloud except that of altitude.

When temperature drops below a certain point water-vapour in the air condenses, and mist or fog occurs at low levels. When this condensation takes place well above the earth's surface we call this mist "cloud," Near to large towns fogs contain a large proportion of smoke particles and dust in addition to water-vapour. (Pages 56, 57.)

(b) Hot, dry weather, with poor visibility owing to haze (page 56). Air calm. Temperature falling several degrees at night owing to rapid radiation in absence of clouds. (Pages 72, 73.) A continuance of a warm anticyclone in Britain in July often leads on to a thunderstorm.

3. In the northern summer ascend the *north*-eastern face of the hill in the morning and descend the *north*-western slope in the evening. In the northern winter ascend the *south*-eastern slope and descend the *south*-western slope. At the equinoxes ascend due east and descend due west. (Page 8.) In the Northern Hemisphere the north-facing hillsides receive the least sunshine and in winter may be in shadow throughout the day. (Page 51.) (Interchange the words "north" and "south" in the above application to the Southern Hemisphere.) In intertropical regions you would ascend the eastern slope and descend the western slope at all seasons. (Page 8.)

## CHAPTER IV

1. (a) The two major factors which determine climatic variations are (1) the main pressure and wind belts which owe their characteristics primarily to the angles of incidence of the sun's rays, and (2) the distribution of land and sea. (Page 75.)

(b) Vegetation is classified as (1) forest, in which trees predominate, and (2) grassland, in which herbaceous plants predominate. Forest degenerates into (3) scrubland, while grassland dwindles through poor steppe into (4) desert. (Page 80.)

2. Representative cities in the Cool Temperate belt are: Dunedin, New Zealand; Paris, France; Vancouver, Canada; Copenhagen, Denmark; and New York, U.S.A.

3. Barriers to animal migration are, chiefly, the deeper channels in the sea, and deserts, and to a lesser extent, forests and mountains. (Pages 78, 80, 81.)

## CHAPTER V

1. (a) The keynote of the physical geography of Western Europe is "diversity." Many changes of climate and vast crustal movements in geological and even in early human times have provided many different types of rock, including boulder-clay, loess deposits, limestones, coal measures and crystalline rocks. (Pages 100, 104, 107.) The deeply indented coastline, due to subsidence or rise of sea-level, is offset by the elevation of high fold-mountains in the Alpine system, while the persistence of ancient plateaux in Scandinavia, the centre of France, Bohemia, and elsewhere, contrasts strongly with the great marshy plains of Finland and the Dnieper basin. (Pages 98, 99.) In the north, the western mountains of the Scandinavian peninsula give way to the gentle slopes and lake-studded plains of eastern Sweden and Finland. (Pages 103, 104.) To the south of these the Great Lowland Plain, occupying a central position, narrows from east to west, and still farther south tower the rocky heights of the Pyrenees, Alps, Carpathians, and Balkan mountains. (Pages 97, 98, 99; Fig. 81.)

(b) The fertile loess lands, and the coal deposits beneath them, running along the hill margins from north-eastern France to Silesia, have been among the more powerful factors in the development of civilization in Western Europe. The presence of large quantities of coal and iron in the centre of the continent has been responsible for the growth of Europe's greatest concentration of industrial towns. The complex tangle of hills and valleys between Rhine and Elbe long encouraged maintenance of small semi-independent units and delayed achievement of broader unification until the advent of the railway.

2. Until the Industrial Revolution, Britain was an agricultural country with London situated in a nodal position on the rich south-eastern lowland. All traffic routes through gaps in the chalk escarpments led to London, and, because, the south-eastern corner of Britain approaches most closely to Europe, influences from the continent reached the rest of England only after they had passed through the capital. (Page 105.)

3. The Industrial Revolution produced much greater changes in England than was the case in Germany. As the change-over from agriculture to industry came far earlier in England, transport was not in an advanced stage and populations had to move towards the raw materials to a much greater extent than was necessary in Germany, where the railway network was already well developed. Whereas in England people were wrenched from one way of life into another, the Germans retained more control over the new mechanical forces and succeeded in grafting new industries on to the existing agricultural framework. By taking risks, Britain obtained a useful initial lead in the rush for markets, but the ultimate results in Germany and Britain were the same, and the danger of neglecting agriculture while relying on exported manufactured goods to support large populations has, by this time, been well brought home to the peoples of both countries. (Pages 114, 118, 119.)

## CHAPTER VI

1. (a) Russian colonists moving eastwards have kept to the route followed (later) by the Trans-Siberian Railway because here, between the southern edge of the taiga or pine forest and the semi-desert plateau of central Asia, lies a relatively narrow corridor of good land, suitable for grazing, with hunting in the adjacent forest, and later for agriculture. (Pages 123, 124, 138.)

(b) In their efforts to develop the great wealth of the eastern areas of the U.S.S.R., the Russians are hampered by a lack of population to fill the huge areas affected. Men are needed, to work not only in the new mines and factories, but also in the fields where food for the workers must be produced, since the Russian aim is to establish new communities which will be as nearly as possible self-sustaining. Poor transport facilities are another limiting factor in the rapid growth of the eastern industrial regions. (Pages 132, 135, 136.)

2. The Ukraine, home of the Little Russians, is united as a political entity by strong ties of nationalism, and owes its economic importance to the extensive "Black Earth" wheat lands of the south-west largely colonized in the last 150 years and to the rich coal deposits of the Donetz basin. (Pages 123, 130.)

3. Air transport is obviously of enormous importance to a country which has an area of nearly nine million square miles and which stretches from the Carpathians and the Baltic Sea to the Pacific Ocean; and from the Arctic Ocean to the Pamirs and the Mongolian plains. Facilities for road and rail transport in many parts of the U.S.S.R. are very primitive (especially in the east), and in any case, the relative speed of aircraft over very long distances is much greater than that of the railway train or the road vehicle. (Pages 126, 127.)

## CHAPTER VII

1. The predominant soils of the Mediterranean lands are those formed from (1) limestone and (2) the material thrown out by volcanoes.

Unless mixed with other materials, limestone forms a poor, infertile soil. Moreover, the underlying limestone rock is soluble in rainwater and is riddled with gullies and subterranean channels which drain away the surface water, leaving the barren surface typified in the Karst district north-east of the Adriatic. Where lime is less dominant and there is more moisture, evaporation in summer draws up dissolved lime and iron salts to the surface which is often reddish. The Mediterranean lands have been described as a region of red soils. They must be scratched frequently to keep the surface from forming a crust.

The materials ejected by volcanoes form very fertile soil, and areas possessing such a covering have encouraged the settlement of man. Occasionally this has led to disaster when a violent eruption from a nearby

volcano has overwhelmed the settlers and their cities. Thus, for example, the existence and destruction of Pompeii may be attributed to the fertility of volcanic soil derived from Vesuvius. (Pages 147, 148.)

2. (a) The basic characteristics of the "mediterranean" type of climate are hot, dry summers and mild, wet winters. (Page 148.)

(b) Regions in other parts of the world which also enjoy a "mediterranean" type of climate are to be found between latitudes 30 degrees to 40 degrees N. and S. on the western margins of continents. They include coastal strips in Western Australia, the Cape of Good Hope and central Chile and California. (Page 89.)

3. The main natural gateways of the Mediterranean are, from the west, the Strait of Gibraltar and the Strait of Messina; to the east, the route through the Dardanelles, Sea of Marmara and the Bosporus, and the Suez Canal; to the north, the Rhône valley, various routes through the Alps for rail and road traffic, and the route from Salonika which traverses the valleys of the Morava and Vardar rivers, and crosses the Danube at Belgrade. (Page 152.)

## CHAPTER VIII

1. The three main climatic regions of the United States of America are: (a) the Pacific belt which includes the west-coast regions with mild rainy winters and warm dry summers; (b) the dry lands east and south-east of the great western mountains; they include desert in the south; and (c) the humid eastern belt where extremes of climate are found. These divisions are subject to variation within themselves. In the south, conditions are sub-tropical, but the northern parts of each division are subject to lower temperatures. These temperature ranges have a considerable effect upon agriculture in the humid eastern belt. In the south, cotton is grown. North of the cotton area are the great corn lands, and, still farther north, dairy farming is typical. The dry area east and south-east of the western mountains is mainly a cattle-raising country, although in some places irrigation has been undertaken, with

the result that wheat, sugar-beet, fruit and vegetables are grown with considerable success. In the Pacific belt, where rain is plentiful in the winter and summers are hot, fruit, vegetables and wheat are the main crops, sub-tropical varieties being grown in Southern California. (Pages 162, 175, 178, 186.)

2. Starting on the extreme west, the border between Canada and U.S.A. begins at the Strait of Juan de Fuca, which separates Vancouver Is. (Canada) from the mainland. The benefits of this sea-way are thus shared, and the border then runs east along the 49th parallel of latitude, and so crosses the Rocky Mountains and Great Plains which have no natural boundary to offer. At the Great Lakes the border follows the central line of the St. Lawrence basin, thus sharing the benefits of water-transport on the lakes, and dividing equally the valuable Niagara Falls. Before reaching Montreal the border leaves the river, so that the land on both sides of the St. Lawrence estuary remains in Canada, and reaches the Atlantic coast at the Bay of Fundy. (Page 164.)

Rich deposits of iron ore are found around the southern tip of Lake Superior, and these, in conjunction with the Allegheny coalfields of Pennsylvania and W. Virginia, have been the mainspring of America's steel industry. This industry, in its turn, supports the immense framework of secondary industries upon which much of the country's wealth has been built. Had the U.S.-Canadian boundary been drawn, for instance, along the forty-fifth parallel of latitude instead of the forty-ninth, this rich store would have greatly increased Canada's assets, while the development of the United States and her importance as a world power would have suffered proportionately. (Pages 180, 181.)

3. Before Europeans landed on the North American continent the soil was protected by forest or grasses, but early development by pioneer groups was characterized by the ruthless clearing of forest, and was followed by the over-cropping of arable land and the over-grazing of pasture especially during the

phase of high prices due to war needs during the First World War. This destruction of natural protection allowed torrential rains and high winds to erode the soil, and natural equilibrium was lost. The process has reached alarming proportions over large areas, and it has been calculated that half the land area has been seriously damaged. The United States government has set up a Soil Conservation Service to give central direction to intermediate and federal planning authorities. Technical measures include the blocking of gullies, tree-planting, grass-sowing, soil fertilization and the practice of contour ploughing which encourages water to percolate instead of running down slopes with resultant erosive action. (Pages 187, 188, 189.)

## CHAPTER IX

1. The great agricultural resources of Latin America have been developed at a slow rate for a number of reasons. These include a shortage of labour, vast areas of untamable jungle, insufficient transport facilities and, in the past, a lack of foreign markets. (Pages 192, 197.) The large indigenous element in the population has brought about other delaying influences.

2. The comparatively low density of the population of South America is due, mainly, to the very large areas of forest and swamp with their characteristic hot, wet climate. Communications, too, are poor, a factor which invariably tends to retard economic development and growth of population. (Page 204.)

3. The Argentine is of vital importance to Western Europe because this South American republic has become one of the most important food-producing countries in the world, her principal exports being meat, wheat, maize, linseed and cotton. The war-ravaged peoples of Western Europe need these staple products and they also require markets for the goods produced by their great manufacturing industries. The Argentine can absorb large quantities of manufactured goods, as her own industries are mainly basic, and for various reasons (chiefly lack of fuel), home

manufacture has hitherto not been practicable. (Page 205.)

## CHAPTER X

1. Communal occupation of land and preservation of traditional customs are the two most important cohesives in an agricultural society. Among most African peoples the occupation of land by a tribe or family is a matter of tradition, subject only to the right of allocation year by year by the local chief. European notions of property, especially land ownership, are completely foreign to these peoples and their introduction to Africa by European settlers often did harm by undermining the chief basis of tribal society. The appropriation and buying-up of land in African communities had led inevitably to proletarianism and to the disintegration of tribal life and culture. This process has been accelerated, too, by the imitation of many of the worst of European practices and the adoption of ideas alien to the traditions of the native races. (Page 220.)

2. Apart from conditions of climate and soil, successful commercial agriculture in any part of Africa depends upon the availability of labour and the existence of transport facilities. The cotton industry of Uganda has flourished because, prior to development, the country had a higher density of population than was usual in a region of this type, and also because rail transport to the sea was made available at an early stage. Other examples of healthy commercial agriculture in areas fulfilling the above conditions are to be found in Ghana (cocoa) and in Senegal (groundnuts). (Pages 225, 226.) On the other hand the widespread absence of manure, the insect-borne diseases affecting cattle, the lack of draught animals and the use of large areas and much labour in low-grade subsistence agriculture on poor intertropical soils that need long periods of rest have all limited the development of commercial agriculture.

3. The British attitude towards colonial peoples in Africa had traditionally been one of paternalism. They accepted the mutual dependence of black and white sections of the African communities and at the same time encouraged the native peoples to maintain and develop their own types of culture and social organization. Much of this well-intentioned attitude was vitiated, however, by the encroachment of European ideas, especially those affecting land-tenure referred to above.

As a colonial power, France, on the other hand, tended to assimilate her African peoples, drawing them ever more closely within the influence of French culture and French metropolitan citizenship. In this way her colonial peoples acquired a much greater measure of social and economic equality in the French system, although at the cost of much that was regarded by others as worth preserving in the native cultures. (Pages 224, 225.)

## CHAPTER XI

1. (a) Nomads driven from the inhospitable areas of interior Asia during phases of drought or of over-population were induced to remain in Indo-Pakistan and China by the fertility of the great river basins where they might dominate a population of cultivators. (Page 229.)

(b) Great mountain barriers obliged the Asiatic nomads to follow definite routes. The way into Indo-Pakistan is guarded in the north by the Himalaya and in the west by the Sulaiman Mountains and the Afghan plateau. To the north-west lie the Ala Shan, Tian Shan and Hindu Kush ranges, and it was through the gorges and valleys of this group—and along the narrow coastal route from Persia—that the early immigrants came. Routes into China were also determined by physical features; in this case by the mountains of Tibet in the west, the enormous sweep of the inhospitable Gobi Desert to the north and the high mountain barriers of Burma and Indo-China in the south-west. (Pages 230, 231, 232.)

2. From the earliest times Indo-Pakistan has included folk groups of very diverse grades of skill and the lowlier ones have usually been avoided and pressed into jungles. The Aryan steppe-folk, descending upon Indo-Pakistan before 1000 B.C.,

found a country of many different peoples, each with its own cultural level and habits of life. In order to attain some measure of unity without so offending susceptibilities as to endanger their own position, the Aryan overlords grouped together numbers of families as castes and laid down certain rules of conduct. Within the caste the family was the important unit. From these beginnings has evolved the extremely complicated caste system which exists today. Some of the advantages of the system have been that the great skill of craftsmen, handed down from generation to generation, has been preserved, individuals have been schooled in the subordination of self to the common interest, and the cultural heritage of the Indo-Pakistani peoples has been kept intact through the centuries. (Page 241.)

3. The industrialization of Japan which began in the second half of the nineteenth century was accomplished in an amazingly short space of time. Until the middle of the century the main industries of the islands had been fishing and agriculture. In the sphere of artistic endeavour her craftsmen excelled in basket work and the fashioning of goods in porcelain, bronze and lacquer; while the women were noted for the spinning and weaving of silk. Then, suddenly, came the change. Copying assiduously the methods of America and of European countries, the Japanese turned to science and machinery and to the development of an up-to-date industrial organization, based upon the power of swift-flowing rivers tapped by modern hydro-electric plant, and upon neglected mineral deposits. Population increased rapidly, so that when the food-producing capabilities of the soil had been exploited to the limit, expansion of people and of commerce beyond the home islands seemed the only solution to the pressing problem of supporting large urban industrial communities. This expansion found its expression in the invasions of Manchuria and China and in growing pressure on world markets. At the end of the Second World War, however, the Japanese, defeated by the Allies, were obliged to give up their over-

seas conquests, and today the problem of a large urbanized population with insufficient food production confronts Japan once more. The institutional reforms effected since the end of the war in 1945 will, no doubt, have a very great effect upon the masses of the Japanese people, and will to some extent colour their relationships with the rest of the world. The new constitution introduced by the occupying powers in 1946 provides for the abandonment of the concept of the divinity of the emperor and for its replacement by one of a constitutionally limited monarchy. The constitution also includes a Bill of Rights for the people of Japan, which, among other things, lays down that all are equal under the law, and which gives workers the right to organize and women the right to vote.

These reforms carry with them the opportunity for the Japanese people to embrace a more democratic way of life. They will certainly bring political advantages to the working classes, who before 1945 were regarded as little better than slaves; and no doubt the fanatical and belligerent nationalism which inspired Japan's attitude towards her neighbours and coloured her relations with the rest of the world will become canalized in time into more civilizing aims.

But the Japanese are a vigorous, highly intelligent and industrious race capable of inestimable pioneering effort; and while the democratization of the country's political organization will be welcomed as an immense step forward in its evolution as a modern society with great potential power, it can by itself do nothing to solve Japan's basic need for an outlet for her swollen population and the dynamic energy of her people and for a more healthy balance of her economy.

### CHAPTER XII

1. The Dutch seamen who first sighted the western shores of Australia made little attempt to explore because of the inhospitable aspect of the coast. When, eventually, the British landed on the other side of the continent they found a great mountain barrier between the narrow coastal strip and the interior of the country. With desert

in the west and mountains in the east, development proceeded very slowly. Another factor which tended to delay the opening up of Australia was the enormous distance separating it from would-be emigrants in England, a very serious consideration during the early days of colonization, when steam power was unknown or in its infancy and living conditions on board ship were so bad as to deter any but the hardiest and most adventurous of emigrants. (Pages 270, 271.)

2. The uneven distribution of population over the Australian continent can be accounted for by the fact that, broadly speaking, it is only the south-eastern and south-western parts of the land mass, with winter rains and mild climate, that are suitable for the white man and his commercial agriculture. Inland, savanna gives way to scrub and eventually to extreme desert conditions. A small proportion of the population is spread along the west coast (mainly in the south) where there are grazing lands and forest areas, but most of the development of this region has been due to deposits of minerals, notably gold. (Pages 271, 272.)

3. The future development of Australia would seem to depend upon a more varied agriculture and the exploitation of her very considerable mineral wealth, which has a wide distribution and which must inevitably be related to the extension of surface transport facilities and the opening up of new air routes. (Page 275.) In addition to solid mineral deposits, small quantities of oil have been found and exploration is being carried out in the hope that larger resources may be discovered. (Page 274.) During the Second World War existing industries were immensely expanded and many new manufacturing plants were established. Much of this industrial potential has been turned over to peacetime requirements, and such activities must have an effect upon the economy of the country.

The above are some of the general indications from which the broad outlines of the pattern of Australia's future development may be glimpsed. The reader will be able to observe for himself other pointers of a more particular nature, applying to specific areas and industries.

## CHAPTER XIII

1. Pastoral and crop-farming industries hold a place of first importance in the economy of New Zealand because both climate and soil are eminently suitable for the rearing of sheep and cattle. At first, the chief pastoral export was wool, but as scientific progress brought faster ships and an efficient refrigeration technique, the New Zealanders were also able to send out of their country large quantities of mutton, lamb, beef, butter and cheese.

Manufacturing industries have developed slowly, largely because of the small home market and the keen competition of more advanced industrial countries. From time to time the government has endeavoured to strengthen home industries by setting up tariff walls against foreign goods and by encouraging the immigration of skilled workers. They have also needed an export surplus to cover interest on external borrowings for capital purposes. There are still large forest tracts in the Dominion, especially in North Island, which, if cleared and sown with suitable grasses, are capable of providing some of the finest pasture land in the world. It is in this direction that the pastoral industries of New Zealand may be expected to expand. (Pages 281, 282.)

2. Although the advent of white people may have brought some material advantages to the natives of the Pacific Islands, there can be little doubt that on the whole the impact of a more advanced society has not been for the general good of the islanders. Diseases introduced by Europeans have flourished among the coloured peoples, whose resistance to these hitherto unknown maladies proved to be almost negligible. Well-meaning missionaries and the better types of trader have done much for the bodily and spiritual welfare of those with whom they have made contact, but the unfortunate influence of beachcombers and other undesirables has also produced its effect. (Page 286.)

3. In time of conflict between powerful nations of east and west, the Pacific Islands assume an importance out of all proportion to their size or economic potentialities. This fact was underlined during the Second World War when in 1941 the United States of America and the British Commonwealth of Nations were obliged to defend their territories against Japanese aggression. Island bases in the Pacific were vitally important to the maintenance of warships and the great air-fleets which both sides threw into the battle. As a result of the war, Japanese political influence has been eliminated from the Pacific Islands and it seems probable that, in the foreseeable future, Western culture will predominate, largely through the agency of the U.S.A. and countries of the British Empire. The day may come, however, when China will settle her internal differences and rise to play a more prominent part in world affairs. Then, perhaps, across the island stepping-stones of the Pacific may be accomplished the unification of mankind. The value of the outlying islands as aerodromes on the long commercial routes across the Pacific is clear (page 287), and perhaps the most immediate advance will be an increase in the number of such bases.

### CHAPTER XIV

1. The chief fear of early Polar explorers was the onset of scurvy. This disease attacked all expeditions which were obliged to winter in Polar regions. The discovery, towards the end of the nineteenth century, that scurvy was a deficiency disease enabled men to adjust their diet so as to obtain the necessary vitamins from fresh meat (seals, birds, fish, etc., previously shunned by Europeans). (Pages 294, 295.)

2. The majority of Eskimos live in Alaska and Greenland and the remainder are distributed throughout Labrador, Canada and north-eastern Siberia. Their staple diet consists of seal meat, fish, caribou and musk-ox. (Pages 292, 293.)

3. Exploration of the Arctic regions was often undertaken with the idea of finding a short route from Europe to the Far East, and many seaborne expeditions were organized to this end. (Pages 293, 294.)

At the other end of the earth there have been, until recently, few practical reasons for exploration apart from the hunting of fur-seals and whales. With the great advance in scientific achievement, however, the probing of the South Polar regions has been given some purpose, and recent expeditions have been carried out in the interests of geology and meteorology—perhaps with an eye as well on the possible discovery of mineral deposits. (Pages 302, 303.)

### CHAPTER XV

1. When, in very early times, many lowlands of Britain were covered by great deciduous forests, the tools available to man were neither strong enough nor sharp enough to fell the great oaks which dominated the forest lands. Man was, therefore, restricted almost entirely to areas in which there were no trees at all or only small trees such as pines and birches. Such areas were usually those kept free from dense woodland by sea winds or the bleakness of heights. (Page 308.)

2. When, in the seventeenth and eighteenth centuries, the cultivation of root crops began to spread over Europe, the old system of strip cultivation was gradually undermined. This was because the new crops were kept in the ground until autumn, which meant that the practice of turning the farm animals out into the big communal fields after the harvest, so that they manured the soil for the next cropping (a feature of the old system), had to be abandoned. The new system meant enclosure of fields and the old schemes came to an end in many parts. (Page 309.)

3. Examples of hunter-collectors remaining today in the Old World are to be found, of pygmy size, in the remote equatorial forests of Africa and Malaya. Then there are others in Australia, India and north-eastern Asia. (Page 316.) Pre-Columbian American peoples are in some cases hunter-collectors, but have rather more skill and equipment.

4. When early man fashioned weapons and tools from stone, the two basic

methods followed were those which produced either the "core" or the "flake"
tools. When the craftsman broke a flint, a
sharp chip or flake flew off, leaving the
remainder of the stone (the core) sharp-
edged along the line of the break. Instead
of using both parts indiscriminately, the
various peoples tended to fashion their
tools mainly from either the core or the
flake. (Pages 314, 315.) The flake tool
triumphed when man learned to fix it in
a wooden haft.

## CHAPTER XVI

1. Among the lowly cultivators of Africa
administration is rudimentary and no
records are kept. There are few institutions
such as organized priesthoods, and although
cattle are kept in some parts they are not
used for agricultural purposes, but serve
merely as currency and as a mark of
prestige. In India, on the other hand, the
lowly peoples have, in many cases, reached
a higher stage of development and there
exists every gradation from the hunter-
collector to the organized village-dweller
who uses a plough to till the soil. Animals
are used in the fields and frequently irrigation work is carried out. (Pages 326, 328,
329, 330.)

2. The classification of men according to
"colour" is very artificial because characteristics such as a brown or yellow skin
colour are largely the results of contact
with environment and have a definite
(though not always simple) relationship to
climate. Brown skin pigments are produced naturally, to give protection against
different conditions, and colouring is
graded from the pure "white" of northern
Europe, through many shades of brown and
yellow, to the "black" peoples of Africa
in the dry zones near the tropic of Cancer
and elsewhere.

3. The plough was used in some parts of
Abyssinia and northern Nigeria before the
coming of Europeans. (Pages 324, 332.)

# INDEX

## ACKNOWLEDGEMENTS

The publishers wish to make grateful acknowledgement to the following for permission to reproduce photographs in this volume:

The Controller H.M. Stationery Office, and the Director, Geological Survey and Museum, Figs. 21, 22, 40, 43, 45, 232, 234, 235 (Crown Copyright Reserved); The Acting Director, United States Information Service, Fig. 124; The High Commissioner for India, Fig. 159; Canadian National Railways, Fig. 112; Canadian Pacific Railways, Fig. 121; National Film Board of Canada, Figs. 111, 113, 114, 116, 117, 118; The High Commissioner for New Zealand, Figs. 183, 186; Royal Geographical Society, Fig. 184; The Prehistoric Society, Cambridge, Fig. 211; G. P. Abraham, Ltd., Keswick, Figs. 27, 28, 38, 39; Aerofilms Ltd., Figs. 32, 44, 88, 106, 109, 145, 209; George A. Clarke, F.R.P.S., F.R.Met.Soc., Fig. 51 (except the photograph of Cumulus cloud); Fairchild Aerial Surveys, Fig. 61; Dr. A. Hamilton-Rice, Figs. 71, 134; Michael Leahy, Fig. 218.